THE EPIC OF MEDICINE

BOOKS BY FELIX MARTI-IBAÑEZ, M. D.

A Prelude to Medical History

Centaur: Essays on the History of Medical Ideas

Ariel: Essays on the Arts and the History and Philosophy of Medicine

Men, Molds, and History

The Pageant of Medicine (Editor)

Henry E. Sigerist on the History of Medicine (Editor)

The Epic of Medicine (Editor)

Ensayo sobre la psicología y fisiología místicas de la India (In Spanish)

Surco (In Spanish)

Obra (In Spanish)

Yo, Rebelde (Novel, in Spanish)

Aventura (Novel, in Spanish)

THE EPIC OF MEDICINE

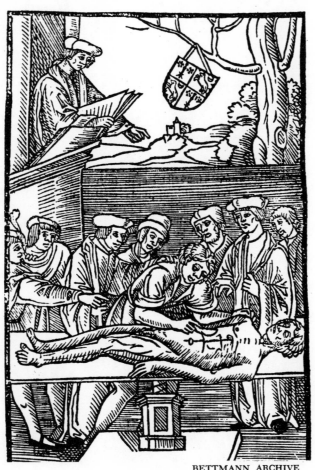

BETTMANN ARCHIVE

THE EPIC
OF
MEDICINE

EDITED BY

FELIX MARTI-IBAÑEZ, M. D.

EDITOR-IN-CHIEF OF MD, THE MEDICAL NEWSMAGAZINE;
FORMER PROFESSOR AND CHAIRMAN OF THE DEPARTMENT OF THE HISTORY OF MEDICINE,
NEW YORK MEDICAL COLLEGE, FLOWER AND FIFTH AVENUE HOSPITALS

Bramhall House

NEW YORK

Acknowledgments

My deepest thanks and gratitude to all those who collaborated so brilliantly and devotedly with me on *The Epic of Medicine*. To Dr. Michael Fry, the Managing Editor of *MD* and the Supervising Editor of this project; to Gerald Goode, the Special Writer on this project; to Verna Sabelle, my Executive Assistant; to Betty Hamilton, my Senior Editorial Assistant; to Ted Bergman, the Art Director of *MD;* to Hans Guggenheim and Federico Castellon, the painters of the specially commissioned paintings; to Alexander Taylor, the Picture Editor of *MD;* to the special researchers for this project, Dr. Ann Pollock and Charles M. Stern (text), and Grace Cardona and Norma Beatty (illustrations); and to all the other staff members of MD Publications who contributed to this project. I am also very grateful to Clarkson N. Potter and his competent staff for their excellent production of this book.

F.M.I.

Frontispiece: *Physicians and philosophers are shown gathered around Plato and Aristotle in one of the buildings of the Academy where Plato founded his most famous school.*

To the memory of Henry E. Sigerist, M. D.
who had the wisdom to envisage the history of medicine
as a facet of the history of civilization

Statue of Aesculapius, made of marble. It was discovered in 1896 and now stands in the national museum in Athens.

Table of Contents

XII

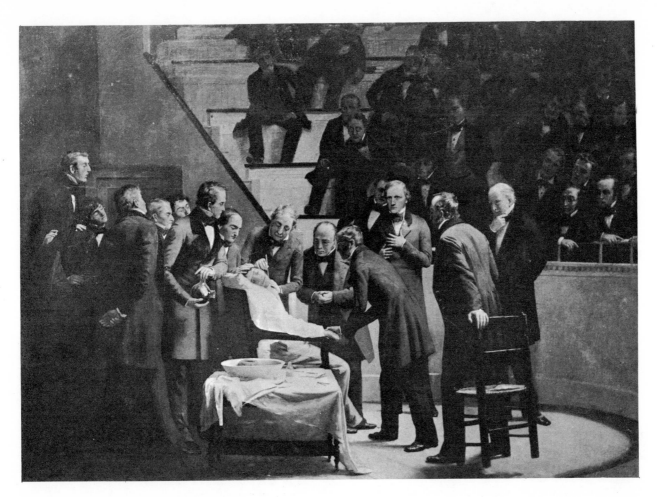

Dr. William Morton demonstrating ether as an anesthetic at Massachusetts General Hospital, October 16, 1846. Surgeon is Dr. John C. Warren. Within a month, Dr. H. J. Bigelow published an account of the efficacy of ether.

Preface

IN man's life dreams always precede deeds. Perhaps this is because, as Goethe said, "Our desires are presentiments of the faculties latent within us and signs of what we may be capable of doing . . . we crave for what we already secretly possess. Passionate anticipation thus changes that which is materially possible into dreamed reality."

To explain the genesis of *The Epic of Medicine* it is necessary first to talk briefly about the medical newsmagazine *MD*, in which it was originally published in twelve installments. Elsewhere I have narrated how as a medical student in Spain—a land generous with the kind of dreams that impelled men of action, like her *conquistadores*, or men of spirit, like her mystics—I realized that every human being carries in his heart a secret wonderland and nurses the silent longing to find during his lifetime his own Northwest Passage.

My most cherished dream as a youth was to bring beauty and romance to Medicine and to make of medical practice the epic adventure it ought to be. To do this, I realized, it would be necessary to inspire the physician with the saga of the "great doctors," to help him reconstruct his whole personality—as a scientist, as a member of society, and as a man—and to integrate his three spheres of action—medical, universal, and human—so as to enable him to look on the world around him through the eyes of an artist and on the world of medicine through the eyes of a human being. This also meant to look at the world as if he were seeing it afresh for the first time, naming each thing anew, spellbound by the same sense of magic that must have possessed Adam in Paradise when for the first time he beheld and named a rose, a bird, a star.

Only a magazine, I further realized, could attempt the difficult task of appealing to the diversity of interests of physicians all over the world. Besides, I deeply believed in the tribute paid by G. K. Chesterton to newspapers and journals when he said: "The roar of the printing wheels weaving the destiny of another day. . . . Here is the school of labor, and of some rough humility, the largest work published anonymously since the great Christian cathedrals." I even felt that only by listening to its heart beats—the medical journals—was it possible to know the condition of Medicine. And thus was eventually born the medical newsmagazine *MD*, which now circulates among all the practicing physicians in the United States, Canada, Latin America, and also to other physicians throughout the world.

Because a magazine is compounded not only of *manu*facture—the integration of paper, ink, and machinery—but, above all, of *mente*facture—the creation of new concepts and their translation into felicitous words and luminous images—*MD*, since its inception in 1957, has always endeavored to bring its readers an imaginative vision of the pageant of medicine and to fill their "inner space," their minds, with ideals that would provide them with the fortitude so necessary today to counteract the menaces lurking in outer space. *MD* is even written in a style that enables the reader to hear in the patio of the written words the thrill of an invisible nightingale. More than a magazine, *MD* strives to be a flying carpet on which the reader can soar through the blue skies of history.

MD has thus become the dramatic scaffold from which we have tried to paint the vast mural of the panorama of medicine throughout the centuries, not as a static chronologic sequence of discoveries, but as a dynamic cavalcade of men down the long trails of history, a procession illuminated by the heavenly caravan of the stars of civilization. I conceived *The Epic of Medicine* as *MD's* greatest project up to now, a history of medicine—Medicine as a profession, an art, a science—related to the history of mankind and civilization, weaving the endeavors and achievements of the physician into a living canvas on which men, events, ideas, things and places would come to life again through the magic of pen, brush, and camera. The basic script for *The Epic of Medicine*, as well as the philosophical concept that guided it and determined its scope, was provided by the texts of my books on the history of medicine, including *The Fabric of Medicine* (in press), and by special outlines I prepared for each chapter, along with the selection of the illustrations. I also wrote the twelve editorials that serve as a poetic and panoramic introduction to each of the chapters of *The Epic of Medicine*. These editorials can be found in this book preceding each chapter.

The decision to launch this series was followed by years of toil and labor. Like mountaineers on the ascent, we broadened our range of vision as *The Epic of Medicine* progressed. We wanted to envelop our readers in the rich fabric of History, and to turn History, which is remembrance and resurrection, into a dynamic instrument for the conquest of the future, which is hope.

In recounting *The Epic of Medicine* we started with the belief that all history, even that of Medicine, is above all pageantry. And so we used a series of living tapestries to portray the joys and miseries of physicians throughout history. Men, ideas, events, and places of memorable import in the story of medicine were resurrected. Like multicolored lamps, words and pictures lit up the still dark corners of the healing art, conjuring the great festival of the medical spirit in the garden of History.

The Epic of Medicine relates the first awakening of medical consciousness in the magic-governed shamans of the primitive world; the struggle between priest-physicians and the demons of disease in Mesopotamia and Egypt; the spinning of subtle philosophies by philosopher-physicians amidst the harmonious geometry of white marbles in ancient Greece; the practice of medicine by slave-physicians in bureaucratic, militaristic Imperial Rome; the monumental compilation of medical works by physicians in walled-in Byzantium, who thus sought to escape their cloistered world, just as the Byzantine artist sought escape through the magic windows of polychrome miniatures; the achievements in alchemy and hygiene of the Arabian *hakims* in the Baghdad-to-Cordova Empire, created at the point of scimitars by Islam; the birth in the unjustly called "Dark" Ages of the first hospitals and universities, plus the Gothic cathedrals and *The Divine Comedy*, which made this an era not of darkness but of blazing splendor; the exploration of the human body by artist-physicians in the Renaissance, which paralleled the exploration of the new world beyond the Atlantic waters; the discovery of the circulation of the blood and the beginning of scientific research in the Baroque, a period characterized by motion and emotion in art; the endeavors of the experimenters and visionaries of the Enlightenment and the Romantic periods, who heralded the advent of the last century's naturalist positivistic medicine; the transition from medicine based on qualitative impressions to present-day medicine, based on quantitative measurements, which has led to the new psychiatry, antibiotic medicine, and space medicine, and is leading to a biochemical, physical, and—once again—philosophical medicine.

The Epic of Medicine endeavors to give substance and meaning to the daily work of the physician. For the History of Medicine *is* Medicine. The physician's work—administering an antibiotic, making a psychoanalysis, performing a laparotomy—acquires meaning only when it is interpreted in reverse, like a film shown backwards. Only thus can be found the historical meaning in everything done in Medicine. This is possible by making, as this book tries to do, *living* history of all medical work, and by doing this with love and imagination so as to let fly once again the many-hued butterflies pressed between the pages of the huge book of History.

There are three ways of handling historical events: if they are minor, they can be *described;* if they have historical dimension, they can also be *interpreted;* if they can be integrated with other events in life, they can be *narrated* like a true tale of wonder. This last *The Epic of Medicine* does. There are many histories of medicine, but there is only *one* History of Medicine that is related to the history of civilization. The magic of interpretative narration—to turn all the different stories of physicians, patients, countries, and epochs into *one* narrative—was the new thread we sought to weave into the fabric of *The Epic of Medicine.*

This book does not quote historical references about each period; instead it embodies in the narrative what we have learned from such references. In this way, the reader will learn about Mesopotamian medicine without more than a passing reference to the Babylonian clay tablets or the Code of Hammurabi, although what was contained in them is incorporated in the text. The contents of the Edwin Smith and Ebers papyri were transformed into data for the narrative, and those of the *Corpus Hippocraticum* into descriptions of the working methods of the Hippocratic physicians. In other words, the source of information no longer appears in awesome academic dress but is turned into pulsating history.

The ward of a women's hospital shown in Florentine fresco by Andrea del Sarto.

The illustrations in the narrative text itself are kinetic in character, portraying events and persons *in action* rather than inanimate objects, and showing monuments not as dead, dusty ruins but as a dynamic part of the physician's daily life in each country and period.

For two reasons we believe that *The Epic of Medicine* will be of interest to non-medical readers.

First, because medicine is based primarily on a symbolic "friendship" between the physician and the patient, a friendship symbolized by the dialogue held between them, which, today as six thousand years ago, is not only the best instrument for diagnosis but also the best therapy. On such dialogue is also based that most precious of all medico-historical documents, the clinical case *history*, another example, a semantic one, of how history is the most important factor in man's health and disease. For biologically man is *nature*, but he is also *history*. He is what he makes himself as he travels down the road of time in his life. Therefore, the more a patient—and we all, including physicians, are patients at one time or another—knows about the endeavors and achievements of physicians throughout the ages, the more friendly the relationship between physician and patient will be and the more impressive will be the therapeutic results obtained.

Second, because, as the great medical historian Henry E. Sigerist said more than thirty years ago, medicine is above all a *social* science that uses the methods of the natural sciences. Sigerist had the wisdom to see this and the courage to proclaim it. Medicine and Science are today the two most important tools in shaping man's fate, and Medicine is much more than just a relationship between a sick person and his physician. Medicine is, above all, the way to improve the health and welfare of nations, the happiness of peoples, and with it peace among nations. The more we know about the past and present of Medicine, the more we all, physicians or not, can cooperate in creating for it—for *us!*—a better future.

May *The Epic of Medicine* be for our readers a picture window open on the amazing wonders of medical history and a way to anticipate the wonders and the grandeur of Medicine in times to come.

Félix Martí-Ibáñez, M.D.

June, 1962
New York, N. Y.

History is drama, and in the drama of History there is no more stirring saga than the epic of medicine. Out of the mists of time man emerged and, braving the everlasting menace of disease, launched on the conquest of the universe. This mighty tale of man's crusade for health is an epic of courage and determination, endeavor and achievement. Through the magic of word and image, of old iconography and modern photography, of historically reconstructed scenes painted especially for this book by famed artists, is created the majestic cavalcade, across the multicolored landscape of the ages, of shamans, magi, philosophers, hakims, physickers, investigators, teachers and space physicians, who fought prejudice and ignorance, malice and adversity, to help ailing mankind. ■ This tale of the great epochs and men of Medicine is unfolded against the tapestry of civilization: the progress of the arts and sciences, the clash of armies, the death of kingdoms, the birth of nations and the discovery of new worlds. ■ A nobler understanding of the role of medicine in the evolution of mankind is presented in THE EPIC OF MEDICINE.

Boar chases man, dog chases boar; drawing by a prehistoric Bushman in a cave in Cape Province, South Africa.

I

Prelude of Mist

Aɴᴅ from the remote mists of Time there emerged some solitary humanoid creatures who started a hard, wandering life over the face of the earth. Between these the first prehistoric men—polished links in a long biological chain—and the original amorphous amoeba there already existed a distance of millions of years.

There was little difference between the preceding anthropoids—our cousins, the apes—and the first prehistoric men, except that when the latter descended from the trees and learned to walk on two feet, they lost their powerful strength of jaw and abdominal muscles, and instead developed a larger cranium to accommodate a heavier cerebral mass. Of these creatures there remains only the testimony of fossils, weapons, tools, and the paintings they did by torchlight on the dripping walls of their caves.

Impelled by hunger, cold, and fear, these creatures roamed the vast natural tapestry of desolate land and steaming jungle, under the silent threat of the myriad eyes that flashed in the immense black velvet of the heavens.

Even before man appeared on the earth disease already existed among beasts. Fossils, bones, and teeth tell the tragic tale of prehistoric man succumbing to disease. A sickly man indeed he must have been, his body and mind wasted by sleeping on the cold, mud-tainted ground, which he shared with snake and toad, by lack of food, by traumas, fears, and stresses. A versatile hunter, he used animal teeth and horns as weapons, and he communicated with his fellow creatures through grunts, gestures, and blows. Two revolutionary discoveries—the flint axe, a stone fingernail that spared his own torn and bleeding nails, and the leather handle subsequently attached to the axe—changed his life, which was further facilitated by the scarlet mystery of fire.

The first physician was man himself; the first medicine, his own instinctive attempts at self-healing, by licking, sucking, and blowing on his lesions. When these individual reactions became stereotyped, the ritual became as important as the treatment. Accidental or battle wounds, cutting up animals, and cannibalism gave man an idea of the visceral content of the human body, as revealed by paleolithic paintings in which the heart is shown as the best spot to strike a mortal blow. And when man began to eat animals' organs, the principle of opotherapic similitude was born.

Tools formerly used as weapons began to be used to make incisions and trepanations. Licking and sucking were replaced by bloodletting, scarification, amputation, and surgery with stone tools. Covering fractures with mud, in imitation of monkeys, provided the first natural cast when the mud dried. And the discovery of fire brought with it burns, but also cautery. A powerful sociological agent, fire beckoned human creatures to gather together in its warm, golden chambers.

Disease developed according to mechanisms identical to those that prevail today: alterations in growth and metabolism, tumors, traumas, and infections. Fossils and carved stones imprisoned the message conveyed by this primigenial humanity, which roamed the earth before the beginning of history.

17

Millennia passed, and out of the prehistoric mists there emerged neolithic man, who, upon learning to grind and shape stone and turn it into weapons and tools—the missile and the hammer—ushered in somewhere around 12,000 B.C. the history of civilization. These primitive men we know about through carved stones, myths and legends, and the primitive tribes of today, people isolated in an isle of Time.

Neolithic man—Caucasians, Mongolians, and Negroes—lived in Europe and Asia, in a world that was turning temperate and humid and where, there being no notion of distances, incredibly long trips were undertaken on foot. Respect for the laws of Nature was born as the only way to conquer it; biologically correct social habits were developed; and community life began. In the endless nights, primitive man (isolated man is perhaps a better term) created astrology and astronomy and came to know the heavens before he conquered the earth. He also devised a mathematical system based on counting his fingers and toes; he learned to use the wheel; lining a basket with mud, he discovered ceramics; he polished stone, horns, and bones, cultivated plants, domesticated animals, and invented textiles.

Diseases—respiratory, osteoarthritic, gastrointestinal, genitourinary, traumatic, arteriosclerotic, infectious, and mental—were treated if minor with domestic remedies (diet, herbs, plasters, massage), often in imitation of wild animals; if severe, like smallpox, serious fractures, psychoses, the patient was killed to relieve the community of his burden, or the healer was summoned.

Besides empirical healers, who employed physiotherapeutic methods, there was the medicine man or shaman, usually a psychopath or schizophrenic, who practiced exorcism, made prophecies, and combined the functions of physician, magician, priest, statesman, and troubadour. The shaman's technique was based on magic. Magic was the precursor of science, man's first attempt to understand Nature. Preventive magic considered disease as a *plus* (entry in the body of a foreign object or spirit) or a *minus* (subtraction of the soul by magic).

The main techniques of the shaman were homeopathic magic, based on similitudes; contagious magic, based on destruction of the enemy; and direct magic, which required special rituals to prevent disease. Defensive magic used *fetishes* (objects endowed with magical powers), *amulets* (protective objects against black magic), and *talismans* (good luck objects). The shaman based his diagnosis on the concept that there was only one disease, which he identified with the cause; the "clinical history" consisted in an interrogation on the existence of fetishes, evil dreams, or broken taboos; prognosis depended on auguries and oracles; treatment was based on the aforementioned concept of intrusion of a foreign object or spirit, or substraction of the soul. Once the direct cause was determined (magic, witchcraft, death dreams, or moral delinquency), intrusion by a foreign object was treated by magic, sucking, extraction rituals, massage, baths, or vegetable drugs; and possession by a spirit, by exorcism, bloodletting, and spells.

The herbalist and prophet, therefore, coexisted with the shaman, who emerged from the millenary mists as the first medicine man, priest, and artist, in whom were joined Medicine, Religion, and Art, knowledge, belief, and creation. His magic was an art of arts, which attempted to govern the demons. It was a pseudoscience, based not on rational observation, as science is, but on the shaman's own experience of emotional states. It sought to treat human-produced and supernatural causes through mechanistic and psychological magic rituals, based on analogies and not on experiment; and "natural" causes through empirical resources, such as setting fractures, giving medicinal herbs, isolating the "possessed" (infectious or mental), practicing cranial decompression to

expel the demons in an epileptic, and variolation. To combat disease, the shaman used sucking, bloodletting, and cupping, accompanying his treatment with dramatic gestures and much drum-beating and rattle-shaking, until the "culprit" incarnating the disease, usually a pebble or tiny insect, was suddenly produced and the patient was declared cured. Other times the shaman used professional "soul catchers" to retrieve the wandering soul of the patient. And in all cases he practiced verbal psychoanalytical exorcism.

Magic medicine, which still prevails in present-day primitive communities, avoided harming the patient and accepted the existence of a psychic component in all diseases. Therapy was of a cathartic nature (bloodletting, purgatives, diuretics). Thus, magic medicine was based on the *who* (the personality of the shaman), the *where* (the sacred place for his rituals), and the *when* (the magic hour); just as scientific medicine today is based on the *what* (what is done), the *how* (the technique used), and the *why* (etiological motive of the therapy).

Seeing and *believing*—empirical experience and mystic faith, natural medicine and magic—these were the first two attitudes adopted by man when confronted with the mystery of disease. These two great channels—*empirical* and *magical*—through which flowed primitive medical thought, would later be widened by the current of *thinking* and *knowing*: the *rational* knowledge of disease and of its treatment.

A man of culture, power, and prestige, the shaman was the first statesman and leader and the most brilliant man in his community. With his attempts at healing he gave man, who ignorant and helpless was a victim of his physical frailties, the first chance to face and solve the riddle posed by the sphinx of disease in the prelude of mist to the Epic of Medicine.

F.M.I.

Massive mammae and buttocks typified female statuettes carved in ivory or soapstone by late paleolithic artists. Shown is an ivory figurine found in Lespugne (southern France).

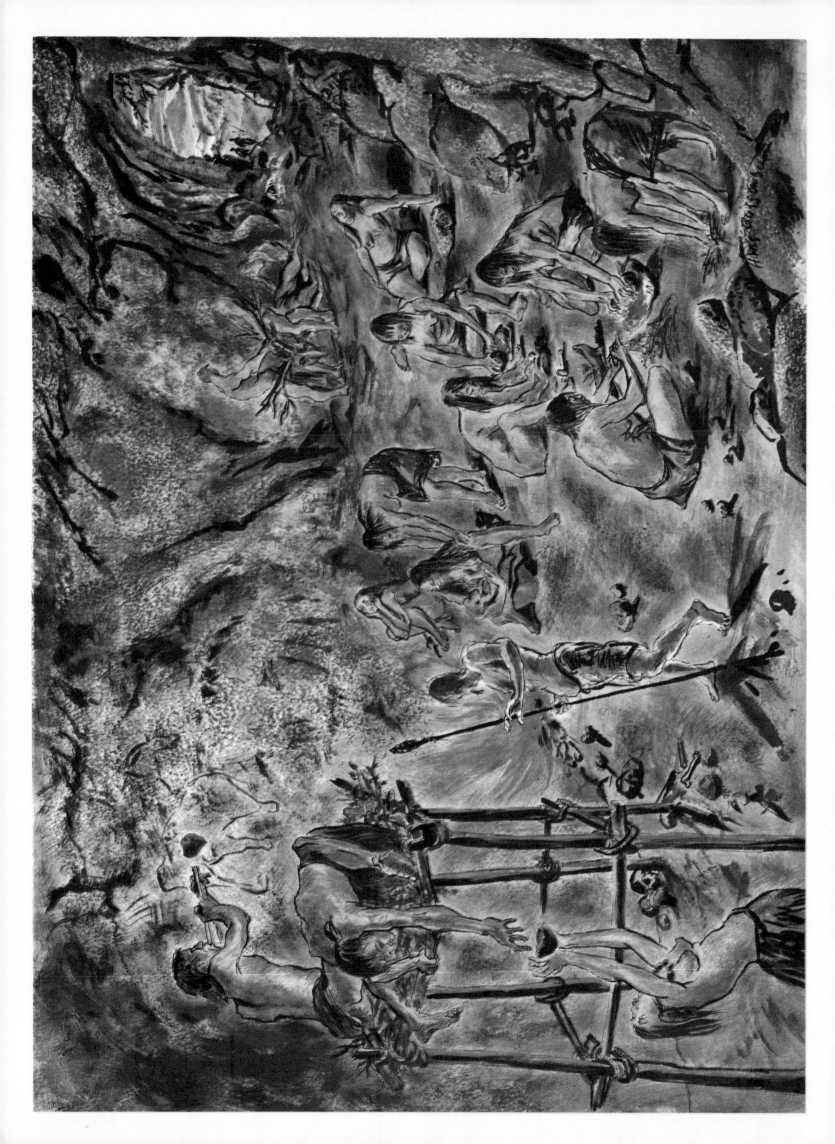

I

PREHISTORIC
AND MAGIC MEDICINE

THE long, primordial rehearsal was over. A million years of evolution had formed a creature who stood erect, could work with nimble hands, knew how to make fire, one who had evolved rudimentary speech.

From a common ancestor many types of human beings branched out to form races adapted to their environment. Some branches withered and were lost, others flourished into communities. All shared a common anguish: sickness and death.

Those who wandered into the European land mass lived in a bleak and unpredictable world whose climate was governed by capricious glaciers, now advancing, now receding. Long winters alternated with brief, brilliant summers when the earth blossomed with alpine primroses, poppies, gentians, flax, and arctic buttercups.

The icecap churned the soil into arable land, creating lakes, rivers, and treacherous marshes. European man clung to his thin thread of life, hunting, suffering, mating, century after century.

Around him roamed the mammoth and woolly rhinoceros, the great carnivorous bear, the hyena and cave lion, creatures that competed with him for the succulent meat of musk ox, ibex, chamois, and alpine hare.

When at last the cold relented and the fens dried out, laurel clung to the slopes, forests gave shelter to deer, herds of small shaggy horses and bison grazed on the grassy plains, salmon leaped in the rivers. Man had achieved a small measure of security, an environment in which he could evolve an ecologic balance.

PRIMITIVE PATIENT. Early European man (Cro-Magnon) was a superb physical specimen, standing about six feet and with a powerfully developed musculature. He was dolichocephalic and his skull contained a brain larger than the average twentieth century organ: approximately 1600 cc. for the male, compared with the present-day average of 1500 cc.

On hunting expeditions from his caves in southwest France, he sometimes met others like himself, tall men with aquiline noses and deep-set eyes who lived at the foot of the maritime alps. In the east roamed the heavy-browed Predmost men who took their living from the mammoths that wandered on the Central European plains.

Also abroad after the elusive game were short, flatnosed Combe-Capelle men who knew how to make long, slender flint blades. Occasionally met were stocky, low-browed, prognathous creatures, remnants of the Neanderthal men who had dwindled out after many millennia. Sometimes European man would meet black men with short torsos and long extremities; some of them were buried in Cro-Magnon caves; they left steatopygous and steatomeric statuettes among their relics.

THE HUNTER. The hunting of game required some 20 square miles of open terrain to feed one hungry cave dweller; hence primitive men were often forced to travel hundreds of miles in a single hunt.

They maneuvered their prey to a man-made pitfall, or ringed them with stone-headed spears and stampeded them with firebrands. The animal world provided food, skins for clothing, bone for implements.

Cave dwellings were usually a shelter under a rocky overhang, facing south to escape the cold winds. Near the opening a fire was kept perpetually

Painting, facing page: *A paleolithic artist of the postglacial era accurately locates the position of heart on a mammoth that he is painting on the wall of Pindal cave in Spain. He is blowing pigment of red ochre through a bone tube while others grind up the natural coloring agent. In background, hunters bring in a deer. Painted by Hans Guggenheim.*

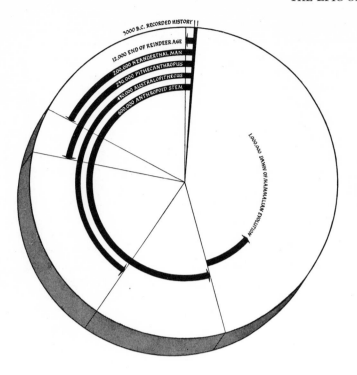

5000 B.C. RECORDED HISTORY
12,000 END OF REINDEER AGE
200,000 NEANDERTHAL MAN
250,000 PITHECANTHROPUS
450,000 AUSTRALOPITHECUS
600,000 ANTHROPOID STEM
1,000,000 DAWN OF MAMMALIAN EVOLUTION

self, then combined with the sky above and the earth below, there dawned on him the magic number seven.

He developed a language slowly, feeling emotion and its muscular expression first, then learning to associate emotion with sound. By imitating nature's noises and by developing significant gestures, man was able to transmit knowledge and build up tradition.

THE SUFFERER. Primitive man's life expectancy was probably little more than thirty years, daily menaced by falling boulders and trees, ravines and bogs, by the slashing horns and fangs of cornered beasts.

Nourishment alternated between feast and famine; meat cooked over open fires or cave hearths was consumed half-raw, thus inviting intestinal parasites. The teeth developed pyorrhea, tartar deposits, erosion, abscesses, and caries.

His reaction to pain was instinctive: stricken with cramps after gluttonous feasting, he massaged his belly; wounds were licked and the bleeding stopped by compression; painful joints were baked by the fire; a feverish body was plunged into an icy stream.

This instinctive medicine in time became formalized in ritual, ritual in turn became as significant as treatment; sucking and licking were supplemented by bleeding, scarification, amputation.

THE MAGICIAN. The most potent defense against disease and death became magic. In this, primitive man sought reassurance for his fears and the answers to such mysteries as birth, dreams, death.

He buried his dead in a sleeping posture, sprinkled them with red ocher, surrounded the corpses with tools and ornaments.

These rites were the task of the natural leader of the community: mediator between his people and the spirit world, the first priest and the first physician.

THE TRANSITION. As the glaciers receded, the mammoth and other paleolithic beasts dwindled away; food-hunting man followed the reindeer northward. Mighty forests stretched across the land so that a squirrel could scurry across the continent through a continous belt of trees.

burning; inside the cave the smell of roasting flesh and drying skins mingled with that of smoke and sweat.

Between hunts, primitive man flaked his flint cores from which he fashioned many tools and weapons: knives, awls, gravers, saws, keeled scrapers, burins for cutting ivory and bone. He learned how to carve bones and horns into daggers, javelin tips, arrowheads, harpoons for fishing, also delicately wrought needles.

Women pierced sea shells and strung them for necklaces, girdles, anklets, and decorative aprons; men preferred necklaces of canines from bears and lions.

THE ARTIST. Prehistoric man spent much of his leisure time in carving animal figures on reindeer antlers and mammoth tusks; he sculptured them in soapstone and clay, engraved them on pebbles, often superimposing one figure on another.

When he worked at his polychrome paintings and sculptures on the cave walls, his lamp was a hollowed-out stone dish of animal grease or fish oil with a fiber wick; his pigments were mixtures of iron oxides and animal fat in shades of red, orange, brown, black; these were blown on the walls through a bone tube. Bas-reliefs and sculptures were modeled in clay or carved out of rock faces.

THE WONDERER. Mathematics crudely began when early man acquired a body image of himself. Discovering that he possessed two hands, feet, ears, and eyes, he arrived at the concept of twoness. Learning that he moved forward, backward, right, and left, he discovered four. Increased to five by his sense of

Oldest example of pathology is shown in osteosis of the femur suffered by Java man (Pithecanthropus erectus about 250,000 years ago).

Bone daggers of Reindeer Age man were embellished with animal art.

BROWN BROTHERS

Shovel used by an early Moravian man was fashioned from the mandible of a wild horse.

Man moved out of caves to the shores of the lakes left by the glaciers; he built a thatched-roof shelter on stilts, fashioned weirs and fish traps, learned to build circular skin boats. His tools were hafted axes, mattocks, maces, fishhooks, net-menders, and barbed spearheads; his weapons were bow and javelin. From the lush earth man gathered fruits, nuts, edible roots. The dog that rooted at his garbage was adopted as a hunting companion and probably became the first domesticated animal.

Communities grew from the cave family group to the larger cluster of clan or tribe. Men developed a binding ethic of ritual and taboo within a tribe, became suspicious of other tribes.

The mesolithic European killed and ate his own kind: to the north on the fresh-water Baltic lake, the Ertebolle men cracked the skulls and split the bones of their human prey, scraped them clean of brains and marrow; to the south, Tardenoisian men cut off the heads of their captives and treasured them in cave pits.

THE FARMER. In the valley of the Nile and the Mesopotamian plains grew wild barley, emmer, and dinkel, and here grazed wild cattle, sheep, goats, and swine. This was probably the setting of the neolithic revolution, when man exchanged the risks of an improvident food gatherer's life for agriculture and animal husbandry. Mediterranean man accomplished this giant stride about 7000 B.C.; European man followed millennia later.

Wherever man learned to produce his food, skills rapidly multiplied. A sharpened stone was attached to a wood handle for a hoe; an adze permitted woodworking and lumbering. From reed or willow baskets, smeared with clay and baked in the sun, was launched the craft of pottery. Invented were ladders, pincers, spindles, looms. Wool and plant fibers were woven into cloth. Wild cattle were tamed, used for milk and hides.

In communal village life, ritual and taboo became the fabric of social structure. Rain, the seasons, and the fertility of earth depended on good relations with the spirit world. The changes of spring and winter were compared with female fertility, giving rise to numerous cults, some of them requiring human sacrifice.

MEDICINE MAN. The earliest human attempts to combat illness seem to have developed in two directions: magic and empiric, moving either parallel or divergently. When neolithic man suffered everyday aches and pains, colds, boils, toothaches, rheumatism, or skin disorders, he sought a natural remedy in water, sand, steam, poultices, massage, and herbs. Finding that bleeding often eased the pain, he developed phlebotomy. Near the Swiss lake of St. Moritz he built a settlement around mineral springs which are still used medicinally today.

As the number of settlements increased across the European-Asian-African land mass, the gamut of infectious diseases expanded. Microorganisms that for hundreds of centuries had found congenial living in other warm-blooded animals changed their abode to human tissues. Living closely in village communities,

AMER. MUSEUM NATURAL HISTORY

Pair of large-skulled children of the Grimaldi racial type, found buried in the Grotte des Enfants (France) facing the blue Mediterranean.

Trephining was practiced for medical or magic purposes among neolithic peoples. Reconstituted bone around openings of skulls above suggests patients survived surgery.

humans easily became seeded with pathogens having an ancestral likeness to diphtheria, smallpox, tuberculosis, the virus diseases.

Primitive man believed that illness was caused by disaffection in the spirit world. The victim had committed an offense against the social code or violated a taboo. Spirits took revenge on offenders either personally or through some agent-sorcerer.

Each man was believed to have an ethereal image, more finely textured than his body. This ambulant soul might make its residence in the kidney, omentum, heart, liver, or gall bladder; it could also be talked to in dreams. Once it was separated from the body, sickness struck; if it failed to re-enter the body, death must follow.

PRIMITIVE ETIOLOGY. Summoned by a stricken person, the medicine man sought an immediate explantation in supernatural causes. The sufferer might have stirred the wrath of the spirits, attracted hovering ghosts, allowed his soul to go astray. Once the diagnosis was established suitable countermagic was initiated.

Probably one of the oldest etiologic concepts was that of foreign object intrusion: a stone chip, wood or bone splinter was believed to have been shot into the body of the afflicted. The medicine man could then extract it by sleight of hand, under cover of an elaborate ritual.

Another grave cause of illness was "soul loss" which could occur while dreaming, after falling down, from sudden fright, sneezing; the soul could also be entrapped by the ghosts of virgins, or by a rope with loops. Only the medicine man, often with the help of professional soul catchers, could return the errant spirit to its owner.

A distant enemy could induce disease by bone-pointing, ghost-shooting, or sympathetic magic. By modeling an effigy or making a drawing of the prospective victim and mutilating it, a sorcerer could cause a victim to fall ill or die. Or the sorcerer might obtain nail parings, hair clippings, a tooth, excrement, spittle, or even the footprints of someone whom he intended to harm. Misfortune or sickness was believed to follow when some envious person cast a glance at another, especially at susceptible children; this was the evil eye which could only be warded off by certain magic signs or amulets.

MAGIC THERAPY. A medicine man made his medical decisions from magic lore in which his people trusted. If illness was believed to be caused by a barbed stick attached to an invisible string, jerked by a spirit and causing pain, he cut the string. If the tribe understood that an enemy had power to shoot a magic shell under the patient's skin, this was his diagnosis; he then scarified the offended part, drew out blood by sucking, magically produced the shell.

Near-hypnotic states were induced by fasting, hallucinogenic herbs, dramatic ceremonies that lasted through many days and nights. Interwoven with these was empiric treatment with emetics, purga-

Preceding pages: *Sunk in a pit, a Congo warrior endures magico-empiric therapy. His shattered leg has been smeared with clay that will harden to form a crude cast. Wattle screen protects patient and medicine man while heat is transmitted to buried leg to relieve pain and bake cast. The Bantu medicine man is waving magic raffia wands to discover the unseen evil agent of the trauma. While medicine man's wives industriously stoke fire, onlookers wait with rapt attention for results of medico-magic ritual. Feathered headdress symbolizes magic power of medicine man, whose face mirrors strength and confidence in his supernatural gifts.*

tives, sweat-baths, massage, and secret herbal formulas.

The psychologic effect of ritual therapy was intensified by an elaborate collection of magic objects, potent for the patient and his kin. An object was charged with power by impregnating it with some magic substance, such as resin, a stone or plume with peculiar markings, or one representing a totem or familiar spirit. The community could also enjoy its potent fetishes, passed down through generations: an image, an ancient tool, or an axe head. The fetish might be pampered, propitiated with gifts or sacrifices; it could be taunted or insulted into working its magic. Its power might require renewal from time to time by some substance from a human body, such as blood.

Amulets either warded off evil or invited good fortune; the medicine man used them as countermagic, to overcome sorcery that had caused disease, or as preventive medicine. His armamentarium rested in a bundle of objects charged with magic energy: shells, stones, animal bones, tools, and implements

Women practitioners were usually herbal healers; their rank was lower than that of the male medicine man; childbirth was usually reserved to them. Delivery was accomplished with the woman in a sitting position, squatting or kneeling, occasionally standing. The midwife chanted while massaging the body

Mummy bundle used for magic purposes in prehistoric Peru.

Rondelles from trephined skull were used as amulets, sometimes strung as necklaces.

downward; if the birth seemed difficult she shook the patient, at the end of labor she might induce her to sneeze.

Wounds were cauterized, sutured with sinews, or clipped together with thorns, or certain types of beetle were made to grasp the lips of the wound with their mandibles; then the body was snipped off and the head left in place. Herbs with astringent or disinfectant properties were applied; with these a dead fly might be inserted for magic effect.

The primitive medicine man frequently scarified, amputated, and incised wounds. Favorite targets of ritual surgery were the digits and genitalia; removal of a finger or figerjoint was commonly part of puberty rites.

Skulls found in primitive caves and communities show signs of having been trephined. By a technique of scratching or circular perforation, rondelles were excised. Evidence of bone healing around the skull opening indicates that the operation was survived. This cranial surgery may have been performed to relieve headaches or to treat epilepsy by permitting

Late stone age engraving made when salmon and reindeer abounded in southern France.

27

the demon that caused the seizures to escape. Rondelles, taken from living and dead, were strung on necklaces and worn as amulets against demons.

The medicine man guided his tribe through crises and natural disasters; as healer he exorcised disease from body and mind. Besides this he knew how to summon rain, turn aside storm and flood, invoke good hunting or good crops. When evil befell the community he was detective, policeman and judge; he discovered the violator of a taboo, passed judgment and executed sentence.

Rigorously trained for his role, he was the revered repository of his people's legends, traditions, drug and herbal lore. He came to his profession as the result of a call, an escape from death, a strange dream or waking experience that marked him; often he courted visions and communion with spirits by fasting, solitude, hallucinogenic drugs.

He memorized with exactitude the chants, dances, costumes, and procedures necessary to invoke good spirits and drive off evil ones; a single error would cause the ceremony to fail in its purpose. He usually possessed great physical strength, carrying on ritual chants and dances through days and nights with little pause. In totem mask and mantle adorned with potent symbols, his graven baton a sceptre of authority in both the real and the spirit world, he inspired awe, fear, and confidence in his powers.

In the primitive community, the medicine man combined both magic and the beginning of religion: magic resided in his personal powers, religion called on supernatural forces. Magic thus represented man's earliest attempts to use his own strength to solve the problems of health and disease; in that sense it stood closer than did religion to the concepts of modern medical science.

As rituals became firmly established by repetition and were handed down from generation to generation, the office of medicine man (or shaman) came to embrace more than healing; it formed the core around which a tribe built its distinctive social and economic culture. The medicine man acted as the interpreter of a community's collective conscience, the link between the living and the dead, the priest-physician-protector.

In the harsh environment of the stone age when mankind lived in constant danger and fear, the medicine man offered the only assurance of victory over a hostile world. In using the power of the mind against disease, he took the first step along the long and frequently fearsome road to civilization, guiding humanity out of its primordial slough into the light of the first recorded cultures in the ancient world.

BETTMAN ARCHIVE

Grotto painting by a Cro-Magnon artist depicts what is probably the oldest known representation of a medicine man, garbed in a reindeer skin and antlers.

African medicine woman slits tongue of young woman as a prophylactic measure. Note modern razor blade.

MAGIC MEDICINE TODAY

Still extant are numerous communities of culturally isolated peoples who practice magico-medical rites that could well be a survival of neolithic times. Some of these people are themselves often living in more or less the same conditions as those of stone age man; they have no settled habitation, gather their food instead of growing it, possess only rudimentary weapons.

Nevertheless the great medical historian Henry Sigerist repeatedly warned that the parallel between primitive medicine still practiced today and the magico-medical practices of 20,000 years ago should not be drawn too clearly. The shamans and medicine men of today may be the direct "professional" descendants of their neolithic predecessors, or they may equally well be perpetuating degenerate remnants of religious rites borrowed from a higher civilization.

Whatever may be the anthropologic link between prehistoric communities and present-day primitive cultures, the photographs in these pages offer a glimpse into the secret and frequently awesome world of magic medicine as it flourishes today on several continents.

Zulu medicine man in Natal (South Africa) using a medicine horn to suck out the evil that is causing sickness in the fearful patient. Sucking rituals are among the most important magic techniques.

Medicine woman throws the "bula" bones to diagnose an ailment. Technique is not far removed from cartomancy.

TERENCE SPENCER

Medicine man's magic bag used in the Bulu tribe in the Cameroons (West Africa). Note bones and pebbles used in disease-healing rituals.

AMER. MUSEUM NATURAL HISTORY

E. VON HESSE-WARTEGG

Member of a secret society in the Bismarck Archipelago (New Guinea). Many of these societies practiced medico-magic rites, often including human sacrifice. In Africa members of these groups also frequently headed anti-white revolts.

Dance of possession is used by Nigerian medicine men to draw evil spirit out of mentally sick patient (lying in foreground). This ritual is common to many tribes.

WORLD HEALTH ORGANIZATION

PIX

New Guinea medicine man is greatly feared and respected. Feathers and shells are supposedly imbued with magic powers.

Australian aborigine using magic bone which he points at the enemy he wishes to harm. Bone pointing is another of the basic techniques of magic medicine.

AUSTRALIAN NATURAL RESEARCH COUNCIL

Babylonian bird-headed deity plucking fruit from the sacred tree. Stone relief in the British Museum.

II

Lands of Sun, Lands of Death

On the sun-drenched shores of the sapphire Latin sea the first civilizations were born. Between the rivers Tigris and Euphrates the Sumerians erected their first cities, while Egypt passed from the neolithic world of the flint to the splendorous world of the pyramids. Mesopotamia, like Egypt, was a gift from the river, a sowing of cultures in the desert that cropped up as bacterial colonies crop up in a Petri dish when one strikes it with a platinum loop dipped in bacterial culture.

The Mesopotamian civilization was man's answer to the desert's challenge to try to survive in its sun-charred, sand-whipped vastness. The Bible has perpetuated the story of Mesopotamia, whose idyllic peace, accented by sheep and palms, was often disturbed by desert nomads and mountain people craving the comforts of the cities in the plains. Located on the route of the caravans, Mesopotamia benefited from the news and ideas that were as much a part of the caravans' cargo as gold, spices, and incense. Sumerians and Semites dug irrigation canals and invented cuneiform writing, passing from mud villages to fabulous cities with soaring towers and hanging gardens. Their leaders blazed a trail of heroic legend: Sargon in Akkadia, Hammurabi in Babylon, Ashurbanipal in Assyria, Nebuchadnezzar in Chaldea. An atrocious deluge, followed by sandstorms that buried buildings and roads, obliterated the Mesopotamian civilization, leaving us only its cuneiform tablets.

The message inscribed on these dusty tablets tells of great cities, of the Tower of Babel and the ziggurats, those skyscrapers of the desert where a table of gold, a soft bed, and a handsome wench waited for the god that ruled the city through his "business manager," the great priest. The tablets also tell about temples crowned with vast terraces, whence the priests tried to probe the mystery of the star-sparkled celestial velvet. Centers of the city were the marketplace and the temple, where virgin-priestesses waited for the stranger who, with caresses and a silver coin, would deliver them from their vows. And there were majestic avenues brilliantly illuminated (by that same petroleum that is still today coveted by nations), flanked by huge bronze lions, threaded with colorful bazaars, and redolent of myrrh.

Writing and metals added new dimensions to human life. The anthropomorphic religion demanded offerings of bread and wine to the Mesopotamians' god, and the slavery-based economy contrasted sharply with their theocratic democracy, which required everyone to labor at the canals in peacetime and to be a soldier in wartime.

Mesopotamian art was an art of duration, static, geometric, massive, agoraphobic. It glorified gods, demons, and the dead. It feared open spaces, the awesome flatland that stretched endlessly all around, and the unfathomable celestial immensity above. It sought to fight the amorphous universal chaos through a rigid geometry, opposing nature's curved lines with man-created straight lines.

Communication was limited by the lack of roads, which barred the use of the wheel except in war chariots. All travel was done on foot, donkeys, or river rafts. Kings were buried together with their courts, their jewels of gold, silver, lapis lazuli, and malachite. Remarkable were their mechanical inventions: the wheel, the pulley, the screw, the level, the wedge, and the inclined plane.

To fight disease (dysentery, the scourge of the river; ophthalmic ailments, the curse of the sands; and arthritis, the bane of humidity), the Mesopotamians resorted to a medico-religious medicine, since they believed that disease was their punishment by the gods for their sins or possession by demons, and they considered the diseased person impure or taboo.

Mesopotamia, therefore, was the cradle of necromancy and magic. In Mesopotamian demonology, in their belief that demons and spirits "specialized" in causing certain diseases, lay the seed of the future doctrine of specific infectious germs. Infections and neuroses were treated through magic rituals. Medicine was a secret art taught only in temples, and all physicians were priests. Surgery progressed as wars increased and the surgeon became the physician par excellence. The Mesopotamians had knife doctors ("surgeons"), herb doctors ("internists"), and spell doctors ("psychiatrists").

Their Code of Hammurabi, inscribed on a pillar of black diorite and set up in the temple at Babylon, represents the first historical codification of medicine. It established both the fees payable to physicians for satisfactory services and the penalties should their ministrations prove harmful. Medical care was completed by laying the sick in the public square so that passers-by might offer advice had they ever had the disease themselves or known of any who had suffered from it. Prescriptions were discussed by the laity as freely as today we discuss dishes on a restaurant menu. The Mesopotamians created an astrology that was concerned not with nativities but with the study of the heavenly mechanics, and that was the precursor of astronomy. After the heavens they studied the earth in search of auguries, the most important of which, together with the flight of birds and the flickering of flames, was hepatoscopy. Examination of the liver of sacrificed animals was a costly practice. The liver was considered the seat of emotions and the most vital organ in the human body, since it appeared so large and full of blood during sacrifices. Its examination was performed in situ, in the "palace of the liver," its scarlet architecture of vessels and ligaments sharply etched beside the green moon of the gall bladder.

Diagnosis, which was based on hepatoscopy, astrology, dreams, and auguries, led to "etiological" therapy through repentance for sins committed, expiatory rituals, the

ELLIOTT ERWITT

expulsion of demons, sympathetic magic, and offerings of milk, honey, and beer. Symptoms were believed to be the disease itself. Also used in therapy were fruit, cereals, spices, flowers (garlic, roses, oats, laurel, and tamarind), mineral and animal substances, massage, plasters, and baths. Besides an extensive pharmacopoeia, the Mesopotamians had a sewage system, they established the notion of certain days for resting, they had a calendar, mathematics, archives, and libraries, and they realized the necessity for isolating the sick. The cradle, together with Egypt, of medical culture, Mesopotamia is an immense wall on which archeologists are still rapping their knuckles in search of the rich historical treasures hidden within its ancient stones.

Mesopotamia's rival, yesterday as today, was Egypt, a "socialist" theocracy in which the Pharaoh was a god, just as Mesopotamia was a "democratic" despotism and the king was a mortal. Egypt was an oasis in the desert, a corridor of fertile land watered by the sacred Nile. On the Nile's periodical inundations (attributed to the tears shed by Isis over her husband Osiris) depended the Egyptian economy. The Egyptians forced the people to erect dikes and dams, adopt a solar calendar, invent geometry in order to delimit private property whose boundaries were wiped off periodically by the inundations. They were also compelled to organize a complex social state to maintain the unity of the people, which was constantly threatened by the river, as well as the greatest bureaucracy in history, with the inevitable loss of human individuality.

BLACK STAR

Limestone figure of Egyptian lady named Nofrit, from about 1500 B.C. Hieroglyphs on both sides of head read "King's friend, Nofrit."

For many centuries the land of Egypt, victim of numerous successive invasions, kept contracting and expanding in the same manner as an amoeba contracts and expands under the microscope. Originally an amalgamation of neolithic clans, unified by Menes, Egypt had a history of feudalism, anarchies, invasions, and vast military powers, which used horse-driven war chariots. Small in size, great in enterprises, a veritable stone coffer locked by rock, sand, and sea, for millennia its language and writing remained local and hieratic, until the Rosetta stone was deciphered.

From a neolithic culture, Egypt, under the Pharaohs, almost jumped to a civilization that knew hieroglyphic writing, metals, how to make papyri for writing purposes, alphabetic signs, colored glass, and metal alloys, and that had a caste of scribes from which would spring the first physicians. They built the pyramids by means of the level,

Wall painting of a funeral procession in a tomb shows attendants bringing mummy in casket accompanied by personal effects.

the ramp, and the roller. They embalmed the human body so as to preserve the soul. Tombs, mummies, and steles reflected the Egyptians' obsession with death and with preservation of body and soul. The climate itself helped to preserve all things: papyri, silks, stones, and the dead. Outstanding among the Pharaohs was Akhenaton, who instituted a monotheistic cult to the sun and who had his wife, who was also his sister, immortalized in art. Thanks to him, she of the swan neck, the beauteous Nefertete, still gazes upon us, her single crystal eye sparkled by some inner dream.

The Egyptians' lack of individuality was reflected in their art—uniform, rigid, massive, and crowded with columns, as if with such optical crutches they sought to combat the visual agoraphobia that bedeviled them. Monumental, monolithic, sepulchral, and funereal, their art made of homes transient places, and of tombs, the eternal dwelling. Each tomb was a temple where the deceased substituted for the god. Not realizing that there was immortality in biological paternity, they sought it instead in death, around which they created a gigantic cult. Ruled by the law of frontality, their art never represented a lifted foot, rarely a woman, never a smile. Instead, it teemed with sphinxes, gods, lotuses, and papyri. An art for the illiterate, it reflected the technology of the times and was a hymn in stone to the immortality that comes only with death.

Stones and papyri describe the Egyptian way of life—their consanguineous marriages, simple garments, and meticulous pulchritude; their meals of bread, fish, dates, and beer; their houses made of adobe or mud and lit by castor oil-soaked salt; the cruel life of the slaves toiling at the mines or pyramids; and the women, their busts gilded, their eyes painted with lead sulfur, and their lips stained green and black.

Mummification was developed to a remarkable degree, for the Egyptians believed that the *ka* or soul returned to the body after death. If the physician's duty was to prevent putrefaction of humors inside the living body, the embalmer's duty was to prevent putrefaction inside the dead body. Sodium bicarbonate, cedar oil, wine, and aromatic herbs were used in mummification; the viscera were removed, the body was swathed in gum-soaked linen, and the face was traced with cloth of gold and precious stones. The mummy was then laid to rest in the sepulchral chamber, together with canopied jars containing the viscera, to wait for the Final Judgment. Yet, though millions of embalmings were performed, not the slightest progress was recorded in anatomy, which was studied only in animals in the kitchen or in sacrifices at the temples.

Medical papyri, written twelve centuries before the *Corpus Hippocraticum*, give us an idea of Egyptian diseases, which were transmitted by water, flies, and food. The Edwin Smith Papyrus reveals the Egyptians' progress in traumatic surgery, though they feared to cut open the major organic cavities. It compares cerebral circumvolutions with "melted copper," cranial fractures with "a crack in a ceramic jug," and it lists surgical symptoms and their empirical and magical treatment. In describing cases and lesions, the author of this papyrus seems to have been moved by a spirit of inquiry. The Ebers Papyrus, of a later date, describes internal diseases and lists traditional therapies, just as household remedy books did in the seventeenth century. Besides amulets and talismans, Egyptians used at least one third of all the medical substances known today— from opium to gentian to castor oil and colchicum—though they ignored their specific indications and collected drugs merely as a child collects toys.

It is important to remember that the most ancient scientific documents are *medical* and *mathematical*, and the most ancient of all such documents is believed to be the *Corpus Hippocraticum* (compiled in the fifth, sixth, and seventh centuries B.C.). But prior to the *Corpus* there existed a scientific tradition that was already old when Greece was young. Pythagoras, Thales, and Hesiod, in the sixth, seventh, and eighth centuries B.C., respectively, linked their work on mathematics with the old Egyptian theories. The *Iliad*, which grants credit to Egypt as the place of origin of Greek drugs, already contains the beginning of a medico-rational system, which dates medicine as far back as the tenth century B.C. But if Greece left us an important literary selection of its writings, Egypt left us only what time itself preserved, chiefly religious breviaries and funeral texts and stones. Greek texts are a product of their Golden Age; Egyptian texts are merely copies of ancient texts made when Egypt's sun was already setting. This explains the inferiority of Egyptian texts, though the Edwin Smith and Ebers papyri record several scientific observations that were repeated twelve centuries later in the *Corpus Hippocraticum*. (The Greek miracle, therefore, was a resurrection of the scientific tradition of Egypt and the Near East).

Medical practice—which was shared by physicians, priests, and medicine men—

Rite of circumcision, wall carving from tomb of Ankhmahor at Sakkara.

reached such a degree of specialization and hierarchy that some physicians were exclusively "guardians of the anus" of the Pharaoh, and most of them were experts in one disease only. The physician was summoned for an ordinary ailment, the priest for a grave one, and their fees were paid in kind. The patient's clinical case history was studied first, after which he was given a general examination, in which the physician's sense of smell was as much a guide as palpation, percussion, and pulse taking. When the diagnosis was etiologico-magical, the demon or spirit that had to be expelled was specified. Empirico-rational diagnoses were symptomatic, and the symptoms—pain, fever, tumor—were believed to be the disease itself.

Therapy was based on diet, herbs gathered from the patient's own garden, enemas (in imitation of the sacred bird of the Nile, the ibis), and external application of animal fat, particularly oxen fat. Physicians themselves, assisted by their servants, prepared all medicaments. They also used lancets, cautery, psychotherapy, and, above all, an eliminative and humoral therapy that made of purgatives a daily cosmetic and of regular bowel movement an eternal blessing.

In Egypt, magico-religious medicine, which was popular because it was inexpensive, coexisted with empirico-rational medicine, which because of its high cost was limited to the wealthy. Only near the end did the latter veer toward magic. A basic etiological cause of disease was considered to be the *whdw*, a substance in the materia peccans in the fecal content of the bowel, responsible for putrefaction. The Egyptian concept of the nature of disease was based on an elemental physiology: alterations in the air, in ingested foods, and in the blood (of which there was so much and loss of which they knew could kill a man). The religion-influenced physiology believed that "conduits" carried the blood and the air through the body, which to the Egyptians was a mass of flesh and bones traversed throughout by canals, with a heart in the center. Since their land was a web of canals through which flowed the most vital element, water, the Egyptian mind conjured an anatomical image of numerous canals through which flowed the blood, air, food, and sperm, and which, like their irrigation canals, were susceptible to obstructions, droughts, and floods.

ELLIOTT ERWITT

Leeches being applied to a patient, depicted in a painting from the tomb of Userhat, a scribe of the Eighteenth dynasty.

Egypt gave birth to Imhotep, "he who comes in peace," a man with pensive eyes and shaven skull, "the first figure of physician to emerge clearly from the mists of antiquity" (Osler). Vizier to King Zoser, physician, priest, astronomer, and architect, Imhotep built the great pyramid of Sakkara, the most ancient stone structure extant. Upon his death, Imhotep was transported up the Nile in a funeral barge, his body swathed in perfumed linens, a necklace of talismans girding his neck, and his flower-lined coffin surrounded by moaning women with bare torsos. This was the beginning of his glorification as hero, semigod, and ultimately god of medicine, and his cult was eventually identified with that of Aesculapius in Greece. Imhotep and Egyptian medicine are the connecting links between the world of calcined deserts of archaic medicine and the sun-lit polished cosmos of Greek rational medicine.

Meanwhile, India, a great nation, was rising in the Orient under the Emperor Asoka, who built hospitals and academies. During the Vedic and Brahmanic periods of its medicine, epidemics were studied, surgery progressed (particularly rhinoplasty, because there were so many punitive facial mutilations), a physicians' oath was introduced, and three classical medical texts were born: *Charaka, Susruta,* and *Vaghbhata,* all based on the *Ayur-Veda,* the supreme mystic document of Hindu medicine.

In its turn, China, influenced by the Buddhist philosophies imported from India and by Confucianism in the North and Taoism in the South, would develop a civilization far more technologically advanced than any Western civilization would be up to the Middle Ages, having invented the compass, gunpowder, silks, porcelain, and printing. The Chinese even "invented" the pocket handkerchief centuries before it was used Europe. Chinese medicine, based on Confucianist principles, after an initial period of magic became cosmological and botanical, developing a fantastic pathology system, a veritable ivory tower with a purely theoretical foundation. Diagnosis was based on examination of the tongue and the pulse, which was regarded as a musical instrument. The Chinese discovered numerous drugs, from ephedrine to camphor, and practiced acupuncture, moxibustion, and variolation. The first consisted in the insertion of fine needles into the "canals" through which flowed the blood and humors, a method inspired by the irrigation canals in their land, and the second required the subcutaneous application of ignited combustible cones.

The Hebrews from Judea originated three great religions—Judaism, Islam, and Christianity—to purify the soul, and a public health system to purify the body. The Bible—which meant even more to the Hebrews than the Homeric epics did to the Greeks—records cases of leprosy and epilepsy and the most ancient prophylactic-hygienic legislation.

The Amerindian cultures—Mayan, Aztec, Incan—followed the same magico-empiric lines of primitive medicine.

And while these cultures sparkled the horizon, there came to happen the Greek miracle, a brilliant epiphany in which man found his full historical dignity.

F.M.I.

Following page: Plainly and scantily garbed Mesopotamian physician-priest in Babylon ponders over clay model of liver brought to him for divination-diagnosis purposes, while patient awaits verdict. In background, a ziggurat towers in the sunset. A constant procession climbs to the temple by well planned ramps.

II
ARCHAIC MEDICINE

Out of the shadows of the stone age the children of the sun moved into the light of civilization's dawn. On the hot plains of Mesopotamia and in the green valley of the Nile emerged man's first golden age.

Some six thousand years ago, human beings knew how to write and do arithmetic; they had discovered metalworking and the wheel, how to channel water and observe the movement of stars, and they counted their long days by the trajectory of the sun.

In those first millennia, monumental architecture and symbolic art forms flowered, primitive awe was transmuted into religious ritual, tribal taboos ex-panded into codified laws, the concept of kingship merged with that of godliness. And medicine began its tortuous ascent from witchcraft to craft.

Mesopotamia and Egypt were both founded on fecund mud and soil-enriching floods that earlier had lured man from untenable deserts, from a nomad's life to settled agriculture. Wrested from the morass by massive toil with carpets of woven reeds to bind the earth, the verdant lands now supported cities and soaring temples. New classes emerged: craftsmen, priests, officials, scribes, merchants, eventually qualified physicians.

Across three thousand years Mesopotamia lived as

Map shows cradle of two archaic civilizations. Mesopotamian kingdoms flourished in what is now Iraq. Course of Tigris and Euphrates has changed considerably since Assyrian times.

a succession of warring states while Egypt maintained an almost unbroken line of nationhood. Each achieved fabulous wealth; each suffered dire breakdowns and invasions. And in both civilizations religion and magic saturated the daily life and institutions of men, shaping their attitudes toward health and disease.

MESOPOTAMIA

The people of the Tigris-Euphrates river region were restless innovators, contributing the largest share to the bold inventions of the archaic world. They invented writing, thereby expanding the dimension of time by linking the past, present, and future. They perfected metallurgy, thus enormously extending the concept of space by impelling far-flung exploration for ores. They founded city-states on soil salvaged by irrigation and by the methodical control of the river waters, thereby establishing the power of man over nature. And Mesopotamia was the first to write codes of law that provided that each man, of high or low estate, should have an equal right to theocratic justice.

Mesopotamian man was probably of Asian origin, speaking a language that was related to no other. In his beginnings, he was dark-haired, roundheaded and short of stature; later intermarriage with Semitic and Aryan conquerors increased his size and altered some facial traits.

Living in awe of the deserts around him, exposed to assaults by nomads who coveted the riches of the plains, Mesopotamians built massive cities surrounded by high walls.[1] Each city was grouped around a temple in which lived the ruler and the local god. The temple priests directed irrigation projects, food supplies, and religious functions. The god owned the city, the high priest was his manager, and all the people were his servants. In return their sustenance and protection were assured by the priests. Each city was also a small state in itself, over which the king ruled in the office of chief steward of the enshrined local deity.

In the religious center of each city-state soared staged towers or ziggurats over 80 feet high. The temples were encircled by inner and outer brick walls within which labored bakers, brewers, smiths, in whitewashed workshops administered by the priests. Huddled around the temple were cramped streets of square, flat-roofed houses. And all around lay the fruitful fields where men and women raised grain and the sacred date palms and tended their herds.

Artisans fashioned beautiful gold and calcite jars and tumblers; they molded and painted pottery, fashioned sculptures and bas-reliefs. Others embellished harps, headdresses, and statuettes with gold leaf and lapis lazuli; out of gold alloy they wrought intricately engraved helmets. Builders devised the arch and vault; chariot makers invented wheels with leather tires. After thousands of years of neolithic stagnation, the inventiveness of Mesopotamian man produced in quick succession copper tools, patterned cloth, textiles, cylinder seals to identify property, astrologic tables, weights and measures, a circle divided into 360 degrees, an hour cut into 60 minutes, a minute containing 60 seconds, and a solar calendar that allowed man to plan his work according to the seasons.

THE GOVERNMENT. The city-states tempered the priest-king's rule by a council of elders. Priests and temple officials formed the guiding class; below them came the freemen, artisans, and husbandmen; lower still were the slaves, usually war prisoners or men who had forfeited their freedom by failing to pay their debts.

The gods of Mesopotamia were believed to live as men did, experiencing their foibles and fears, driven by the same good or evil impulses. Most solemnly revered were the nature deities of sky, sun, earth, and water; they were enshrined in temples and offered daily food and drink; as a religious duty every woman was expected to offer herself to any passing stranger in the temple once in her lifetime and contribute her fee to the earth-goddess Ishtar.

When a king died, his body was accompanied into the tomb by his brightly attired wives, his concubines, musicians, attendants and guards, by his horses and cattle; the members of the royal household arranged themselves in their lifetime hierarchic positions, then drank a soporific to render their suffocation painless and serene; for Mesopotamians, who were not concerned in a life after death, such immolations were considered merely as acts of loyalty.

THE PEOPLE. The fertile valleys supplied the cities with plentiful food, mainly vegetables, barley bread, malted cereals, cereal porridges, milk, honey, occasionally meat and fish. The wealthy enjoyed garlic and sour cream, roast salmon, pork or lamb, unleavened wheat bread, dates, grapes, and pomegranates; their beverages were wine made of grapes or dates, or beer.

Public buildings were faced with brilliant blue, yellow, and white enameled tiles, blazing in the sunshine, standing on broad avenues crossed by canals and winding streets. The odor of hot asphalt from the paved sacred pathways between the temples mingled with the stench of garbage that was allowed to rot in the sun.

The dark men with trimmed beards, some bewigged and perfumed, wore cotton tunics under linen robes, the women were veiled unless they were slaves or unmarried temple prostitute-vestals; their

Reconstruction of Babylon (after Unger) as it was rebuilt by Nebuchadnezzar (Sixth century B.C.). Bridge over Euphrates leads through outer and inner walls into temple and processional area, with ziggurat at left.

long cotton tunics of blue and red stripes or dots left one shoulder bare; they also wore elaborately coifed hair, shapely sandals, many bead necklaces, amulets, and bracelets.

Marriage auctions were held in the public squares, where girls who had not found a husband privately were brought by their families. The prettiest girls were offered first to fetch the highest price, part of which was applied as a dowry to increase the chances of the plainer ones.

In the Babylon of King Nebuchadnezzar (ca. 600 B.C.) one avenue was flanked by 120 ceramic lions; the palace itself was all of yellow brick. Supported by tier upon tier of colonnades soared the Hanging Gardens (one of the seven wonders of the ancient world) built by the king for his Median princess when she pined for her native green hills; its exotic shrubs and flowers were freshened by water pumped from the Euphrates by an ingenious irrigation system.

Food was brought to the cities in wheeled carts drawn by small Asiatic asses (onagers); camels brought textiles, dyestuffs, glassware, and precious stones across the long caravan routes. River boats manned by sixty oarsmen transported copper, gold, and silver, oil from the fields northward of the Tigris for a city's many lamps. Beyond the cultivated fields prowled fierce desert lions, ever ready to raid flocks and villages.

THE SICK. Unlike Egypt in its protected sea and mountain girdle, Mesopotamia sat astride numerous caravan routes, was open to plagues and other diseases carried by man and beast. Sudden dust storms, searing heat by day and cold by night, bred afflictions of the nose and chest; polluted irrigation canals and the myriad flies carried malaria, dysentery, eye ailments; lepers were many and were kept apart by law.

When a Mesopotamian fell ill it meant that the sufferer or one of his family or clan had committed a sin. Illness was the punishment for this sin, ordered by the gods and meted out by demons, vagrant ghosts, or evil spirits that stealthily possessed the sinner's body and caused havoc therein.[2]

Also waiting in ambush were the dreaded disease demons such as those in the service of the powerful earth-goddess Ishtar, also the goddess of witchcraft and pestilence; they sought to corrupt man's body and spirit. Other demons caused diseases of the head by gripping it in a tight band, or they stormily occupied the breast, the throat, or the loins, bringing fever and pain.

A sin was any act that displeased or angered the gods, or any transgression of their commandments, or any neglect of their needs. Deities hungered for more than homage, they also required gifts of food, clothing, money, women. Sin was to spit or urinate in canals, eat out of a sick person's plate, dip the feet into unclean water, touch a menstruating woman with unclean hands, unnecessarily handle the sick. If an illness could not be traced to a moral misdeed, the sufferer acknowledged that the ways of the gods were too mysterious for his understanding and resigned himself to the priest.

Babylonian-Assyrian bronze amulet. Third row from top shows sickroom scene with two physician-priests garbed as fish demons; two others with animal masks (right) fight a mock battle. In the Louvre, Paris.

THE PHYSICIAN. Medicine was a sacred art taught in the temple; the most learned man in a city-state was the priest-physician or *âsû* ("he who knows the waters"). He was versed in reading and writing, science, religion, literature; he had knowledge of ritual and magic, divination and astrology. When attached to the court he served the king's family and officials, tended the poorer sick without fee. He worshipped the healing deities, Ninib, Gula, and Ninazu and his son, whose emblem was a rod and serpent.

The *âsû* was not called on to diagnose a disease or predict its course; these duties were performed by the *bârû* who was a master of divination. When evil spirits needed to be exorcised, or restless ghosts invaded a sufferer, the *âshipu* (incantation priest) was called in to take over the case.

The task of the physician was to treat the sick with charms, drugs, and minor operations. He made no calls on five days in a month,[3] nor would he tend a patient whose condition was hopeless. He embodied

authority and a knowledge of magico-empiric medical lore. His fees were regulated by law, so were legal penalties if any treatment caused death or injury to the patient.

The *bârû* read the portents of an illness in the animals or insects he encountered on the way to the sufferer: a falcon seen on his right promised recovery; seen on the left it meant death.

The most costly form of divination was hepatoscopy, devised by the Mesopotamians in the belief that the liver was the seat of the soul and center of life.[4] The ritual was performed before the statue of a god who made his intentions known in the liver of the sacrificed sheep. This was examined in its every detail in the search for malformations or peculiarities; each real or supposed deviation was interpreted by the diviner as the god's answer to specific questions. When the right lobe was shaped like a purse it was an omen of disaster; when the common duct inclined to the right the patient was expected to live. The art of hepatoscopy was taught in the temples with the aid of clay or bronze models of a liver.

Physicians were also well versed in the relationship between certain movements of the stars and the outbreak of disease and epidemics, thereby forging the first conscious understanding of the links between man and his environment. They could interpret dreams as clues to the outcome of an illness or a form of treatment. And they knew which gods to invoke for help against the demons of disease: Nabu, the Assyrian god of the healing art, or Babylon's Marduk, who held the power to overcome all disease.

Clay model of a sheep's liver used in divination (Babylon, ca. 2000 B.C.) is divided into 50 quadrangular fields, each square containing inscriptions and omens, used to teach the art of hepatoscopy. When inspection of the liver of sacrificial animals showed alterations these were noted by pegging holes. In British Museum.

THE TREATMENT. Physicians treated illness with drugs, fumigation, medicated baths, hot or cold water. They recognized diseases of the eyes and ears,

Limestone relief with figure representing King Hammurabi of Babylon (2100 or 1700 B.C.) who drew up first Code of Laws regulating medical practice. Monument was dedicated to a goddess for having preserved the king's life.

rheumatism, tumors, abscesses, heart trouble, skin and venereal disease, jaundice, respiratory ailments.

Fumigation for chest disease was done by spreading powder of tar on a thorn fire and letting the smoke enter the anus, the mouth, and the nose; the whole body was covered with curd, then bound in pulverized linseed for three days; fumigation was also done with smoke from the dung of pig, dog, jackal, fox, and gazelle, or from hartshorn, sulfur, bitumen, and human bones.

Drugs were given in anal suppositories or in enemas, or the physician blew them into the urethra through a tube. Potions prepared at night were taken before sunrise on an empty stomach, in the evening they were drunk when stars appeared.

Recommended for a cough were ground darnel and pounded roses eaten in oil and honey, a soup of pig's meat, a fire lit under the sufferer when he defecated. Cramps were treated first by pouring cassia juice on the head, then by manipulating the spine, arms, and head and by rolling the patient on the ground.

In Mesopotamia's many wars physicians gained an empiric knowledge of surgery, including eye operations, phlebotomy, and cupping. If an operation caused the loss of an eye, the physician's hands were cut off, if a highborn patient died he lost his life. The lawmakers were evidently aware of the power that could be wielded by a man who knew how to use poisons and the knife; the Draconic laws were most probably a means of protection against malpractice or lack of dexterity in physicians.

Remedies used included garlic, onion, leek and bean, cereals, spices and condiments, resins and gums, the roots, leaves, and fruit of the date palm, cypress, pine, tamarisk, or laurel. Popular herbs were hellebore, mandrake, opium, and hemp. Animal sub-

stances came from cows, donkeys, lions, mice, frogs, ravens, storks, owls, falcons, or vultures, including the urine, feces, hair, or ground bones. Minerals in use were white and black sulfur, arsenic, black saltpeter, antimony, iron oxide, copper dust, mercury, alum, naphtha, calcined lime.

Out of their fertile triangle of the Tigris and Euphrates the people of many mighty kingdoms forged a civilization whose traces are still clear to see in present-day living cultures. Innovators in many fields, they supplemented their demonic beliefs with numerous practical methods of treating injuries and disease, vastly enriching man's lore of herbal and mineral medicine. They codified laws to preserve the public health and defined for the first time in recorded history the duties and responsibilities of physicians. With its sister civilization to the west, Mesopotamia helped to guide medicine on its relentless course of rendering aid to suffering humanity.

World's oldest prescription in cuneiform writing. Front face of a Sumerian physician's tablet dating from about 2100 B.C. found at Nippur. It reveals acquaintance with large number of drugs. Tablets were made of clay, baked in oven or under sun; writing was done with sharpened reed. These tablets were then stored in libraries.

MESOPOTAMIAN MILESTONES

ANCIENT CITY

UR OF THE CHALDEES
Important center of Sumerian culture, given in the Bible as the home of Abraham. About 2800 B.C. it and other Sumerian cities were conquered by the Semitic King Sargon of Akkad, thereby creating the first Mesopotamian empire. It vanished in the fourth century B.C., was not rediscovered until the nineteenth century.

BABYLON
On the Euphrates, this center of the empire of Babylonia flourished as early as 300 B.C. Its city-god was Marduk. The city acquired a reputation for luxury and licentiousness. It was destroyed by the Assyrians under King Sennacherib (ca. 693 B.C.) but was rebuilt, more brilliant and luxurious than before. In 538 it was captured by the Persians under Cyrus the Great and its glory ended.

ASSUR
First capital of Assyria, 200 miles north of Babylon. Inhabited by people of Semitic-Akkadian ancestry who developed a formidable military state equipped with cavalry, war chariots, siege machines, battering rams, and armored scaling towers. Around this city on the upper Tigris developed the nucleus of a Semitic state in the third millennium B.C. The city later gave way to Babylon and Nineveh.

NINEVEH
Capital of Assyria, on the Tigris (near modern Mosul, Iraq). The city reached its fullest glory under Kings Sennacherib and Assurbanipal. It was more than 3 miles long, with magnificent buildings and walls 50 feet high. It is mentioned several times in the Bible, which also describes its fall (ca. 608 B.C.) under a combined attack of the Medes and the Babylonians.

HISTORIC RULER

SARGON I
(Sarru-Kinu). He was one of the earliest empire builders in Mesopotamia, a fierce warrior and ruthless conqueror. He became the overlord of numerous Sumerian cities and extended his loosely knit empire as far as the Mediterranean in the west and the Black Sea in the north. His dynasty lasted for about two centuries.

HAMMURABI
King and founder of Babylonia's greatness. His code of laws consisting of 3600 lines of cuneiform was carved on a black diorite column. He reigned around 2100 B.C., but other systems of dating place him near 1700 B.C. The Biblical Amraphel is identified by some with Hammurabi.

TIGLATH-PILESER I
King of ancient Assyria (died ca. 1100 B.C.), a mighty hunter and empire builder. He subdued many provinces and conquered tribes in Syria, Cappadocia, Armenia, and Kurdistan. He built many temples and palaces and developed the Mesopotamian irrigation system. One record said that he killed with his own hand 10 elephants and 920 lions.

ASSURBANIPAL
(ca. 668-626 B.C.) Last of the great kings of the Sargon dynasty, called Sardanapalus by the Greeks (the Bible calls him Asenappar). In his reign Assyria achieved great prosperity and splendor, while art and literature flourished. He was (in his own words) "endowed with attentive ears," which made him a patron of literature; he ordered all the cuneiform writings of that time to be collected in the royal library, part of which now rests in the British Museum. About a score of years after his death the Assyrian empire fell to pieces.

EGYPT

Unlike their Mesopotamian neighbors who were peoples of the plain and reeds, the people of the Nile lived inside the safety of natural bastions: rocky hills, desert sand, and sea. The unfailing flood of the Nile brought yearly abundance, the gentle climate bred cheerfulness and serenity. Century after century of sun-drenched peaceful existence evolved a culture unlike any other in western Asia. And an orderly society allowed medicine the security required to flower at leisure.

GOVERNMENT. At the start of the transition from neolithic life, the inhabitants along some 600 miles of river were loosely clustered in nomes (ruled by nomarchs), divided into the regions of the upper reaches of the river and its spacious delta.[5] Some time in the third millennium B.C. the semilegendary King Menes welded them into one kingdom, thereby founding the first of thirty dynasties that were to last almost 4000 years and end with the poisoned bite of an asp in the breast of Cleopatra.

During the first thousand years of recorded history the king became identified as a god, the son of the sun-god Re. In the name of that god he was absolute monarch over all Egyptians. The nation's affairs were administered by a vizier who served as prime minister, treasurer, and chief justice. The Pharaoh's house-

hold staff included military leaders, guardians of the wardrobe, launderers; he was daily attended by barbers, manicurists, cosmeticians.[6] He was held in such awe that his name could not be pronounced and he could only be addressed as *Pharaoh* ("royal house").

During the earlier dynasties the king appointed the monarchs in the role of provincial governors; in time they transformed themselves into petty local rulers, occasionally rebelling against the king's authority.

Justice was administered by the king's officials serving as temporary judges. Transgressors were given a fair trial; punishment could include beating (for tax evasion), ablation of nose, hands or tongue, impalement, beheading, or burning; an extreme penalty was burying alive in caustic soda (natron).

THE PEOPLE. The Egyptians were physically robust, strong-boned, and slender. Their hair was dark and smooth, frequently completely shaved in both men and women; the nobility wore elaborate colored wigs. The wealthier women rouged their faces, painted the lips and eyes, gilded the breasts, and colored their nails; they used creams, oils, perfumes, combs, and mirrors, shaved their body hair with bronze razors.

In the earlier centuries men and women went naked to the waist, a linen wrap covering the loins and legs; servants and priests wore only a loincloth. Children lived nude until puberty, though girls wore earrings and a bead belt around the hips.

The daily provender included cereals and fish eaten raw, cooked, or sun-dried. Vegetables and fruits included onions, leeks, garlic, beans, cucumbers, olives, melons, dates, figs, and grapes. Cooking was done in olive oil, honey was the sweetener, wine and beer were the favorite alcoholic beverages. Luxuries on the rich man's table were wild ducks, geese, and quail, snared by nets.

The children played with tenpins and tops; adults played a form of backgammon; men also enjoyed watching wrestling and boxing. At the homes of the wealthy, guests were entertained by dancing girls to the music of drums, lyres, and flutes.

During most of the dynasties the people were divided into five classes: the royal family, priests, nobles, middle class (scribes, merchants, artisans), the farmers; during the empire period (ca. 1500 B.C.) were added the class of professional soldiers and thousands of slaves captured during forays into neighboring states. Persons of one class could by their own efforts improve their social position.[7] In the course of three thousand years, the predominant classes were in turn the nobles and priests, then the commoners, finally the powerful hierarchy of government officials.

Society rested on monogamy: not even the god-king could have more than one wife. The practice of sister-brother marriage, first introduced by the Pharaohs to protect their power and family property, became common in all classes. Women had almost equal social and economic rights with men; in many cases the husband made over his property to the wife as part of the marriage contract.

Premarital sexual freedom was allowed youths and

maidens;[8] men were allowed to keep concubines after marriage, but adultery in a woman was cause for divorce. Children were taught to respect their parents; Egyptian parents in turn were generally kind to their offspring and allowed them many liberties.

THE RELIGION. Woven into every facet of Egyptian life was the belief in a multitude of gods and goddesses, friends or foes of puny man. One group of earlier beneficial deities was merged into the one sun-god Re (Ra, Amen, or Amon); the life-giving gods of nature and vegetation were fused into the god Osiris who was also god of the Nile; these two competed for supremacy throughout the dynastic era.

The worship of Re, the god of righteousness and justice, was the official religion of the king and the priests; the cult of Osiris grew among the lowlier folk to whom he promised rewards in afterlife. While Re personified life, Osiris came to represent death.[9] In the span of centuries these two faiths were merged into one religion.

The only interruption in this gradual fusion was the attempt by King Amenhotep IV (began reign ca. 1375 B.C.) to reform the state religion, which had by that time been degraded by corrupt priests into a system of magic ritualism. He boldly banished the priests, erased the names of traditional deities from the temples, proclaimed only one true god, Aten (Aton, the ancient sun-god). He changed his name to Akh-en-Aten,[10] built a new city for the deity and spent fifteen idyllic years with his beautiful queen (and sister) Nefertete and their children.

Medical interest in Akhenaton's monotheistic experiment is that his solar religion was based on worship of the vital force emanating from the sun disk, source of all life; as such it was a form of heliotherapy.

The kingdom meanwhile was attacked from outside and thrown into disorder internally; Akhenaton was finally obliged to make concessions to the priests (which caused Nefertete to leave him), and to accept his brother as co-ruler. When he died his new city fell into ruin, his solar religion was abandoned, and Egypt's priesthood returned to power and to its ancient ways.

In the official religion Egyptians came to believe that man did not die but was destroyed by a vengeful god, a malign spirit, or an escaped ghost. Death became merely a momentary interruption of life. At first the dead were believed to continue their life in the tomb; their immortality must be assured with food and all the essentials of life.[11] Then it was believed that, if the body were preserved, the soul and the *ka* (the spiritual self, small double of the body) could also be given immortality.

Reserved for kings and nobles was the highest form of the embalmers' art, in which the brain (not regarded as especially important) was first drawn out through the nostrils with a hook and the cranial cavity washed out with salt water. Through a lateral incision in the abdomen (between 3½ and 4¼ inches long), made with a stone knife, the viscera were withdrawn, but the heart, believed to be the seat of the personality, was left in place.

After washing out with wine and aromatic herbs, the abdominal cavity was stuffed with myrrh, quassia, spices, and occasionally linseed, sand, sawdust, soda, and onions; the incision was sutured and the body immersed in a 70 day soda bath. It was then covered with fiber wrappings smeared with gum, a plaster image of the face of the deceased was set in place and the body was placed in the mummy case, this in turn was laid in a stone sarcophagus in the tomb. Four canopic jars containing the viscera accompanied the body into the burial chamber.

The least expensive form of mummification extracted part of the intestines by liquefying them through an anal or vaginal injection of natron; the body was then soaked in soda for the regulation 70 days; for a slightly higher price, cedar oil was injected before the soda bath, leaving only dried bones and flesh.

As Egyptians shrank from cutting dead human flesh with a knife, they assigned the task of making the abdominal incision to the *paraschistes,* who performed the operation, then ran from a mock onslaught of stones and taunts. The *taricheutes* who eviscerated the body and prepared it for the tomb were revered as priests.[12]

Protection of the dead also played its part in the construction of the royal and noble tombs, Egypt's monumental contribution to architecture and elementary engineering. Beginning as a modest *mastaba* or vault over an underground mummy chamber, the royal tombs grew more massive until they reached the immensity of the great pyramid at Gizeh, built by King Khufu (Cheops) in the second millennium B.C.[13]

In the building of these gigantic structures, Egyptians developed notable engineering skills such as the ramp and the lever; they also amassed stupendous sculptures in the round, enormous bas-reliefs, countless painted figures, superb pottery, metalware, and jewelry, hieroglyphic accounts of earliest times.

Egyptian art represented a collective social life, hence architecture was the most highly developed art. The Egyptians invented the column (later refined by the Greeks), the illusion of perspective, the use of massive blocks of stone. The total effect was one of grandeur and massiveness, evidently expressing the Egyptians' belief that their cities and temples

King Akhenaton with his wife, Nefertete, and their children. Bas-relief in Berlin Museum.

would dominate the valley of the Nile into eternity.

Religious rebel Akhenaton also tried to revolutionize the strictly formal method of painting figures; he had himself, Queen Nefertete, and their children painted in informal lifelike poses. His own face he allowed to be portrayed in all its misshapen ugliness. The "new art" persisted for a time under his successor Tut-ankh-amen but in a century or two it was submerged in the old traditional system of representation.

PHYSICIAN. Neither medicine man nor shaman, the Egyptian physician was a man of culture and learning; his skill was admired abroad and he was often called to attend royalty in foreign lands, as when Persia's King Cyrus sent for an Egyptian oculist to attend his mother.[14] He possessed empiric judgment, manual dexterity, a background of training under experienced physicians; the texts of his medical studies held the lore of centuries. In the early dynasties he was a member of the priesthood; later he attained an independent professional status. Indicated in the medical papyri is that he became a physician, an exorcist, or a priest of Sekhmet (surgeon and specialist).

Most of the royal physicians were specialists, including physicians of the eyes, the teeth, the belly, a specialist in internal fluids, and a "shepherd of the anus." At the bottom of the hierarchy were physicians without special titles, dominated successively by a chief of physicians, inspector, superintendent. The royal staff had in addition a senior physician; at the pinnacle of the medical structure reigned the Greatest Physician of Lower and Upper Egypt.

Egypt's medium of exchange was not money but barter or payment in kind; hence physicians were remunerated by gifts; those attached to a royal or noble household were also given their living. Physicians employed by the temples were paid out of the temple budget; also attached to the temples were medical training schools. Wealthy physicians frequently gave their services to the poor without charge. The general practitioners practiced among the poorer people, supplementing their meager fare with the sale of cosmetics, hair dyes, and insecticides.

The most vivid personality to emerge from the early dynastic centuries was Imhotep,[15] architect and physician to King Zoser (ca. 3150 B.C.). He also served as a priest, scribe, astronomer, and grand vizier.

He built the first pyramid at Sakkara, oldest stone structure in the world, introduced fluted shafts and bas-reliefs in the funerary temples of Zoser, thus laying the foundations of Egyptian art for millennia to come. When he died his body was taken up the Nile in a ceremonial funeral barge, the beginning of a glorification that was to transform him into the god of medicine many centuries later and link his cult with that of Aesculapius.

49

Votive offering shows a woman in labor assisted by animal-headed gods.

THE CONCEPTS. Whereas Mesopotamian physicians regarded the liver as the seat of life, Egyptian medicine placed the vital function in respiration and the circulation of the blood. The heart was placed at the center of the blood system, attached by 22 or 44 vessels to every part of the body. The enormously intricate system of canals along the Nile banks encouraged the Egyptians to liken the human body to a system of ducts for the transport of air, blood, food, and sperm; illness thus became basically an obstruction or flood in the normal circulation. In their mythologic anatomy each organ was connected with its own particular god. While demons and spirits were important causes of disease, the demons were overpowered by gods, the spells were broken by prayers.

The concept of disease also included parasites as the possible cause of certain ills common to western Asia. In the religious legends, the sun-god Re became ill from the bite of a worm, and Horus was stung by a scorpion. Parasites could be expelled by purgation.

An important part of the Egyptian concept was the belief in a close relationship between the anal region and the cardiovascular system. A number of prescriptions noted that retention enemas were valuable because they refreshed the anus and the heart.

THE PRACTICE. An extremely wide range of medical lore was enclosed in the various Egyptian papyri preserved from dynasty to dynasty.[16] They most likely included lore that was handed down from prehistory.

Medical practice was divided into two schools: the empiric, which was costly and reserved for the royal family and the wealthy, and the magico-ritual, which was inexpensive and popular.

In the empiric method, diagnosis by observation and palpation (possibly auscultation) was fairly advanced. The physicians were able to describe dysfunctions of the digestive tract, the heart and circulation, and the liver and spleen; other ills diagnosed included menstrual disturbances, eye disorders, tumors.

Remedies included almost a thousand prescriptions compounded of honey, beer, fruits, spices, opium, portions of animals (fat, blood, excrement), substances such as salt, alum, antimony. Purgation was a routine procedure, so was vaginal irrigation; suppositories were in common use. Surgery included the lancing of boils (a frequent ailment) and abscesses, excision of tumors, and circumcision for both boys and girls.

For the public health, the people were exhorted to frequent fasting and the regular use of emetics and enemas.[17] The daily life of the people was strictly regulated by hygienic laws governing the burial of the dead, diet, sexual intercourse, care of infants, and cleanliness of the body and in the home.

The Egyptian medical papyri demonstrate a ra-

50

tional approach to medicine and surgery, based on clinical observation, and an early separation between magic, religion, and medicine.

There was no magic in the treatment of injuries and surgical conditions; also completely rational was the establishment of a relationship between hematuria and schistosomiasis.

Basic concept among Egyptian physicians was the (putrefaction) as a biologic process of decay and corruption; for them the *materia peccans* resided in the fecal contents of the bowels, the absorption of which led eventually to the destruction of the body. Hence the widespread concern with prophylactic cleansing of the bowels by enemas and purgatives to avoid pathogenic material that might arise from absorbed excreta. This concept was reflected in both medicine and religion: the embalmer's duty was to prevent putrefaction in the dead body; the physician's task was to prevent it in the living organism.

Much of Egyptian medical practice was based on magico-religious beliefs, but it also contained the seed of scientific medicine, as Egyptian engineering contained the rudiments of physics. These seeds germinated slowly in the rainless valleys of Egypt, until some 2500 years ago they came to flower in the Hellenic islands, to usher in the next and brilliant era of the epic of medicine.

THE MEDICAL PAPYRI

Generally used to illustrate ancient Egyptian medicine are eight medical papyri[18] located in the United States, Britain, and Germany and dated between 1900 and 1200 B.C.

FROM THE EBERS PAPYRUS:

If you examine a person who suffers in the region of the stomach and vomits frequently, and you find a protuberance in the anterior parts, and his eyes are tired and the nose is stopped, then say to him: It is a putrefaction of the excrement, the excrements are not passing through the intestines; prepare for him white bread, absinthe in large amounts, add to it garlic steeped in beer, give the patient to eat of the meat of a fat beef and a beer to drink composed of various ingredients, in order to open both his eyes and his nose and to create an exit for his excrements.

To drive away inflammation of the eyes, grind the stems of the juniper of Byblos, steep them in water, apply to the eyes of the sick person and he will be quickly cured. To cure granulations of the eye you will prepare a remedy of cyllyrium, verdigris, onions, blue vitriol, powdered wood; mix and apply to the eyes.

FROM THE EDWIN SMITH PAPYRUS:

Instructions concerning a break in the column of

the nose: You should cleanse it for him with two plugs of linen. You should place two other plugs of linen saturated with grease in the inside of his two nostrils. You should put him at his mooring stakes until the swelling is drawn out. You should apply for him stiff rolls of linen by which his nose is held fast. You should treat him afterward with lint every day until he recovers.

THE ABOVE TRANSLATED INTO THE HIEROGLYPHIC CHARACTER

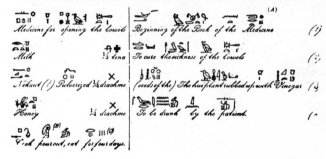

Prescription from the Ebers Papyrus, with translation into hieroglyphic characters below.

OTHER ARCHAIC CIVILIZATIONS

INDIAN MEDICINE

Paralleling the Mesopotamian and Egyptian civilization, although not quite as ancient, was the civilization that flourished in the Indus river valley of India, comprising people of unknown origin and the great Aryan migration that peopled India and parts of western Asia and Europe.

Some of the most ancient Indian medical texts such as the *Atharvaveda* contain magic formulas against demons; at that time medicine was almost entirely in the hands of the ruling caste of Brahmins.

The chief god of medicine in India was Dhanvantari, physician to other gods. He received the *Ayurveda* (medical traditions) directly from Brahma. Ayurvedic medicine is still widely practiced in the countryside today.

In the Brahmanic period (800 B.C.–1000 A.D.)

physicians belonged to a caste lower than the priests, and took an oath similar to the Hippocratic one. Classics of the period were the medical books of Atreya, Charaka (100 A.D.), Susruta (500 A.D.), and Vaghbhata (600 A.D.), founders of Indian medicine.

The basic concept was the equilibrium of the three body elements, air, phlegm, bile, the disturbance of which caused disease. Diagnosis was advanced (more than 1000 diseases described). Pulse lore was developed and the taste test was used to diagnose diabetes mellitus. Therapy was based on hygiene and diet and eliminatory measures. Surgery was highly developed, more than 100 surgical instruments being described; laparotomies, cataract extractions and above all oto- and rhinoplasty were far advanced. Hypnosis was used for anesthesia and variolization was practiced.

Many of the Indian medicinal herbs found their way into Western medicine, notably *Rauwolfia serpentina*.

HEBREW MEDICINE

Growing directly out of Mesopotamian medicine was the specialized medical lore of the Hebrews, cousins of many of the Tigris-Euphrates peoples.

The great contribution to medicine of the Hebrews was the first great codification of private and collective principles of hygiene, thereby laying the foundation of public health legislation.

The Bible and Talmud contain extensive descriptions of diseases (infectious, endocrine, mental), laws, precepts, and practices of hygiene mostly related to diet and sexual practices, important epidemiologic anticipations (transmission of plague by rats) and little surgery (circumcision).

An important innovation was the practice of bleeding animals before eating them, thus avoiding the role of animal blood as a culture medium for germs.

Disease was considered a punishment for sin, and Jehovah was accepted as the giver of disease as well as the supreme healer. Physicians and bleeders are mentioned in the Talmud, although the Bible generally merged the concept of physician with that of saint or apostle (St. Luke, the "beloved physician"). Mosaic laws (transmitted from Egypt through Moses'

education in that country) were among the first organized public health measures to be clearly codified.

CHINESE MEDICINE

China is the youngest of the archaic civilizations, and its tradition places the origin of Chinese medicine with three legendary emperors: Fu Hsi (ca. 2800 B.C.), who originated the philosophy of *yang* and *yin* in nature; Shen Nung (ca. 2700 B.C.), who originated herbal medicine and acupuncture, and Huang Ti (ca. 2600 B.C.), author of the most ancient medical text (stiil studied), *Nei Ching*.

Chinese philosophy established that man, like everything else, is composed of wood, fire, earth, metal, and water, to which five elements correspond five planets, seasons, colors, sounds, senses, viscera, and tastes.

The two opposing qualities in metabolism, as in the universe, are *yang* (the male element) and *yin* (the female element); health and tranquility rest on the perfect equilibrium of these two principles, disease being a disharmony among the five organs created by interference of corresponding planets, seasons, sounds, and colors. *Yang* being always dominant, revulsive medicines are used to excite this principle and effect a cure in case of disease.

Chinese diagnosis grew into an extremely intricate art, including the study of some 200 types of pulse and 37 shades of tongue.

The basis of treatment in ancient Chinese medicine (still practiced today) was acupuncture aided by moxibustion: small needles were introduced into imaginary canals called *chin* (these images of the canals being probably inspired by the irrigation canals in the land) in which were supposed to circulate the two vital principles. Twelve of these canals were related to vital organs; by puncturing them, obstructions or bad secretions were allowed to escape, thereby restoring the body's over-all equilibrium.

Among the contributions of Chinese medicine were almost two thousand substances, some of which were ephedrine, chaulmoogra, and camphor, opium, and sodium sulfate.

Preceding pages: In the palace hall of King Akhenaton, who introduced heliotherapic-monotheistic cult of sun disc, sculptor works on bust of King's sister-wife, Queen Nefertete. Uncomely appearance of King, probably suffering from rickets or an endocrinal dysfunction, contrasts with the serene beauty of his Sun-Queen wearing ornamental headdress, royal bracelets and necklace. Physician to the Court, wearing ceremonial wig and leaning on golden staff, watches sculpting of Nefertete's famous head.

Aswan dam backs up Nile 250 miles, irrigates thousands of acres.

ARCHAIC VERSUS MODERN IN
NEAR EAST TODAY

Jet planes now roar through the skies over Egypt and Iraq, while on the ground is fought a constant battle between the archaic and the modern ways of life. In thousands of details of daily life the ancient customs of Pharaonic and Babylonian days can still be discerned in Egypt, Syria, Lebanon, Iraq, and the lands that were once Palestine.

Enormous progress has been made since the last war in the fields of public health, largely through the untiring work of teams supported by various agencies of the United Nations. Working either directly or through governments they are steadily conquering the three worst diseases in the Near East, schistosomiasis, trachoma, and malaria.

Two historic scourges of the ancient world, plague and cholera, are today infrequent and limited to local outbreaks. One ironic problem is that new irrigation canals frequently cause a rise in schistosomiasis, for which snails are the intermediate hosts.

Leading country in public health in that region today is Israel, where there is a ratio of one physician to 450 of the population (1 per 3600 in United Arab Republic).

One of the most difficult problems to solve in the Fertile Crescent is that of the numerous nomadic tribes who live much as their ancestors must have lived in Biblical times. Another problem is that of the thousands of refugees left over from the wars and disturbances in the Near East.

Modern epidemiologic control in Iraq. Woman suffering from bejel is given penicillin injection.

Basketlike boat called kurfa, seen on Tigris, goes back to prehistoric times, is similar to the Celtic coracle.

III

At Dawn the Sun Shines

THE golden sun of Attica for many years had already been sparkling the orange and olive groves of Greece when a small band of courageous men, the first philosophers, dared for the first time in History to formulate formidable questions: What is man, and what is Nature?

These were the men who initiated the Greek miracle: the awakening of human conscience. The small rock-girded peninsula, washed by the wine-colored waters of the Latin sea sung of by Homer, thus contributed to the "time-axis," that momentous period in History when philosophers from Greece, prophets from Israel, Confucius and Lao-tse in China, and Buddha in India, six centuries before Christ, created the first great religions and philosophies of mankind.

The first great task accomplished by Greece was the unification of its peoples, dispersed throughout the isles surrounding the mainland. Two things maintained this unity: First, the epic hexameters of the *Iliad* and the *Odyssey*, compiled about one millennium before Christ by a wandering blind bard called Homer. These poems reveal the existence of an empirical, chiefly surgical, medicine. Before Homer, the seat of life was placed at the liver; with Homer, it was transferred to the heart; after Homer, it passed to the brain. Second, the Olympic games, which, held every four years, served to measure time. Their Marathon race commemorated the feat performed by an athlete who ran without pausing from Marathon to Athens, whereupon he fell dead, probably as a result of acute hypoglycemia.

Half a millennium later, the Greek philosophers opened the luminous path that would lead Greece to its Golden Age. Thales of Miletus, Heraclitus, Anaximenes, Democedes of Croton, Empedocles of Agrigentum, Pythagoras, and Alcmaeon of Croton—these men advanced the basis of the two great doctrines that for many centuries to come would rule medicine: the humoral and the pneumatic.

In this sunny landscape there blossomed two great systems of medical philosophy: the Aesculapian cult, or temple medicine, based on religious suggestions and psychotherapy; and empirical medicine, based on rational thought.

Just as today people go to spas, in classical Greece people made pilgrimages to the temples of Aesculapius. From Greek mythology we learn that the god Apollo, jealous of the nymph Coronis, had her slain with arrows. The lovely Coronis fell dead, her slim torso bejeweled with rubies of blood, whereupon her son Aesculapius was secreted to a mountain by the kind and gifted Chiron, the centaur, who taught Aesculapius the healing art. Aesculapius performed numerous miracles of healing, became a god, and was worshipped in Asclepieia throughout Greece.

To these temples, erected on scenic grounds with natural springs and provided with stadiums, theatres, and bathing pools, came flocks of miracle-hungry pilgrims, avid to read the temple tablets—their equivalent of our electronic newsboards—listing the miraculous cures performed, and to practice the healing ritual known as "incubation" or temple sleep. At the foot of the marble and gold statue of the god, they lay down to sleep, and during the night the god, incarnated in the Asclepiad or priest, appeared in their dreams, followed by his daughters Hygeia and Panacea, and prescribed healing herbs and even performed operations. In the morning the patients departed, often cured, after making a sacrificial offering of gold and sheep or songs and prayers, according to their means.

Side by side with this psychotherapeutic temple medicine there blossomed an empirical medicine that regarded disease as a disharmony in the *physis*. This medicine was practiced by *periodeutai*, or itinerant physicians, by court physicians, and by military surgeons. The *periodeutai* were wandering craftsmen who traveled ceaselessly. In the public square of the town they would exercise the art of oratory, sing, and recite poetry, in an effort to attract people to their *iatreia* or offices. They were also experts in the art of *pronoia*, and often bombarded the onlookers, before they had a chance to say a word, with a detailed description of their ailments. This empirical medicine, which used diet, herbs, and drugs in treatment, was represented by the old school of Cnidus, which was interested in diagnosis, and later by the school of Cos, which specialized in *pronoia*.

One man was responsible for this new attitude in medicine. We know little of his life—even less than we know of Christ's youth—yet Hippocrates of Cos has passed into History as the Father of Medicine. Like Homer, Christ, and Socrates, Hippocrates never wrote a word, yet the *Corpus Hippocraticum* consists of no less than seventy-two volumes and contains an exposition of the knowledge of this great physician, the first to treat *patients* instead of diseases and to prepare clinical case histories with a modern biographical approach.

In the center of the town of Cos, there still stands the plane tree in whose shade Hippocrates is reputed to have taught his pupils while examining his patients. He accepted the existence of *many* diseases instead of just one, and regarded them as natural processes that altered the humors of the body, of which he believed there were four, based perhaps on observation of the four layers formed by clotting blood. He believed in the curative powers of Nature. With the advent of Hippocrates, the sick ceased to be considered sinners, while sinners began to be considered sick people. Patients became human beings who went through a certain process in their life history that was called disease. This biographical approach prevails every day more in medicine. Like a wreath of laurel crowning his work, there remains the *Hippocratic Oath*, a great code based on the golden rule that to be a good physician one must first be a good and kind man.

Many schools sprang up in those times, the most outstanding being the dogmatic, the empirical, the methodist, the pneumatic, the eclectic, and the peripatetic. Eventually Hellenic knowledge leaped from Athens to the shores of the Nile when the Greek Ptolemy I Soter founded in Alexandria the *Museum* or home of the muses, which housed

one of the most famous libraries in the world with more than half a million volumes. Here taught Archimedes, Euclid, the Hippocratist Herophilus of Chalcedon, father of anatomy, and the Galenist surgeon Erasistratus, who discovered the tricuspid valve. Here also was born the first great clinical school and university in the world, complete with laboratories, cafeterias, and publishing house. In this school anatomic dissection was first practiced, ushering in the concept that the seat of disease was the *organs*, not the humors.

Greek art reflected the Greeks' attitude on life. The Nike of Delos, the first effigy ever made of a woman not only running but *smiling* as well, is a symbol of the Greek spirit, which humanized the gods, while deifying man. Whereas Egyptian temples were fortresses, the Parthenon atop the sacred hill was more like a marble harp suspended from the radiant blue, an eternal symbol of the Greek miracle.

To the work of the Greek philosophers modern civilization owes an immense debt. Socrates taught man to think; Plato regarded the brain as man's most noble tool, established the unity of body and soul, founded the Academy, and in his *Symposium*, through the lips of Eryximachus the physician, described medicine as "the art of understanding the love affairs of the organs of the body." His pupil Aristotle, whose mind was a vast empire of knowledge, restored medicine to the kingdom of biology. Whereas his master Plato accpted all knowledge as emanating from *within*, Aristotle contended that everything emanated from the *outside* and was absorbed through the senses and perception.

Greek medicine is not the beginning, but the *middle* of the history of medicine. More than two thousand years separate Hippocrates from Imhotep, and about as many years separate Hippocrates and Fleming. Only by being aware of this fact can one realize how ancient medicine is.

Great and noble is our Greek medical heritage: the objective observation of the patient; the concept of disease as a process of natural causes, cured spontaneously by Nature; and the creation of a new type of physician—a humanist and a humanitarian, conscious of his mission and his destiny, as the kind and good Hippocrates himself was.

F.M.I.

Artist's restoration of the Temple of Aesculapius at Epidaurus, the most famous of all the temples.

The figure of Hippocrates, sitting in the shade of a plane tree on the island of Cos, is explaining the symptoms of a respiratory complaint to a group of students. The Hippocratic school was familiar with nasal catarrh, laryngitis, pneumonia, pleurisy and phthisis.

III

GREEK MEDICINE

During the thousand years before Christ the center of civilization moved from the hot lands of Egypt and Mesopotamia to the Aegean scene of dazzling colors, blue seas, temperate days and nights.

Along the craggy shores of the Greek peninsula and the necklace of islands stretching to the coast of Asia Minor, the concepts of rational medicine and medical ethics were born, part of man's search for objective truth.

To be a Greek in the classical era was to be a part of a communion where man aspired to glory, reason, and beauty. No longer a groveling pawn of tyrants, man now saw himself as an individual capable of infinite enhancement.

The sense of national identity was forged in an epos of heroes and heroic deeds. Minstrels wandered from shore to shore, reciting their tales, until some time in the ninth century a blind bard named Homer gathered the tales of the war with Ilium and the travels of Odysseus into two great epics of adventure.

Early Hellenes were loyal to their chieftains, violent in their passions, and admirers of physical prowess. They gained their livelihood from the earth or from plunder and piracy.

Among the many city-states, the greatest was Athens, ruled by men who did not claim divinity.

Although Persians and Spartans threatened Athenian supremacy, the years from 500 to 400 B.C. saw the gathering of Aeschylus, Sophocles, Euripides, Herodotus, Hippocrates, Socrates, Plato, and later of Aristotle. The art of living, science, ethics, politics became subjects for philosophic inquiry. In one hundred brilliant years, literature, art, philosophy, and medicine soared to an unprecedented apogee.

THE FOUNDATIONS. The first Greeks were an Aryan people who migrated from plains beyond the Dan-

ube. Vigorous, bearded men with horses, chariots, and bronze weapons, they overwhelmed the Stone Age inhabitants and settled in kinship groups around walled citadels where they installed their chieftains.

They formed links with riper Eastern cultures by way of Crete,[1] at about the same time as Confucius and Lao-tse appeared in China, Buddha in India, Zoroaster in Persia, and Isaiah in Judea.

In that fertile age the Ionian Greeks launched into speculative thought unlike that of any people before them: they generalized from observed facts, saw principles of nature where others had seen only magic phenomena.

To the aging Egyptians these Greeks seemed like prattling children, to the religious cultures they were pagans without faith or discipline. But they borrowed Egypt's mathematics and Babylonia's astronomy, the wealth of knowledge uncritically assembled through millennia by older cultures, and wove them with free and reasoning minds into philosophy, history, and logic.

Their arts escaped from two-dimensional conventions to portray figures as seen in nature. They built white marble temples on rocky heights, oriented so that in the rising and setting sun the dark base sank away into shadow and the shrine appeared to float on shafts of light.

Commerce flourished in the cities, releasing men to engage in philosophy and politics. The *agora* in a Greek city became a marketplace not only of goods but of ideas. There developed the *polis*, the city-state with a government sometimes elected by its freemen citizens, sometimes headed by a tyrant who overthrew the aristocracy with the support of peasants and merchants.

THE PHYSICIAN-WARRIOR. In the great days of which Homer sang, every warrior was skilled in extracting an arrowhead; he could stop the flow of blood, bathe the wound with warm water, lay on a healing balm. Achilles himself had been instructed in the medical arts by no less a teacher than the wise centaur Chiron.

The warriors knew the bones and joints, muscles and sinews of the body. They observed how the beating heart could make an arrow in the chest quiver, and how the large neck tendon holds the head erect.

Most deadly were wounds in the forehead, the throat, and windpipe where the departing breath of life carried the soul with it. Homer's physicians knew that a spear striking the breast might pierce the lung, that a mighty thrust into a buttock could pass through to the bladder.

Of infection, suppuration, fever, gangrene, tetanus, or internal hemorrhage they observed little; a wounded hero died or he rallied; with stimulating drinks and healing herbs he recovered to fight again. Seven or eight out of every ten wounded did not recover; least dangerous were arrow wounds, but those made by the new and terrible weapon, the iron sword, were most often mortal.

THE OLYMPIANS. The gods venerated by the Greeks were the gayest, most human, most inspiriting that the ancient world had yet known; they spent

Ancient Greek cupping instruments.

timeless, deathless lives in feasting, love-making, meddling in earthly intrigues. They suffered human frailties without loss of dignity, and in their dealings with man they neither humiliated him nor demanded his abasement.

In Greek religion mortals were fated to die, were not promised deification. The Homeric heroes faced their world stripped of illusions; they were aware that gods do not succor the weak, that aristocracy signifies more than wealth and inheritance, that strength and personal glory (*kudos*) were the highest

good; the most grievous sin was *hybris*, the assumption of more than mortal power, of immoderate self-importance.

Beginning in 776 B.C. pilgrims from all Hellas swarmed to the games at Olympus where Zeus was enshrined. Religious in origin the quadrennial event served to unify discordant factions; wars were interrupted under a sacred truce effective while the festival lasted. Only Greeks were permitted to compete; the Hellenic ancestry of entrants was strictly scrutinized, and women were barred from attending. Toughness and endurance were admired; wrestlers were known to prefer strangulation to defeat. Among many contests were races run in deep sand and in soldier's equipment. Those with unique skills also performed: acrobats, conjurers, lecturers, even authors who gave readings of their works. Victorious athletes were feted on homecoming, given free meals for life.

THE PEOPLE. Frugal Greeks had no taste for oriental opulence; aristocrats' homes were spacious, free of excessive ornamentation and luxuries. Personal fortunes were not flaunted, though gold, ivory, and marble were lavished on sculpture and public buildings; 44 talents of gold weighing 2545 pounds[2] were used on Athena's 45 foot statue in the Parthenon.

The common people lived in dwellings of sun-dried brick, built on rubble, dark and cramped, in streets strewn each day with litter hurled from houses to the warning cry of *exodos*.

Diet was limited in variety, included porridges of barley or wheat mixed either with honey and oil or with grated cheese and eggs. Lentils, chick-peas, string beans were heavily consumed. The wealthy ate game, veal, eel, caviar, and oysters from abroad. As banquets and *symposia* grew popular, menus improved with the addition of more meats, sardines, herrings; a favorite sauce was made by pickling small hake.

Clothes were simple: women wore a *chiton* or flowing long tunic, men a shorter version reaching to midthigh. Over this both sexes wore a *himation,* an outer cloak usually made of wool and weighted with metal at the four corners so that it could be draped in a variety of ways. Physicians followed a characteristic fashion in their mode of draping their *himatia* and by wearing strips of fur wound around their calves. Some fashionable Athenian women attended private gatherings garbed only in chitons of transparent silk especially spun for them on the island of Cos.

Privileged youths enjoyed unique status; a mark of honor was to be chosen by older men of education and taken under protective wing, to be taught wisdom and ethics often in the *palestrae* where they exercised. Teacher-disciple attachments were considered acceptable if the ideal was a noble relationship, but condemned if carnally pursued or frivolously motivated.

Wives were restricted to housekeeping and childbearing; well-to-do husbands could openly take concubines. The *hetairai,* women of education, wit, and beauty, were the partners of distinguished men and were groomed for their vocation. They alone of all women were invited to banquets and gatherings of philosophers and leaders, receiving large fees for their services; some became wealthy and contributed generously to the building of temples and public shrines.

The ratio of slaves to free citizens was about ten to one. Aristotle considered them excellent human instruments; he estimated that 100 slaves were required to maintain the comfort of one philosopher.

THE PHYSICIAN-PHILOSOPHER.   The pioneers of rational medicine were early Greek philosophers, the Milesians, the Pythagoreans, the Sicilians, who sought to explain the universe by pure reason. Unencumbered by magic, religion, or tradition, these heralds of natural science were the first to surmise that natural events were not miracles but were explicable under systems of immutable law. Some explained the world process by monistic theories; others projected a dual or multifaceted version of phenomena.

Observing the need of human, animal, and plant life for water, Thales of Miletus propounded the primary principle that water was the cause of all things. His fame spread beyond his native Ionia when he correctly foretold a total eclipse of the sun on May 28, 585 B.C. His fellow citizen Anaxagoras later advanced the opinion that the sun was not a god but an incandescent stone as big as Greece. Still another Milesian, Anaximenes, observed the role of winds in nature and of respiration in human life and reduced the diversity of the world to the single element of *pneuma* or air.

Somber-minded Heraclitus of Ephesus was the first man to declare that dreams were a retreat into a personal world and not a journey into supernatural spheres.

Majestic in purple tunic and golden laurel wreath, half convinced that he was a god, Empedocles of Agrigentum explained the world in terms of four elements: earth, water, air and fire. Synthesizing Egyptian myths, he proclaimed the blood and heart to be the seat of the *pneuma* or vital spirit, saw in the alternating motions of attraction and repulsion the antagonism of love and hate. Empedocles composed a volume of dietary prescriptions in 400 verses.

Pythagoras of Samos constructed an orderly universe based on the harmony of numbers, combining this mystic concept with scientific experiments in music theory and acoustics. His secret sect, founded for the study of mathematics, in time became a quasi-religious brotherhood aiming at purification of the

Hygeia, goddess of health and one of the daughters of Aesculapius. She appeared with her father in the healing temples.

63

soul through knowledge and a systematized way of life; ritualistic accretions eventually weighted it with taboos against eating beans, stirring the fire with iron, leaving impressions of the body on the bed. Pythagorean science and cosmology served as beacons to later giants of Greek philosophy; to Hippocratic thought they contributed the principle of days and crises of disease.

Phythagoras' pupil, Alcmaeon of Croton, pursued the science of anatomy with the dissection of animals; among his achievements was the separation of blood vessels into veins and arteries. His was the doctrine that harmony or disharmony of the body's component materials resulted in health or sickness; his treatise on nature became a fundamental medical text.

Other philosophic pioneers were Parmenides of Elea, a logician who declared that heat loss was the cause of death; Diogenes of Apollonia who practiced comparative anatomy; Democritus of Abdera, who first conceived of the universe as composed of space and atoms; as a physician he sought the causes of epidemic diseases.

THE CULT. Rising rational inquiry did not exclude a parallel rise of magico-religious medicine in Greece; this centered around the god-head of Aesculapius. From families tracing their ancestry to this sacred source evolved a secret medical lore that was later shared with others who took the oath that became the oath of Hippocrates and of all physicians.

Aesculapius was worshiped in magnificent temples throughout the Aegean lands. Serene but never awesome, he calmed with soothing suggestion and magic ministration the sick and maimed; his symbol was a staff entwined by a single serpent.

Aesculapius was mythically born of Apollo and the nymph Coronis. Her dalliance with a mortal brought down Apollonian jealousy and his lethal arrows; in death the god delivered her of the infant Aesculapius who was taught the arts of medicine by the wise and kind centaur Chiron. Turned partly into a horse by a jealous wife, Chiron was learned in music and healing art, he also educated Jason and Achilles.

On this myth arose a cult of divine medicine that brought the afflicted in vast numbers, afoot or on donkeys, to the god-physician's shrine. The temples of Aesculapius were built in healthful pastoral settings, usually with mineral springs at hand; they were equipped with bathing pools, gymnasia, gardens. At Epidaurus the most splendid of the temples included exercise grounds, race track, a theatre seating 20,000 persons.

Admission to the healing sanctum was preceded by elaborate ritual: in preparation the patients underwent purification by rigorous fasting, sea baths, fumigations. Each day they read at the temple's entrance votive tablets describing medical cures re-

Greek physician palpating patient's abdomen, particularly the liver, which was regarded as an important seat of health.

cently performed. Invited at last to the inner court of the temple, the sufferers were often already relieved of pain and worry. They made offerings before the gold and ivory image of the god, then priests, acolytes, masseurs, and bath attendants prepared them for the temple sleep.

On pallets made of the skins of animals sacrificed to the deity, they dreamed that Aesculapius walked among them, followed by his daughters Hygeia and Panacea and his ever-present serpent.

Priests were paid in money, supplications, or songs according to a patient's means; votive offerings were frequently of silver and gold. At Epidaurus were recorded such cures as the delivery of a woman pregnant five years, as a blind man whose eyes opened to see the temple trees, and as a bald man whom the god endowed with hair overnight.

Mythical surgery was also reported: when a Spartan girl suffering from dropsy besought him, Aesculapius cut off her head, held her upside down to drain the fluid, then replaced her head on her neck. Aesculapian miracles so depopulated Hades that, on Pluto's complaint, Zeus struck down the healer with a thunderbolt.

Simultaneously, an empirio-rational school of medicine throve on the peninsula of Cnidos off the Asia Minor coast; here therapy focused on symptoms and diagnosis was the primary interest. On the ad-

Grateful patients bring tributes to a Greek physician. Note serpent symbol coiled in tree.

joining island of Cos a rival school was mainly concerned with the art of *pronoia*, or deducing the past, present, and future of an illness from the symptoms.

THE FATHER. Illumined in the fifth century's sunburst of Greek intellect was the towering figure of Hippocrates, myth and man, obscurely born among the olive groves of seagirt Cos in 460 B.C., more than one thousand years after Imhotep. No physician before him matched his accomplishment. To him were attributed 72 texts, 42 clinical histories that vastly swelled the sum of medical knowledge; he added to medical terminology such words as chronic, exacerbation, relapse, resolution, crisis, paroxysm, and convalescence.

Legend proliferated around him; the magnetic core of his wisdom attracted the thinking of others until, centuries after his death at an age perhaps close to a hundred years, Hippocrates the man, in life an errant Asklepiad, gave way to the Hippocratic *Corpus*, a compilation made during the third century B.C. by Alexandrine scholars.

Hippocrates winnowed out philosophy from medicine, expelled the gods in one incisive stroke: "I am about to discuss the disease called sacred (epilepsy). It is not in my opinion, any more divine or more sacred than other diseases, but has a natural cause, and its supposed divine origin is due to men's inex-

perience, and to their wonder at its peculiar character."

He conceived of disease as a natural process born of natural causes: environment, climate, diet, way of life. The body possessed its own means of recovery; fever expressed the struggle of the body to cure itself. Health resulted from the harmony and mutual sympathy of all the humors; a healthy man was one in a balanced mental and physical state.

Hewing close to naturalistic data, tending toward prognosis rather than diagnosis, focusing more on the diseased patient than on the disease, the Hippocratic writings were rooted in the authority of observed facts. They established firmly the existence not of one disease but many, singled out the curative powers of nature. Important in therapy were exercise, massage, sea baths, diet, and drugs; physicians were urged to know seasonal effects of hot and cold winds and the properties of water peculiar to each region.

Hippocrates and his disciples collected scientific case histories as none before had done; in *Epidemics* he described the events of illness with cool detachment. He observed pneumonia, pleurisy, tuberculosis, and malaria. In *Airs, Waters, Places* appeared the first treatise on public health and medical geography, the first descriptions of urinary calculi, and the first observations of sexual impotence. His writings on children's diseases, injuries of the head, fractures, and articulations were masterful; his aphorisms and precepts, like the physicians' Oath, were responses to the humanism and love of man that characterized the noblest of the Greeks.

Hippocratic pathology, essentially humoral, directed attention to the correspondence of the fundamental elements (air, water, earth, and fire) to blood, phlegm, yellow bile, and black bile, each humor having its specific seat respectively in the heart, liver, spleen, and brain.

The mechanism of disease proceeded in stages: *apepsis*, when the offending material, *materia peccans*, brought the humors into their raw or crude state; the state of *pepsis* whereby nature, aided by heat, brought the disease to maturity; the *crisis*, usually lasting three or four days, when confrontation occurred between nature and the disease, an event characterized by increased secretions. Thus nature was viewed as a resisting force: "untaught and uninstructed."

Hippocratic teaching clearly enunciated in the Oath the moral and ethical codes of professional practice; the Greek world saw a new, reassuring image of the learned physician, a man wise, modest and humane; medicine once again became the possession of men.

THE PRACTITIONER. Through the towns and villages of the Aegean lands wandered the *periodeutes*, itinerant physician, knocking on doors, asking if there were any sick who needed help. If he found enough demand for his services he opened an establishment, his *iatreion*, and remained as long as there was sufficient practice. His status was that of an artisan, he had no medical license, but he had systematic training; if he had studied with a distinguished teacher or had attended one of the great schools, Cos or Cnidos, his qualifications were respected.

In a city the physician might hold a municipal or state appointment with an annual salary raised among citizens by a special tax; from his private practice he might also receive rich remuneration and handsome gifts. Greek physicians rarely remained poor, some became exceedingly wealthy; they moved as equals among philosophers and poets, were honored at banquets for their medical skill, and became the friends and companions of kings.

The physician had a reputation for devotion to duty and a high standard of ethical behavior; when his city was struck by earthquake, siege, or pestilence he labored without pay, tending the sick, burning bonfires in the streets to drive out disease; often he earned his city's decree of thanks. He served the poor without fee and prescribed for sick slaves to save their masters the trouble of caring for them.

His principal concern were the men of wealth and

Marble head of Socrates in Farnese Collection.

leisure who devoted themselves to government, philosophy, and the arts. He gave lectures on health and hygiene and made generous gifts to his city's institutions. Yet if he attended a play of Aristophanes or Euripides he might well hear himself criticized for taking fees for services that he should give freely. Plato rebuked physicians for prescribing in a tyrannical and cursory manner for slaves, whereas with an upper-class patient they discoursed and sought to instill confidence.

At the public games physicians treated the athletes without fee, also any spectators who became ill. They often held an appointment from an organization; the *epheboi*, youths newly arrived at citizenship, had their own physician. Or they worked in a gymnasium, especially versed in therapeutic exercise and medical dietetics.

Obstetrics and gynecology were left to midwives and women physicians, among whom were several skilled herbalists and medical botanists. One famous midwife, Agnodice, dressed in male attire to attend medical lectures; when she was arrested and brought to trial the Athenian women rose in her defence.

When a city went to war, physicians accompanied troops on campaign, decided on a sanitary location for the camp. The men were ordered to observe moderation in eating, boil their water, and keep fit with exercise. Campaigns were rigorous; in the mountainous lands men froze to death, suffered frostbite and snow blindness. Military surgeons were skillful at removing arrows and treating wounds; wounded prisoners of war were unchained and given medical care. But a general's physician might also be put to death for failing to cure his illness or that of a favorite aide.

THE GIANTS. Nearing the fourth century B.C., Hellas was riven by war, faced dissolution and ruin. Yet the great works of Pericles had not yet vanished; his enlightened leadership had made Athens the center for art and thought; literature reached its zenith, philosophers came there to think and study and teach. So keen was popular thirst for knowledge that a class of Sophists or wisdom-mongers flourished, spreading the wares of rhetoric and facile debate before an eager generation.

Athens tottered at last; hunger stalked the imperial city; the ideals of citizenship became corroded. In this fretful era of political eclipse lived Socrates, a lowborn sculptor whose mission was to sting the accepted order like a gadfly, cross-examining, discussing and debating with all who would listen. Married to a shrewish wife, never angry, buoyantly optimistic, frequently feigning total ignorance, he taught philosophy without fee to a devoted following and finally paid for his intellectual integrity with his life.

Highborn Plato, who could trace his ancestry to Solon and the god Poseidon, was 24 years old when

Portrait of Plato after sculpture in Vatican Museum.

Athens fell to the Macedonians. Charming with women, robustly built and good-looking, he had wrestled at the Isthmian games, fought in three battles, and won a medal for bravery. Excelling in music, mathematics, and rhetoric, composer of youthful epigrams and love poems before turning to philosophy, Plato wove his philosophic principles and those of his master into 27 dialogues of imagined argumentative conversations. Platonic thought differentiated between the material world, perceived through the senses, and true reality, which was conceived as a suprasensory world of abstract ideas.

The medical beliefs of Plato assigned to man an immortal soul residing in the head while a mortal soul dwelled in the torso. The heart was the fountainhead of the blood, the liver was the mirror of the soul, the spleen the organ for cleansing the liver; the unsatisfied uterus roamed in the body like a goldfish swimming in its bowl.

Viewing the human body as formed of triangles and the world's only perfect geometric figure, Plato indicated that the blood circulated and was first to employ the term *anaisthesia*. The figure of the physician Eryximachus appeared in the *Symposium* where medicine was spoken of as "the knowledge of the loves and desires of the body, and how to satisfy them."

Friends purchased for Plato a suburban recreation grove that had been dedicated to the god Academus; here rose the Academy on whose portal was inscribed "Let none without geometry enter here." Students paid no fees; the school was supported by philanthropists to provide philosophers with leisure.

Here for two decades studied Aristotle, younger than Plato by 43 years. Son of a physician to the King of Macedon, called the Stagirite after the Thracian city of his birth, he tutored young Alexander for three years. He undertook the monumental task of classifying all existing fields of knowledge, of founding biology, psychology, formal logic, deductive reasoning, and scientific method. His works treated such medical subjects as respiration, longevity, dreams, sleep, and sensation, as well as classical rhetoric, poetry, ethics, political theory.

Aristotle founded his Lyceum in the buildings of an elegant Athenian gymnasium dedicated to Apollo Lyceus, god of shepherds. Here he established zoologic gardens, a museum of natural history, and his famous library, and he paced the shrub-lined walks while students took notes on animal biology, botany, metaphysics.

Aristotle's basic thought opposed that of Plato in some areas, particularly in the separateness of sensory and ideational worlds. He adopted the heart as the seat of emotions and gave teleologic explanations of body organs. One of his precepts was that the philosopher must begin with medicine and the physician must end with philosophy.

BETTMANN ARCHIVE

Head of Aristotle in Palazzo Spada, Rome.

Preceding pages: *In the gardens of a Temple of Aesculapius, sick people and their relatives or assistants await their opportunity to enter the healing halls. Aesculapian temples were always set in beautiful surroundings, this being considered part of the required therapy.*

Other schools of thought made sporadic entrances in the philosophic area: the Dogmatists, who introduced speculation as a basis of medicine, and also schools of empiric, ecletic, methodist, or encyclopedic persuasions. Among the Peripatetics stood forth Theophrastus, the divine orator, one of Aristotle's most celebrated pupils; his *History of Plants* was a masterpiece of botanic observation. To him Aristotle bequeathed his library and museum, arranged for him to be his successor at the by then famous Lyceum.

Founded by Alexander the Great in 332 B.C. was the city of Alexandria, a port on the Mediterranean. The foundation of anatomic dissection as a means of study was one of Alexandria's contribution to the history of medicine. The horror of contact with corpses, springing not only from religious prejudice but also from the natural terror of death, had prevailed even with Hippocrates, for the Greeks flinched from touching a corpse for fear of being pestered by the spirit of the deceased. The systematic practice of anatomic dissection in Alexandria changed the face of medicine and opened the way to the concept that diseases have their particular seats in certain organs and not in any system of mysterious humors.

A leading figure in Alexandria was Herophilus of Chalcedon, founder of anatomy, whose name still endures in the torcular Herophili; he studied human viscera, described numerous organs, and named the calamus scriptorius and the duodenum.

Erasistratus, who flourished a generation later, dissected animals and human organs and by experiments in metabolism laid the first foundations of pathologic anatomy and physiology. He discovered the tricuspid valve and opened the abdomen in an access of surgical audacity. A great surgeon, with Galenist principles, he adhered to the established pneumatic doctrine.

Ancient mortars and other pharmacy instruments found on the island of Cos.

Centuries later, followers of Herophilus and Erasistratus succeeded in forming the empirical school, concerned with the practice of healing, observation, practical comparison, and therapeutics; outstanding among them were Heracleides of Tarentum and Serapion of Alexandria. But the rot was slowly setting in, and mysticism, occultism, and magic practices were steadily creeping back into the domain of science.

The school of Alexandria vanished in 30 A.D. when Cleopatra put an asp to her bosom and died. But its learning was by that time well disseminated throughout the civilized world and the seed of Roman technology in medicine was already firmly rooted and rapidly growing, providing the bridge to the next important milestone in the epic of medicine.

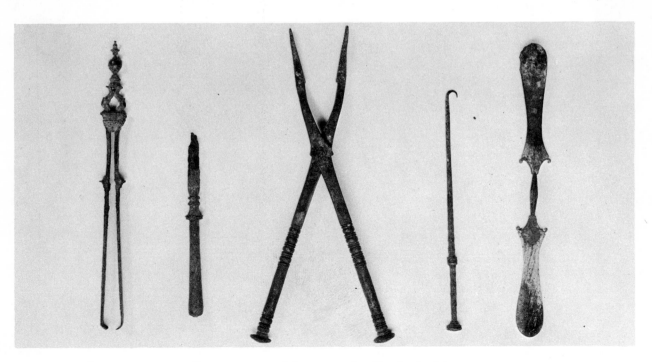

Instruments used in surgery by Greek physicians.

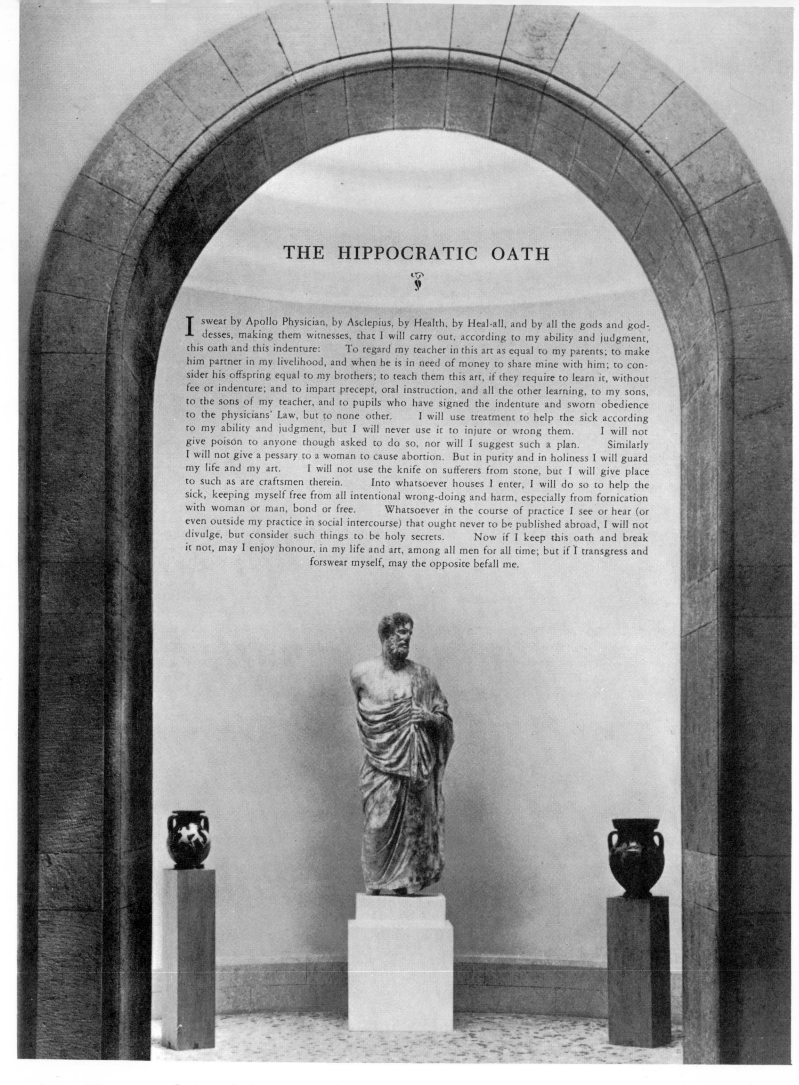

THE HIPPOCRATIC OATH

I swear by Apollo Physician, by Asclepius, by Health, by Heal-all, and by all the gods and goddesses, making them witnesses, that I will carry out, according to my ability and judgment, this oath and this indenture: To regard my teacher in this art as equal to my parents; to make him partner in my livelihood, and when he is in need of money to share mine with him; to consider his offspring equal to my brothers; to teach them this art, if they require to learn it, without fee or indenture; and to impart precept, oral instruction, and all the other learning, to my sons, to the sons of my teacher, and to pupils who have signed the indenture and sworn obedience to the physicians' Law, but to none other. I will use treatment to help the sick according to my ability and judgment, but I will never use it to injure or wrong them. I will not give poison to anyone though asked to do so, nor will I suggest such a plan. Similarly I will not give a pessary to a woman to cause abortion. But in purity and in holiness I will guard my life and my art. I will not use the knife on sufferers from stone, but I will give place to such as are craftsmen therein. Into whatsoever houses I enter, I will do so to help the sick, keeping myself free from all intentional wrong-doing and harm, especially from fornication with woman or man, bond or free. Whatsoever in the course of practice I see or hear (or even outside my practice in social intercourse) that ought never to be published abroad, I will not divulge, but consider such things to be holy secrets. Now if I keep this oath and break it not, may I enjoy honour, in my life and art, among all men for all time; but if I transgress and forswear myself, may the opposite befall me.

Statue of Hippocrates in the Cos Archeology Museum. Above is superimposed Oath of Hippocrates in the translation of W.H.S. Jones.

CAS OORTHUYS

Theatre above the Temple of Apollo where many mythologic dramas were performed.

GREECE: ANCIENT AND
MODERN

Greece today continues to present startling contrasts between the ancient world of classical Greece and the country that is made up of a large peninsula and numerous islands in the Ionian and Aegean seas.

The history of Greece since the eclipse of its glorious centuries is a sorry one of conquest and persecution. During and after the reign of Alexander the Great of Macedonia in the fourth century B.C., the warring Greek city-states continued to nurse their rivalries. Greece was weakened by warfare while the power of Rome was rising. In the year 146 B.C. the remnants of the Greek states fell under Roman domination and Greece became a mere backwater of the Roman empire.

73

Although Greece lost its political and economic importance, its culture and philosophy dominated the Mediterranean world, giving rise to the Hellenistic civilization that lived on through the Byzantine Empire after the fall of Rome to the barbarians.

During the centuries after the fall of Rome, Greece was frequently overrun by barbarians (Huns, Avars, Slavs, Bulgars). The Turks began their inroads during the eleventh century. It was finally conquered by the Turks in 1456, and Greece did not regain its independence until 1832.

Panoramic view of Athens, showing
the Acropolis with Parthenon; the
Theatre of Dionysus is below it. To
the left is Theatre of Herodes Atti-
cus. High point in background is
the Lycabettus crowned by a
monastery.

CAS OORTHUYS

WHO

At Metera (Gr., mother) Baby Center in Athens a physician explains baby care to
a group of student nurses.

Following page: *A Roman battlefield showing a physician attending a wounded legionnaire. The inscription on
the votive stone at right is a form of shorthand and reads:* SACRED TO APOLLO AND TO AESCULAPIUS, SALUS,
FORTUNA, FOR THE SUCCESS OF LUCIUS PETRONIUS FLORENTINUS, PREFECT OF THE FOURTH MOUNTED COHORT OF
THE AQUITANIANS, ROMAN CITIZENS. MARCUS RUBRIUS ZOSIMUS, PHYSICIAN OF THE ABOVE COHORT, RESIDENT OF
OSTIA, WILLINGLY AND GLADLY HAS DULY FULFILLED HIS PLEDGE. *Found at Obernburg-am-Main, Germany. Painted
by Hans Guggenheim.*

IV

A Torrent of Lions

L IKE a torrent of lions the Romans fell upon the historical scene, and their proud imperial eagles swept across the skies of the world.

Strong warriors the Romans were, as well as highly adept in law and administration. Originally a handful of Aryan merchants ruled by Etruscan kings, the Romans created an aristocratic republic, with a caste of patrician families lording it over the masses. Their history encompasses bloody triumvirates, mighty emperors—sadists and philosophers, schizophrenics and saints—who created a vast and powerful empire, only to succumb to a plague and inflation. Military curse of the world, Rome was redeemed by its genius in jurisprudence and organization, by its men of letters, its patricians, and, above all, its physicians.

Mining and agriculture for slaves and laborers, and war for all and at all moments, were the main occupations, which engendered an aristocracy of force. A world of athletes and adventurers, empire of the javelin and the lance, the sword and the bow, the Romans ascribed great importance to that *offensive* weapon par excellence—the shield, for no one who is innocent of the desire to attack his fellow men would trouble to provide himself in advance with a means for protection.

The Romans boasted of splendid brick, clay, and marble cities, with fine torch-lit streets and wide roads. They made exquisite painted ceramics and porcelains, wrote on parchment (nontanned lamb hide), had arsenals and central heating, travel agencies, draining canals, food inspectors, and military hospitals. In their *prandium* and *convivium* they ate bean porridge and nonfermented bread dipped in honey, and drank diluted wine and hydromel. Their technology was based on slavery until they realized that horses, though they ate more than slaves, were stronger and therefore more economical. Their art reflected their megalomania for the colossal, just as Greek art reflected a craving for beauty. With its triumphal arches and colonnades, vast coliseums and arenas, Roman art epitomized the Roman cult of force.

Originally Roman medicine was magical. When the pendulum of world knowledge swung to Rome, side by side with the Aesculapian cult there flourished all sorts of quacks who dealt in wholesale healing, though often their only medication was goat fat or, as in the case of Cato the Censor, cabbage juice, which he prescribed for all ailments alike. He even ordered his patients to bathe in the urine of persons who had fed on cabbage and with his experiments finally succeeded in killing his own wife.

For a long time practiced only by priests, which therefore made it inferior to philosophy and poetry, medicine was left chiefly in the hands of slaves, until the first Greek physicians arrived in Rome, particularly Asclepiades of Bithynia, who with his golden tongue conquered Rome and created a solidistic philosophical system based on the notion of atoms. Thereafter several schools of thought flourished. There were Methodists—Themison of Laodicea and the great gynecologist Soranus of Ephesus—who considered disease an alteration in the organic pores and thus simplified the treatment of the great masses of slaves in the plantations; Pneumatists—Athenaeus of Attalia, Archigenes and Aretaeus of Cappadocia—who recognized as vital force the *pneuma*, or soul of the world, any alterations wherein produced disease; and Eclectics, such as Pliny the Elder, Dioscorides, the naturalist and master of medicinal plants, Rufus of Ephesus, almost as great as Galen, and the elegant, sophisticated, erudite Celsus, of golden Ciceronian eloquence.

The first physicians in Rome were slaves. Later they became *medici liberti manumitidis*, when Julius Caesar granted freedom to all freeborn Greek physicians practicing in Roman territory. A kind emperor, Antoninus Pius, instituted state regulations protecting municipal physicians, enabling some of them, Antonius Musa, for instance, to amass great fortunes and, though they were only liberated slaves, to be honored with monuments. Physician-slaves, on the other hand, could be bought for some $340, less $60 if they had been castrated. Physicians of the invincible Roman legions and of military hospitals or *valetudinaria* coexisted with palatine or imperial physicians and with "specialists." After the establishment of medical licenses in A.D. 200, medical societies and civil hospitals were created, and imperial laws for medical students, such as the one prohibiting the visit to brothels, were passed, much to the grief of the students.

Even then therapeutics comprised magic. Next to the polished effigies of the new gods hung ancient Etruscan mirrors of polished bronze engraved with images of succubi. A barbaric polypharmacy (turtle blood, camel's brains, crocodile excrement) was used as much as new drugs and techniques in the treatment of epilepsy. Fear of

Roman bireme, a fast galley favored by the legionnaires as invasion craft. Note fortress-like structure forward, also curious crocodile figurehead. In Vatican Museum.

touching the dead body paralyzed all progress in anatomy, which was studied only in animals and during vivisection of criminals. To study the great organic cavities, so feared by the ancients, they dared practice short and quick—to forestall putrefaction—dissections in Barbary monkeys.

The most important Roman contributions to public health were the marvelous aqueducts, which to this day make Rome the best irrigated city in Italy, public baths and swimming pools, sewers, fountains, and wells. At its zenith, Rome could boast of having more than 122 gallons of water per inhabitant. Yet, the poor had to bathe in the Tiber, the streets were filth ridden, and in small towns and villages excrement streamed down the streets. The Romans had public health inspectors, but personal hygiene degenerated into an end instead of a means, into effeminacy and depravation. Sports evolved into athletics, and hygiene into weakness. Later, with Christianity, the body was neglected and the filthy body became the only possible dwelling for the pure soul, and the naked Greek statuary of fluid line was replaced by the rigid, austerely robed statuary of Christianity. Overindulgence in the pleasures of the body—succulent banquets of highly spiced food, torrents of wine and hydromel (the Roman Coca-Cola), torpid siestas in the shady atrium, massages by the sensuous hands of expert slave girls—set the Romans far on the road to degeneration and destruction. Little or nothing could the Roman physician do against all this, even if the physician was the great Claudius Galen.

To this day Galen excites a feeling of ambivalence among physicians. Since Roman medicine is linked to such unpleasant things as slavery and dogmatism, which is exactly the opposite to what medical progress requires, that is, a climate of absolute freedom, Galen's glory must be constantly revindicated. But Galen, whose word and work were articles of faith for fifteen hundred years, is really a *modern* author.

Born at Pergamum, Galen was baptized Galenos, meaning a tranquil sea, he who was so atrabilious! In his seventy years of life, he served as physician first to gladiators and later to the Roman emperors—Marcus Aurelius, the gentle philosopher, Commodus, Pertinax, Didius Julianus, and Septimius Severus. Galen conquered the Imperial City with his gifted tongue and his great culture, and he left a pyramid of more than 500 works, which would be the basis of his dictatorship in Medicine for fifteen centuries. His anatomy, based exclusively on dissection of monkeys and only two human corpses, was nevertheless correct; his physiology and pathology were speculative; his therapy was empirical; and his endorsement of the Aristotelian notion that the body is the vehicle of the soul was the basis for the monotheism of Arabs and Christians.

Galen believed in the Hippocratic nosology and in humoral pathology to the effect that the blood *moved*, not circulated, through the arteries; he also believed that the body was made of *parts*, not humors. Later, in the Renaissance, Paracelsus would destroy Galen's pathology; Vesalius, his anatomy; and Paré, his "first intention cures."

Ruins of the baths of Caracalla, showing two remaining columns of the calidarium. Caracalla (Marcus Antoninus) was Roman emperor from 211 to 217 A. D.

Galen's theological viewpoint, which made him the spoiled child of Christian psalmists, did great damage to his physiological investigations.

While Hippocratic medicine was humoral and philosophical and therefore antiquated, Galenic medicine was anatomic and consequently modern. His concept of a *pneuma* breathed by man, which at his death returned to its source of origin, becoming a universal *pneuma*, was that such a spirit turned into *natural* spirits in the liver, was distributed through the veins and transformed into *vital* spirits upon reaching the left heart, was then distributed through the arteries and finally became *animal* spirits in the brain, and was then distributed through its "branches," the nerves.

Galen initiated the use of "Galenicals" or vegetable simples and turned practical hygiene into applied physiology—the Eclectic application of rest, diet, sleep, and exercise. In accepting the Aristotelian concept of the relation between body and soul, the responsibility of the individual, and the Christian interpretation of life, Galen once again reunited medicine and philosophy, which had been separated by Hippocrates.

After Galen, Christianity imposed a curative religion and disease became an act of purification and divine grace. Galen's disciples were excommunicated and priest-healers were glorified. Upon his death, Galen's writings disappeared and were not resuscitated until they were translated into Latin in the thirteenth century, which helped prolong the cultural coma that was to last one thousand years. In decreeing that every human organ was made perfect by the Creator, Christianity discouraged anatomical studies and experimental medical research.

CULVER

Constantine's triumphal arc in Rome (fifth century). View is from the Coliseum.

80

A Torrent of Lions

The Roman contribution to the progress of mankind included improved collective hygiene and public health, irrigation, draining, aqueducts, thermal baths, gymnasia, inspection of markets and brothels, antimalarial measures, military hospitals, legalization of the medical class by such means as title-licenses and examinations, medical insurance, social and military medicine, systematization of medical instruction, and a higher social standing for the physician.

Then one day the barbarians from the North invaded Rome and their boots trampled the imperial purple and the blood-soaked togas strewn all over the floor of the Roman Capitol, which rang with the clang of bronze and steel, announcing the beginning of the Middle Ages.

F.M.I.

Roman sarcophagus decorated with the story of Endymion. Late second or early third century. Metropolitan Museum of Art.

Romulus, legendary founder of Rome, and his brother Remus being suckled by a she-wolf, statue is in the Vatican Museum.

IV
ROMAN MEDICINE

Rome burst into history with an ambition to conquer the world. Its people were an ethnic fusion of tribes from Central Europe and Asia Minor, Italic, Sabine, Etruscan. Their morality was based on courage and an unshakeable conviction that they were superior to all other peoples.

As Hellenic society declined, Rome developed military might, wrote out laws, built up a governmental administration, and forged new instruments and techniques.

Rome inherited most of its early culture from the Etruscans who were its first rulers. These strange people, whose language is still undeciphered, were fond of music, games, and racing.[1] They were a practical people, mostly concerned with commerce.

Theophrastus declared in the third century B.C. that the Etruscans were rich in medicines and that the Etruscan race was one that cultivated medicine. Etruscan bronze mirrors show female aphrodisiac demons which have a function of protecting women in labor. One circular mirror in Rome's Gregorian Museum depicts a haruspex examining a liver, evidence that the Etruscans practiced some of the magico-medical rites of Assyrian and Babylonian priest-physicians.

There is some evidence that the Etruscans excavated tunnels and leveled hills to combat malaria in Latium. They appear to have understood that drainage of swamps could combat the disease.[2]

There is also proof that the Etruscans practiced surgery and that they were adept in dentistry: in several Etruscan tombs have been found teeth bound with gold wire (dentes auro juncti). This dental procedure was passed on to the Romans and was found in numerous Roman tombs.

The hub of empire was built on seven hills overlooking the Tiber, on a fertile peninsula bisected by the spine of the Apennine mountains. After expelling their Etruscan overlords (ca. 500 B.C.), the Romans founded a republic that lasted four centuries. The patricians at first controlled the government, but in time the bulk of the population (plebs) were able to elect their own consuls. Three popular assemblies (comitia) developed gradually, until they eventually

Bronze model of a liver, used by Etruscan physician-magicians to diagnose maladies by Hepatoscopy. In the Museum at Piacenza.

took most of the legislative power from the patricians. By the third century B.C. the senate was the supreme power in Rome.

Roman arms meanwhile conquered all of Italy, the whole Mediterranean, annexed Greece and the Hellenic states, Asia Minor, Syria, Judea, finally Egypt. Greek culture infiltrated Roman life until religion, art, and education bore the Hellenic imprint. Wrote Horace: "Captive Greece has taken captive her rude conqueror."

In the course of these formative centuries, foreign conquest, civil war, and provincial rebellion proved to be beyond the power of the senate to control. The republic made way for the triumvirates, which in turn were absorbed by the first Roman emperor, Caius Octavius, great-nephew of Julius Caesar, who as Augustus established the foundations of the Roman empire.

CITY LIFE. The city and suburbs of Imperial Rome swarmed with a million and a half people housed in 46,600 *insulae* or apartment blocks three to eight stories high, flimsily erected of wood, rubble, and brick. Windows were simple openings with shutters or hangings to deaden the daily cacophony of street sellers. Carts with iron-rimmed wheels were permitted in the streets only at night, thereby maintaining a stupendous nocturnal uproar.

Water was fetched from the many public fountains, as only the rich could have a private well or tap the city's conduits. Excretion was done in public lavatories during the day, at other times in receptacles which were frequently emptied into the street.[3]

The state doled out free grain to about one half of the population. An annual income of 2400 sesterces was usual; a man was considered rich who possessed three million sesterces yielding five per cent yearly. Capital was invested in farming, mining, cattle ranching, buying and renting buildings, training and hiring out gladiators, book publishing.

Corrupt public officials were expected to reap fortunes from tribute, bribery, and plunder, then to retire into virtue and luxury. Menial work was done by 400,000 slaves; a middle-class citizen owned about eight, the rich from 500 to 1000, an emperor might possess 20,000.

In summer the working day began around five, in winter at eight o'clock. At the height of imperial prosperity free urban workers enjoyed seventeen to eighteen hours of leisure out of every twenty-four. Public baths, sports, and gladiatorial contests were generally free.

In the Coliseum huge naval battles were staged in the flooded arena, also gory battles between gladiators or between gladiators and wild animals; occasionally sexual exhibitions were performed after the arena was cleared of corpses.

The basic diet of the average Roman was bean meal mash and unleavened breadcakes cooked on cinders and dipped in milk or honey. A light midday meal, the *prandium*, consisted of fruit, a sweetmeat, cheese, and watered wine frequently consumed standing up in public eating places. At night the *convivium* offered meat, fish, cereals, a porridge of breadcrumbs and onions fried in oil, seasoned with vinegar and chick-peas.

Rich banquets included eels, snails, wings of ostriches, tongues of flamingos, flesh of songbirds, livers of geese; mullet (at 1000 sesterces a pound).

THE PEOPLE. Family life retained an outward sobriety; well-to-do parents hired Greek nurses and pedagogues; domestic and foreign schools of higher learning taught Roman youth politics, philosophy, history, astronomy, literature; girls received training in music and dancing. Trajan awarded 5000 scholarships to needy youths; under Hadrian the state financed secondary schools and pensions for teachers.

Roman women kept slender by exercise and diet; they wore their predominantly brunette hair in a knot at the back, sometimes adorned it with blonde wigs from Germania or wired it in a high coiffure. Cosmetics were applied with skillful elaborateness; unique was a facial treatment of dough and asse's milk. Nero's empress Poppaea traveled with a herd of asses for her lacteal baths.

The growing equality of the sexes permitted some women to work in shops and textile factories, to become lawyers, physicians, actresses, poets, even gladiators. Married and single women could move about unescorted at country resorts, banquets, amphitheatres, parks, and temple courts.

Male and female prostitutes were available at varying fees; erotic poetry, notably the *Priapeia*, was widely read by the immature. Unmarried girls of nineteen were a rarity; adultery was commonplace. Wrote Ovid: "Pure women are only those who have not been asked; and a man who is angry at his wife's amours is a mere rustic."

A Roman of modest income attended business until noon, when he ate lunch and took his siesta. He spent afternoons at the baths, played dice or chess until his evening meal; the higher his status, the later he dined. On formal occasions he wore tunic, toga, thonged sandals or full-length leather shoes, large-stoned rings on many fingers. Most men wore their hair cropped; dandies affected curled hair and some wore wigs. Shaving was customary; a youth's first shave was a holy day, when he dedicated his beard to a god.

Roman men of imperial times loved power, blood, women, and money above all. But some also appreciated music, theatre, poetry readings, sculpture and painting and elegant conversation with scholars, usually Greek.

TECHNOLOGY. In war equipment, bridges, roads,

Relief of a dancing maenad, one of nymphs who attended Dionysus. This marble work is a Roman copy of a Greek sculpture of the fifth century B. C. In the Metropolitan Museum of Art.

aqueducts, architectural interiors, transport, and the decorative crafts, the Romans outstripped the Greeks. Public highways 4000 miles long stretched from Scotland to the Persian Gulf, from Morocco to Turkistan. Topographic obstacles were overcome by embankments, viaducts, tunnels, and cuts and fills. An army with eight men abreast traversed a six-arched, granite bridge 200 feet high over the Tagus river in Spain; two thousand troops could occupy it at one time.

Walled cities fell easy victims to Roman siege-craft; ingenious engines breached walls fifty to sixty feet high. Wooden towers with platforms at several levels were wheeled into battle supporting batteries of mechanical slings and powerful catapults. Metal-nosed rams pounded gates under cover of massed bronze shields resembling tortoise backs; engineers undermined wall foundations.

Wherever the Roman eagle was planted, *thermae* were certain to be built soon. The Baths of Caracalla in Rome covered twenty acres, contained reading rooms, auditoria, running tracks, covered walks, planted gardens; the main building alone covered six acres, accommodated thousands. Vaulted ceilings intricately ornamented, vast stretches of mosaic flooring, costly marble veneering, impressive statuary, gaming rooms, and gymnasia dazzled the populace, diverted their minds from politics. One swimming pool was 200 feet long; the steam room alone was half the size of the Pantheon.

Beneath the baths were copper boilers heated by open-hearth fires equipped with high brick flues. Water from boilers was conducted in flexible lead piping to the sweating rooms and the tepid pools; cold water was separately piped from aqueducts. The premises were kept comfortable and warm with hot air sucked up through labyrinthine passages. Underground, slaves toiled like moles in humid caverns, tending fires and hauling wood to the intricate maze of furnaces.

Transportation on land and sea was efficient and fast; Romans built their sailing ships up to 420 feet long, with fifty foot beams. One commercial carrier had room for 200 sailors, 1300 passengers, 93,000 bushels of wheat. A swift boat aided by wind and oars crossed the Adriatic in one day; another took six days from Sicily to Alexandria. Travel on public roads by horse-drawn chariots could average 100 miles a day.[4]

Factories and artisans produced exquisite silverware and glassware, pottery and utensils; highly developed also were the engraving arts. Unequaled in ancient architecture was the skill of the Roman builders; their ingenious use of concrete made possible huge arched roofs and domes such as the Pantheon.

THE PIONEERS. While tribute from conquests poured into Rome, science remained an encrustation of stale

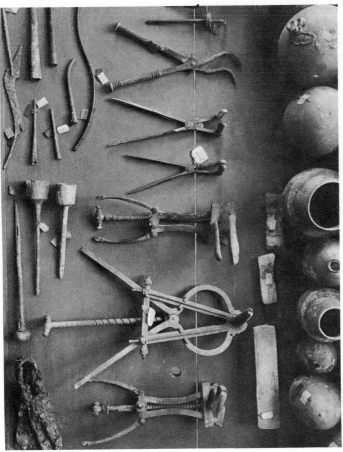

*Collection of a Roman physician's instruments. Easily
recognizable are forceps and speculum.*

facts and medicine a conglomerate of magic and
empiricism.

The first physicians to arrive from Greece were
charlatans who gradually replaced the medical ministrations of family slaves, priests, barbers, and masseurs. Alexander of Abonitichus, flaunting an Aesculapian serpent, built a thriving practice on his panacea of goat's grease.

Probably the first Greek physician to attain fame
and honor in Rome was Archagathos, a freed slave
endowed by the senate with a *taberna* where he engaged in surgery. But so free was his scalpel that he
soon lost his honorary title of wound curer and became known as the *carnifex*, or executioner.

From Bithynia came an orator and teacher of
public speaking named Asclepiades. Having induced
all of Rome to hang on his golden words, he revealed
himself as a physician. A single incident brought him
professional recognition: seeing a funeral procession
moving toward the pyre he was struck by the thought
that the cadaver might yet be alive; he interrupted
the ceremony, applied restoratives, and turned weep-
ing to rejoicing. Thereafter he was patronized by
Cicero, Crassus, and Mark Antony, wrote a score of
treatises, founded a solidist system that opposed the
humors and espoused the belief that atoms moved

through pores or canals and that health and disease
depended on the constriction or relaxation of solid
particles.

Asclepiades' maxim for medical care was *cito, tute,
jucunde* (promptly, safely, pleasantly). He advocated regimens of sunshine, warmth, cold baths, diet,
liquids, wine fasting; for some ailments he prescribed
continence; for others, intercourse.

In his distinguished career, Asclepiades originated
distinctions between acute and chronic disease and
was the first physician to calm the insane with gentleness, sunshine, and music. He recognized the psychic
effects of pneumonia and pleurisy, clearly defined
such conditions as frenzy, lethargy, catalepsy.

THE SCHOOLS. Disciples of Asclepiades fashioned a
system upon solidist pathology; a prominent follower
was Themison of Laodicea, said to have been bitten
by a mad dog and rendered incapable of writing on
rabies without showing its symptoms.

Themison (first century) founded the methodist
school, based its principles on the existence of narrow pores (*status strictus*), loose pores (*status laxus*),
and a mixed condition of pores (*status mixtus*). His
therapeutic method was to cure "contraries by contraries," reducing large pores and enlarging small
pores. Satirist Juvenal poured vitriol on Themison's
professional repute in a tract on old-age infirmities;
listing hundreds of ills, he concluded: "I could soon-
er tell you . . . how many patients Themison has killed
off in a single day."

Another target of Roman derision was Thessalius

Asclepiades of Prusa, born ca. 125 B. C.

Aulus Cornelius Celsus, First century.

Pliny the Elder, First century.

of Tralles, a notorious braggart who offered guarantees to teach the medical arts in six months. Cobblers, housepainters, blacksmiths, tanners, eager to change occupations, followed him on his rounds, clustered around sickbeds as he lectured; they were called Thessalius' jackasses. Complained epigrammatist Martial: "The hundred pawed me all over with hands congealed by the north wind."

Founder of obstetrics and gynecology, the celebrated Soranus of Ephesus belonged to the methodist school. Philosopher, grammarian, gentleman, he wrote a memorable treatise on diseases of women, obstetric care, contraception; addressed to midwives, it was inaccurate in anatomic details.

THE ENCYCLOPEDISTS. Standing apart from warring sects were the Encyclopedists, men who sought to select, record, and interpret the best of medical knowledge up to their time. Among these were patricians, placed by their class above the practice of medicine but drawn to it by their interest in science and their literary gift. From their hands come two great Latin classics of medical writing, those of Celsus and Pliny.

In the reign of Tiberius, Aulus Cornelius Celsus set himself to write on all the knowledge of all the arts then practiced. His *De Artibus* treated of agriculture, warfare, rhetoric, philosophy, jurisprudence, and medicine. A man of intellect and calm judgment, he wrote the first organized medical history, tracing its evolution from the simple remedies of the "most

barbarous" nations, through Hippocratic and Alexandrian medicine. Called the "Cicero of Medicine" for his fine literary style, he divided therapy into three forms: dietetic, pharmaceutic, and surgical; he was the first medical writer to translate Greek terms into Latin. As a son of military Rome he was interested in wounds; his four cardinal signs in their treatment were redness, swelling, heat, pain: *rubor et tumor, cum calore et dolore.*

A nonmember of the profession and therefore above the competitive battle, he exercised a restraint in writing of physicians that was remarkable for his time.

His considerable technical knowledge was gained by faithful attendance at operations and dissections; wrote he: "I am of the opinion that the art of medicine ought to be rational . . . to open the bodies of the dead is necessary for learners."

Celsus described minutely the surgical instruments of his day and many surgical procedures; in listing the qualifications for a surgeon, he gave this graphic impression of a surgeon's qualifications in Roman times:

"A surgeon ought to be young, or at any rate, not very old; his hand should be firm and steady, and never shake; he should be able to use his left hand with as much dexterity as his right; his eyesight should be acute and clear; his mind intrepid, and so far subject to pity as to make him desirous of the recovery of his patient, but not so far as to suffer him-

Following pages: The scene shown is in the main reading room of the famous library at Alexandria, later destroyed by fire, where about half a million volumes were stored. In foreground medical students are studying a skeleton. Others are copyists and students. At right is the curious foot statue of Sarapis, the Egyptian god, maker of all things. The magnificent marble colonnades connected the various buildings, all white marble and stone. Painted by Hans Guggenheim.

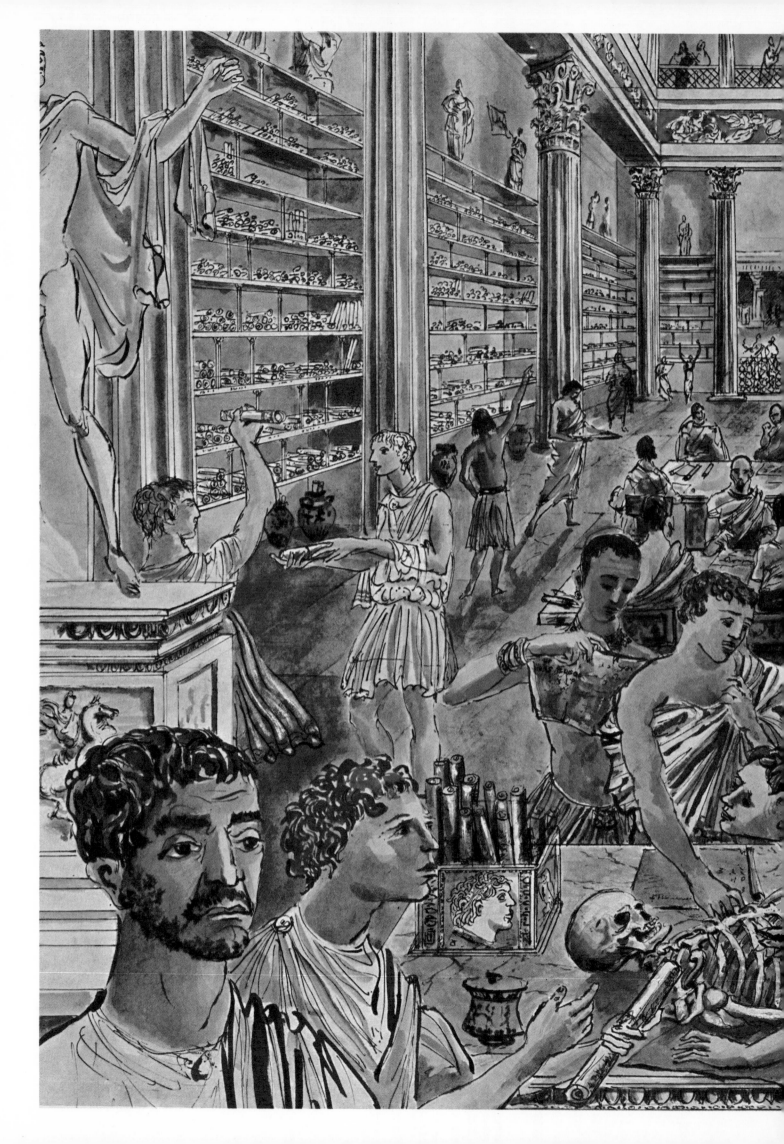

self to be moved by his cries; he should neither hurry the operation more than the case requires, nor cut less than is necessary, but do everything just as if the other's screams made no impression on him."

A scientist of a different order was Caius Plinius Secundus (Pliny the Elder) who rose before daybreak to begin his reading and had his secretaries read to him even while in his bath. Born a patrician, a proconsul in Spain, he was in command of the army at Misenum when, on the fateful twenty-fourth day of August in 79 A.D. he climbed a hill to observe the eruption of Vesuvius. For his curiosity he paid with his life as had the Greek Empedocles in the crater of Mt. Etna: the holocaust that engulfed Pompeii and Herculaneum asphyxiated Rome's great naturalist with its fumes.

With insatiable appetite for knowledge, Pliny crammed everything he read or heard about into his capacious *Natural History*: plants, animals, the races of man (some one-eyed, some one-legged, some with eyes in their shoulders, some lacking mouths who eat by inhaling fruit and flower scents), also anatomy, physiology, pathology, pharmacology, diseases and therapies both magic and rational.

He believed every wonder: that a horse deceived into committing incest would kill itself or its groom, that an elephant existed which could write Greek, that a menstruating woman by a look could dim mirrors, blunt steel, cause a gravid mare to miscarry; she could also cure quartan fever by cohabiting with the patient, clear a wheat field of caterpillars, worms, or beetles by walking through it nude.

Enthusiastic, gossipy, Pliny indiscriminately recorded fact and fantasy; he wrote in his dedication to the emperor Vespasian that he intended his work for humble folk. Yet he was the first scholar to cite his authorities, name scores of antiquity's physicians; of 37 volumes he devoted 13 to drugs, listing remedies from human excretions, blood, hair, woman's milk and spittle, the dead, 19 remedies being from the crocodile alone.

THE PRACTITIONER. The practice of medicine during the Republic was thought by Romans to be a slave's work, at best a freedman's; Greek physicians enjoyed no status, earned resentment and often ridicule, until Julius Caesar granted them citizenship in 46 B.C., a memorable medical milestone. Thenceforth they were exempt from taxes and military service, given salaried posts in the army and in theatres, assigned to the care of private families, athletes, and gladiators. Physicians called to service at the emperor's court received salaries up to 100,000 sesterces a year.

During the imperial decadence, Greek physicians improved their social position; Roman municipalities selected their own *archiatri populares* who treated rich and poor alike. Court physicians, *archiatri palatini*, were high functionaries, supervised the five to ten physicians appointed to a particular territory. Especially honorific was the appointment of a physician to tend the health of the Vestal Virgins whose promise to remain virgin for 30 years, if broken, earned lashing and burial alive.

Some physicians became involved in dark political intrigue: Stertinius Xenophon supplied the poisoned mushrooms that killed Emperor Claudius; Euterion joined the conspiracy ending the life of Drusus; Vetius Valens became the confidential counselor to the evil Messalina.

Medical education became regularized; licenses were introduced in the third century A.D., issued on recommendation of a collegium of physicians. Medical students were required to obtain good conduct certificates from the local police, were prohibited from joining illegal societies, visiting brothels, or taking prolonged holidays; they were expected to complete their studies before the age of 20. Greek was the language of instruction.

Military medicine reached a peak of efficiency in the early empire; a corps of 24 surgeons attended an army legion; maintained at encampments were hospitals and field ambulances. Warships had their own

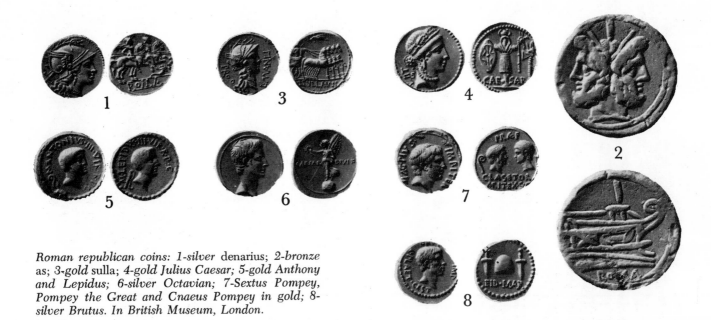

Roman republican coins: 1-silver denarius; 2-bronze as; 3-gold sulla; 4-gold Julius Caesar; 5-gold Anthony and Lepidus; 6-silver Octavian; 7-Sextus Pompey, Pompey the Great and Cnaeus Pompey in gold; 8-silver Brutus. In British Museum, London.

physicians; during their period of service in the military forces, practitioners were relieved of every civil obligation.

The day of a physician in Rome began at dawn when he journeyed to the atrium of the Temple of Peace where Galen or another distinguished physician lectured in resounding prose on medicine, literature, philosophy, or grammar. After discussing these subjects with colleagues, he visited patients in his *iatreion*, then made the round of patients at their homes. If he chanced upon colleagues along the way he engaged them in controversial conversation often so violent that they came almost to blows. Returning home to dine and take an afternoon siesta, he spent the rest of the day in thought and study.

THERAPY. In imperial Rome, rational medical procedures were intermixed with eccentric physiotherapy and a barbarian polypharmacy. Serapion's popular antiepileptic remedy was a compound of camel's brain, turtle's blood, and crocodile dung. Antonius Musa had a statue erected in his honor and placed next to that of Aesculapius, for curing the ailing Emperor Augustus with massive draughts of cold water, lettuce, chicory, and endive. Theriac and mithridate, containing scores of ingredients, staved off many a royal poisoning.

Cold douching displaced therapy in warm sulfur springs, so that at one time the brimming baths at balmy Baiae were deserted for the freezing waters at Elusium. Wine was prescribed as freely as massage,

BETTMANN ARCHIVE

Roman chariot race. Sculpture in the Lateran Museum.

Physicians carried their instruments and pomade pots in small cabinets, used mortars to prepare their own medicines, usually of herbs from abounding gardens. In Rome there were no apothecaries, no anatomic texts containing diagrams or morphologic sketches; physicians paid a penalty in ignorance for the Roman horror of human dissection.

Experimentation on animals, especially apes, and the occasional vivisection of criminals permitted them to study the physiology of the nervous system, digestion, and muscular action.

Among the considerable population of practicing physicians in Rome were urologists, gynecologists, ophthalmologists. Dentists fitted patients with wired teeth, dental plates, gold teeth. Women physicians who wrote manuals on abortions were the favorites of court ladies and prostitutes.

diet, and rest. When therapies failed, patients placated Scabies, goddess of the itch, or Febris, goddess of marsh malaria, or Angina, goddess of quinsy.

Up to 200 different surgical instruments were available for operations; massive ligature of blood vessels was performed; anesthesia was accomplished by sponges placed in the patient's mouth, which dripped soporific juices such as mandragora into the digestive tract. There were plastic surgeons who specialized in replacing the prepuce of circumcized Jews seeking to attain Roman office.

The vaginal speculum, obstetric labor stool, gentleness instead of violence in expediting childbirth were known to Greek physicians in Rome. Soranus enriched pediatric practice with suggestions for the removal of the vernix caseosa; he wrote on infants' feeding habits and bowel movements.

Claudius Galen (138-201).

GALEN. To the Rome of Marcus Aurelius in 162 A.D. there came from Pergamum in Asia Minor a brilliant, egotistic young Greek, heavy with learning after ten years of study in the medical capitals. Boastful, brutally honest, with a nimble mind and a fondness for theory, classification, and sound logic, Claudius Galen at age 34 was determined to win fame and fortune.

Born of a devoted father and a shrewish mother, the newcomer scorned to ally himself with any of the quarreling sects. He won attention by astute diagnoses for distinguished patients: he correctly traced a philosopher's paralysis of three fingers of one hand to a nerve injury in the seventh cervical vertebra; he discovered that a Roman matron's insomnia was due to lovesickness for a famous actor by noting the acceleration of her pulse when the performer's name was mentioned.

Rome's elite crowded into the public theatre where he gave lecture demonstrations on anatomy and physiology; a dozen scribes wrote down his treatises which he dictated at high speed. His practice grew; he boldly charged the consul Boethius 400 gold pieces,[5] fifteen times the customary fee, for a night call on his wife. The consul not only paid the fee but proclaimed him the "wonder-worker."

After four whirlwind years, on the verge of an appointment as physician to the Emperor, Galen unaccountably left Rome, possibly to escape a threatening epidemic; his own explanation was that he feared assassination by rivals.

Recalled within a year, he evaded a summons from Marcus Aurelius to accompany the Emperor on a military campaign, recounting a dream in which Aesculapius warned him that he would be needed to attend the royal children. The infant heir did in fact fall ill and require his care; he later successfully diagnosed and treated the Emperor's gastritis from rotten cheese.

Galen habitually castigated all charlatans, irritably berated professional rivals as fools, asses, robbers. He delivered his theories as infallible dogma, declared: "Whoever seeks fame need only become familiar with all that I have achieved."

The solid core of Galen's method was anatomic and experimental; he pursued physiologic studies with dogs, swine, horses, birds, fish (once an elephant), created cerebral and spinal lesions to trace the nerve pathways, proved the mechanism of voice production by finding the link between brain and larynx.

Galen's conception of disease was anatomic, but his thinking included pneumatic and teleologic elements. His theory of temperaments attempted to classify humans into four humoral types. Following his predecessors in the theory of the *pneuma* (or vital spirit), he astutely sought a specific life-sustaining component in the air. Wrote he, anticipating oxygen: "When we know what supports a flame we shall know the cause of the body's heat."

He declared that arteries and veins "anastomose with each other throughout the whole body, and exchange with each other blood and spirits by certain invisible and exceedingly minute passages." He believed that blood moved through the body in a system of ebb and flow.

Roman law prevented the use of human cadavers for study, obliging Galen to confine himself to a criminal's skeleton picked cleaned by vultures and the remains of a corpse washed out of a cemetery in a flood. Nevertheless his anatomic findings, mainly studied in Barbary apes, were largely correct: he described in detail the two eyelid and six eyeball muscles, the maxillary group, many muscles of the head, neck, trunk and limbs.

He accurately described the bones and sutures of the skull, traced a number of the cranial and spinal nerves, made vertical sections of the spinal cord, cross sections between the vertebras. His extensive *materia medica* included 540 vegetables, 180 animal and 100 mineral substances, the basis of what became the famous herbal "galenicals."

Galen acknowledged Hippocrates as his master and maintained that he alone pursued the true path of Hippocrates. He was an authority on baths and gymnastics, enjoyed a wrestling match before his bath until he suffered a dislocation of the collarbone. He produced 500 works on every aspect of medical science and practice; a large part of these were lost in a fire that destroyed the Temple of Peace.

PUBLIC HEALTH. The Roman poor bathed in the polluted Tiber; in small villages ill-smelling ordure ran down the streets in rivers. Nevertheless, the empire's citizens were the most washed, best bathed people in antiquity.

Galen's method of binding up a head wound.

Fourteen aqueducts, totaling 1300 miles in length, theoretically gave each person in Rome the use of 130 gallons of fresh spring water every day. A few palaces and brothels cheated by tapping the mainstream, once causing a drought. Usually, however, there was sufficient water for the city's homes, fountains, gardens, one thousand or more swimming pools, eleven great *thermae*, artificial lakes for mock battles.

Nearly all dwellings had cisterns; swamps and marshes were methodically drained; laws enforced the burial of the dead outside of city limits. Army physicians served as public health inspectors; even food supplies were inspected. Prostitution was controlled.

The practice of mass balneology in settings of architectural splendor proved no guarantee of national health; a few clear Roman minds vainly called

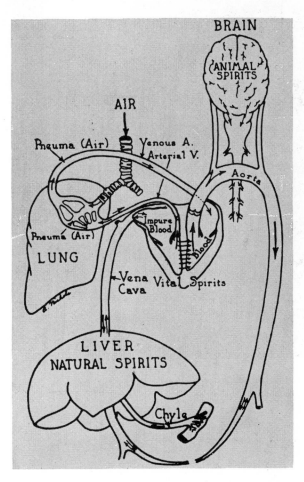

Galen's concept of the circulatory system (shown in a modern diagram).

for a halt to the bathing obsession, holding that soft living and effeminacy would result. Bathing and exercise did in fact lose their original hygienic purpose, deteriorating into a cult of sensuality.

As the shadow of the Dark Ages drew nearer,

Roman physician patronizing blacksmith's shop where surgical instruments were forged. In Vatican Museum.

Richly ornamented lid of a Roman physician's surgical instruments case. In Altes Museum, Berlin.

Wall painting in Pompeii depicts Aeneas being attended by a physician.

Portrait of an unknown physician; he appears to be consulting a papyrus roll. On shelf at upper right is a case of surgical instruments.

Antoninus Musa, personal physician to the Emperor Augustus, sculptured as Aesculapius. Musa cured Augustus of a liver complaint by hydrotherapy.

Rome's legacy to medicine could be assessed: public health, personal hygiene, inspection of food, control of prostitution, antimalarial campaigns. Its military hospitals were the forerunners of civilian hospitals. The medical profession was given a legal status; medical teaching was organized.

But one of the weaknesses in Galen's teaching was to cast a blight on the development of medicine for centuries. The teleologic content of his ideas was quite acceptable to the growing theology of the Christian faith, to challenge them in due course became a serious offence.

Moreover Galen's overestimation of the power of the mind over the body caused a decline in experimental interest in the body, particularly after the Church gained temporal power and became the repository of most knowledge.

The zest for experiment seemed to vanish with Galen, leaving man to become a mere pawn in a vastly complicated heavenly machinery.

The last century of the Roman Empire accelerated the decadence of mores; wars and civil strife ruined the countryside, terrible epidemics wiped out entire cities; whole regions succumbed to famine and drought.

Both a closer contact with Oriental peoples and the growth of religious fervor among the poorer classes helped to divert medical progress into mystic bypaths, such as the sects of Essenes and the Therapeutists. Some sects tried to revive the traditions of the ancient Aesculapian temples, combining these with Orphic or Pythagorean myths to form a hopelessly obscure mélange of magic medicine. The seeds of rational medicine sown in Greece now seemed to be lost to mankind for ever more.

Thus a long time was yet to elapse before medicine could emerge from barbarian superstition and magic. The knowledge stored in Byzantium by past cultures, including the Roman, was vast, but it was to remain fallow for many centuries until it could return to the new nations of Europe.

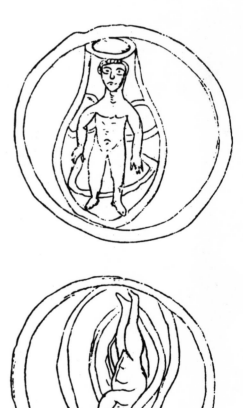

Sketches of the fetus in utero in the work of Soranus of Ephesus (first century) regarded as the founder of obstetrics and gynecology.

Modern biochemistry class at the ancient University of Bologna, one of oldest medical schools in Europe.

ROME: DECLINE AND
REBIRTH

The date commonly accepted for the end of the Roman Empire is 476, when the last Emperor of the West, appropriately called Romulus Augustulus, was deposed by Germanic chieftain Odoacer. Thereafter Italy and other European countries sank into what are commonly called the Dark Ages.

The history of Rome during medieval centuries is largely a record of the papacy and of the commune of Rome. The city was at various times ruled by princes from without, some of them in conflict with the reigning Pope or in league with the papacy against a third party.

A last effort to restore the Roman republic failed in 1453, after which the city's fate was more than ever closely bound up with that of the papacy. During the Renaissance, the papal courts became opulent and encouraged numerous great artists, including Michelangelo and Raphael.

Rome was sacked by the French emperor Charles V, but it managed to recover and prospered through the succeeding centuries. The city was quite badly damaged during the last world war, largely by street fighting between rival Italian forces. It has since made another remarkable revival, is now considered the equal if not the superior to Paris as a center of modern arts and civilization.

Justinian the Great. Sixth century mosaic in Church of St. Vitale, Ravenna, Italy.

V

Through a Stained Glass Window

O N entering a Gothic cathedral today one feels as if a weird fauna were rushing down from windows and capitals. Griffins, gargoyles, and dragons, long imprisoned in the Gothic cage, that "trap of fantasy," seem ready to set off in chase of the elusive quarry of the Infinite. Man must have felt much the same at the beginning of the Middle or so-called Dark Ages, when upon him descended the avalanche of beauty and squalor, romanticism and roguishness, chivalry and sadism that characterized the age of the Crusades, the Gothic cathedrals, the *Divine Comedy,* and the *chansons de geste.*

We should not call "Dark Ages" a period that gave birth not only to such men as St. Thomas Aquinas, Albertus Magnus, and Arnold of Villanova, but also to the three great bases of modern medicine: universities, hospitals, and public health. True, in the first four centuries of this period, man wallowed in magic, and the invisible threads binding him to stars and amulets ruled his life; but for the remainder of the Middle Ages he valiantly combated the ignorance and bigotry surrounding him. Rather than the "Middle Age," that is to say the maturity, of Europe, this was her childhood, when she began to awaken to a new view of man and of things.

In the fifth century the pendulum of history had swung from Rome to Byzantium, the city with a thousand gilded domes bathed by the waters of the Golden Horn and the Bosporus. Thereafter, for the next thousand years, until the fall of Constantinople to the Turks, or, if a medical date is preferred, until the publication of Vesalius' *Fabrica,* Greco-Latin medical learning would flow through three channels—Byzantium, the Arabian empire, and the monastic universities—which would later converge into the resplendent broad stream of the Renaissance.

Byzantium, later called Constantinople, and now called Istanbul, kingdom of God on earth, was for ten centuries the unattainable dream of the barbarians, who coveted its rich treasures. A walled bastion in a hostile world, defended by the walls built by Theodosius and the azure waters of the Bosporus, Byzantium defied the pagan hordes for a thousand years after Rome herself had succumbed. Century after century, Mongols, Turks, and Tartars, attracted by the glittering domes and the legend of its treasures, vainly attacked the invincible city.

Life in Byzantium was cloistered. The people, deprived by the city walls from looking ahead, looked up and back: at heaven and at the past. Their emperor, the basileus, was regarded as Christ on earth; his political code was the Bible; his parliament, the holy apostles; his offices were the basilicas, vast and towering and ablaze with gilded mosaics in all the colors of the rainbow. He appeared in public "pale as death," robed in white and surrounded by his twelve apostles. His meals were replicas of the Last Supper; his garments and countenance, of those in sacred icons. His palace was yet another church where even the porter was a priest. The finest silks and porcelain, gilded mirrors, carved ivory chess sets, damask tapestries, jeweled enamels,

99

coats of mail, diamonds and other gems, gold chalices, sandalwood and ebony caskets, jewelry and table services inlaid with precious stones, carpets and ceramics jammed the treasury of the city, which like a golden cloud gleamed above the Bosporus and the Golden Horn. Founded by Romans, Byzantium was inhabited by Greeks, Romans, and Asiatics. Its basilicas were the house of God; its palaces, the house of the church militant.

The lack of statuary was compensated for by the abundance of paintings—the "books" of the illiterate ancients—in which the Byzantines depicted what they *felt,* just as the Egyptians depicted in their art what they *knew,* and the Greeks what they *saw.* In Byzantium the dung-piled streets contrasted with the splendor of the palaces; the strange Christian democracy, with the stern ruling theocracy.

Under Byzantium's three great emperors—Constantine I, Julian the Apostate, and Theodosius—Byzantine culture developed in flight from the present to the past, its art turning from the classical portrayal of the human being to the introvert world of mosaics, bas-reliefs, and miniatures, and its medicine taking refuge in endless compilations of Greek learning.

The Crusades introduced Europeans to the cultured world of Byzantium, a world protected by its geographical position on the confines of two worlds, at the end of a landlocked sea, by the principle of unity known as "Hellenism"—a community of language, ideas, and culture—and by the intricate web of Byzantine diplomacy and their genius for weaving political intrigues.

In Byzantium—whose art was the art of Eastern Christendom, just as Roman art was the art of Western Christendom—the basilica was the house of God, an arrogant granite mass symbolizing the Church on a war footing and its everlasting might capable of resisting all sieges. The basilicas contained no statuary, for that was a symbol of paganism; in fact, they contained nothing that did not reek of religious asceticism. Religious imagery was prominent in mosaics, which were placed on walls and ceilings and not in the pavements as in Rome; for man, in his greater meekness, now looked toward heaven rather than to earth. The Oriental aversion to depicting the human form turned Byzantine art toward abstract and geometric motifs. The mosaics and multicolored paintings in the basilicas were an inspiration to visionaries, and its gems, to which were attributed magic properties, bore an obvious analogy to the mystical descriptions of heaven.

Typical of this art were the painted glass windows, ivory and metal filigrees, and illuminated initials sparkling with golden luster and precious stones. Stained glass windows in the Middle Ages were intended to inspire emotional ecstasy. Later, when the printing press was invented and, with the advent of the Reformation, the Bible

Carved figure of Constantine the Great, founder of Constantinople.

Capture of Constantinople by the Turks in 1453. This marked end of Byzantine Empire.

was read inside the churches, church windows were made of transparent glass. Fraught with perfectionism and preciosity, Byzantine art was symbolic of the besieged capital, where man's only escape from his walled-in existence was to roam the limitless regions of time.

Renouncing travel in space, since fierce enemies were ravening on the other side of the walls, the Byzantines journeyed into time: the artists devoting themselves to time-consuming stained glass and filigree work; and the physicians turning to the past in search of knowledge, since learning makes man lose his sense of isolation. As a result, Byzantine medicine turned backward, and was based not on investigation but on compilation. To Oribasius of Pergamum, Aëtius of Amida, Paul of Aegina, Alexander of Tralles—to these men we owe the monumental tomes in which is preserved the medical lore of ancient Greece.

There being no one in Byzantium to garner the heritage of Galen and again raise the torch of experimental medicine, medicine became a matter of faith. The sick person was regarded as a potential saint; prayer was adopted as the best medicine, the priest as the best physician, the Church as the best hospital, and Christ as the Supreme Healer.

In the Byzantine Empire, medicine was in the hands of priests and Magi. The guardian saints, Cosmas and Damian, shed their light over the city. Nevertheless, the Roman appetite for luxury and sensual pleasures endured. Paradoxically, philosophical mysticism and the Oriental influence of demonology, magic, and alchemy existed side by side with the influences of Christianity. A medicine of priests, Byzantine medicine bowed to ecclesiastical authority. Taking their example from Christ, their first physician, the fathers of the Church practiced medicine. They also erected hospitals, one of which with its annexes could accommodate 7000 patients. The sick were fed on fruit and wine, temple sleep was practiced, and physical and spiritual healing was

101

promised to the faithful. Smallpox plagues, which scourged Constantinople often, were described by the priest-physicians.

The ancient pagan cults survived solely among the healthy. Christianity, with its appeal to the unclean, the diseased, and the sinners, became a powerful revolutionary force. The diseased person became a privileged being, and medicine was founded on faith and miracles, the Divine Word, and prayer. Faithful Christians renounced classical hygiene. The patients of the priests were mostly laborers and the needy, not the well-to-do classes, and the diseased body was extolled as the only possible dwelling for a healthy soul.

After surviving the ventures of the Crusaders, Constantinople finally fell in 1453, after a siege lasting several months, when the Ottoman Sultan Mohammed II, commanding half a million men, with the aid of greased log rollers hauled seventy-two galleys from the heights of Pera in twenty-four hours and in a single night, placed them on the waters of the Golden Horn opposite the city, using his artillery to support his attack on the coveted prize.

One tragic day, through the *Kerkoporta*, at the shout of the war-cry *Yagma!* (Plunder!), the enemy poured into the thousand-domed city. Constantinople fell before the fury of the invaders who, scimitars in hand, spared neither Byzantine man nor Byzantine art, but set the seal of Ottoman art and religion on them both. In Istanbul today one can still see traces of that fatal hour: the shattered walls of Theodosius, which for one thousand years guarded the colossal basilicas, that miracle of architecture, symbol of an unprecedentedly beautiful and mighty civilization. Concurrently, Byzantine medicine yielded to the Ottoman medicine of the invaders.

With the fall of Constantinople, Hellenic learning migrated to the West, driven by the force of *humanitas*, that is to say, culture and the heritage of "man as a measure" of Nature.

The Byzantine contribution to medicine was the creation of hospitals and the monumental compilations of medical knowledge by men who seem to have given no thought to the approaching storm, who, ignoring the fact that they stood on the brink of an everlasting night, toiled as if they were bathed in the light of dawn. Byzantium stands in history like a bridge across the ocean of Time, thanks to which the Renaissance was enriched by the Greek classical learning imprisoned in the Byzantine compilations, whose pages were as subtle and eternal as the moon's reflection on the waters of the Bosporus.

F.M.I.

Silver chalice from Antiochus, possibly Fourth century.

*Altar in monastery of St. Naum on Lake Ochrida, in
Yugoslavia. It dates from the Tenth century when
Ochrida flourished as the capital of Bulgaria.*

V

BYZANTINE MEDICINE

Under barbarian pressure and internal decay the Roman empire slowly but steadily disintegrated. Although Greco-Roman man had glimpsed the peaks of rational thought, his successors turned back time to mysticism and magic. Exhausted by wars, plagues, and famines, man sought solace in the mystery cults of Mithra, Eleusis, Dionysius.

During the last century of the Western Roman Empire[1] the civilized world was divided into two magnificent orbits: the splendor of Rome and the opulence of Byzantium, called the Eastern Roman Empire. The political and spiritual gap between these two giants grew wider decade by decade, until by 395 they were permanently divided. When the last Roman Emperor in the West was deposed by the barbarians, Byzantium remained as the sole fortress of civilization throughout five centuries of the so-called "Dark Ages."

As an empire and a center of culture, Byzantium survived more than a thousand years, bridging the turbulent transition between Roman hegemony and the opening centuries of the modern world. When Constantine I built his capital on the banks of the Bosporus in 330, Rome was still the center of the known world; when the last Byzantine emperor Constantine XI died in battle against the Turks in 1453, the Hundred Years' War between England and France had just ended, Dante and Chaucer had already penned their masterpieces, and Europe was on the brink of its stupendous expansion across the seas.

The heart of the Byzantine empire consisted of the Balkan Peninsula, embracing what are today Greece, parts of Yugoslavia, and Asia Minor. In the course of eleven and a half centuries, the empire gained and lost Syria, Palestine, Egypt, North Africa, Italy, Corsica, and Sicily.

It was successively attacked by Visigoths, Huns, Bulgars, Persians, Arabs, Venetians, and Christian Crusaders. At one point in the thirteenth century it almost vanished, only to be rebuilt and revived for another two hundred years.

Byzantine civilization conserved a vast body of classical learning, much of which would have perished after the fall of Rome. While it brought forth no giants in philosophy, literature, science, or medicine, it encouraged scholarship, promoted education, produced some of the most dazzling handicrafts and art works in the world.

From the year 313, when Constantine I and his fellow emperor in Rome officially tolerated Christianity, the Church steadily gained influence in Byzantium. Although Constantine himself was no more than a half-Christian, he dedicated his new capital to the Virgin, banned pagan religions from it, and helped the quarreling fathers of the Church to put their ecclesiastical establishment in order.[2] By the time of Justinian I (sixth century), Christian culture mixed with some Oriental strains was ascendant and dynamic; it had seeped into the marrow of government and possessed the daily life and thought of the people.

THE CITY. The glittering hub of the Byzantine Empire was "the city guarded by God": devout, cruel, corrupt, cultivated, sensuous Constantinople.[3]

At its zenith in the eleventh century, it held a million inhabitants, representing a mixture of a dozen peoples. Resplendent with marble, mosaics, frescoes, sculptures, colonnades, tapestries, carpets, jewelry, and silks, Constantinople outshone Rome and Alexandria in wealth and trade, surpassed all antiquity in the refinement of its decorative art and its elaborate religious ceremonies.

Facing page: In foreground a monastic physician-scribe in a Cappadocian monastery is seen writing a new version of an ancient medical text being dictated by a fellow priest. Richly ornamented vaulted ceilings, carved out of rock, are typically Byzantine. Painted by Hans Guggenheim.

Empress Theodora (d. 548) and members of her court. Detail of mosaic in Church of St. Vitale in Ravenna.

Man and nature made Constantinople a nearly impregnable fortress with towering land walls, sea walls, and water on three sides. Pointing at Asia, the Byzantine capital bestrode the commercial crossways of the world; it stirred the wonder and greed of Islam and eastern barbarians; even crusading Christians strove to loot its wealth.

Gold was paramount; Byzantine artist-craftsmen threaded it into textiles, leafed it over acres of vaulted ceilings, spread it lavishly on frescoes and mosaics, painted portraits in goldwash, covered the domed roofs of five hundred churches with solid sheets of gold that blazed in the sun.

The two mile long Mese teemed with shops offering merchandise from many lands; torches lit its fabulous silk bazaars at night; offered for sale were jewels, carved ivory, sumptuous cloths and dyes, also farm produce and animals.

Within the city proper and in its suburbs were built oases of serenity comprising monasteries, churches, schools, houses of meditation, and religious retreats.

106

The imperial Sacred Palace was a city within a city, containing thirty acres of palaces, pavilions, barracks, baths, libraries, churches, prisons, galleries, terraces. In one 650 foot reception hall the emperor reviewed his troops; in another called the Building of the Nineteen Beds, he held state dinners for over 200 guests. A separate palace for the empress, which no male except the emperor might enter, was spacious enough for her to conceal indefinitely any fugitive from royal disfavor.[4] In another structure, the Fresh Breeze Palace, the empress took her ceremonial bath.

The harbor and docks of the six mile long bay, the Golden Horn, swarmed with merchants: bearded Asians, turbaned traders from Babylon, Syria, Egypt, Persia, primitive Bulgars wearing an iron chain as a belt, elegant visitors from Spain and Italy.

In an old basilica transformed into a library, its walls lined with 150,000 books, students wearing Greek *chlamys* and kilt stood at the reading desks; beyond were the streets where goldsmiths, silversmiths, and bronzesmiths shaped miraculous miniatures, carved and inlaid massive doors for the wealthy houses. On one of the city's seven hills stood the university founded by Theodosius II in the fifth century, and the Nymphaeum, a festival hall in whose arcades prostitutes paraded, wearing strips of purple cloth on their breasts as required by law.

The greatest glory of the city was the Basilica of Hagia Sophia (St. Sophia) built in the sixth century by the emperor Justinian. It was and still is a marvel of architectural daring, combining Roman and Oriental forms into an awe-inspiring structure of multicolored marble, blue and gold mosaics, cupolas and arches, and a fabulous dome that seems to be suspended from the sky.

In contrast with the palaces and plazas were uproarious overcrowded quarters, some of them containing vaulted alleyways where the sun never penetrated, swarming with a squalid humanity in low, cramped houses, crisscrossed by narrow streets where mud and filth were often deep enough to bog down man and beast.

THE SOCIETY. The Byzantines were a conglomerate of Greeks, some Latins and an assortment of Phrygians, Hittites, Gauls, Semites, Persians, Armenians, Slavs. Christian rituals and symbols permeated virtually all facets of society: diplomacy, court etiquette, official acts and orders, even military life, were set in a religious framework.

Theology was interwoven in the life of the people; in times of peace it was often a popular pastime: the everyday conversations of people bristled with theologic allusions and arguments; a common dispute concerned the sex of angels. Noted a visiting churchman in the fourth century: "If I ask for my bill, the reply is a comment about the Virgin birth; if I ask for the price of bread, I am told that the Father is greater than the Son; when I ask whether my bath is ready I am told that the Son was created from nothing."

Theologic quarrels often rent the empire, as in the formidable Iconoclastic Controversy that lasted for more than a hundred years. At the beginning of the eighth century, Emperor Leo III (the Isaurian) attacked the excessive wealth and power of the monasteries by proscribing icons; monasteries were closed or secularized, and monks were beaten, exiled, or forced to marry. The monks responded with equal violence, even appealed to Rome for help.

Christian ethics did not deter physical cruelties: hands, feet, and noses were cut off and eyes gouged out for minor crimes; burning at the stake was a popular spectacle, alternated with having people roasted in a bronze animal.

Parents ambitious for their sons' careers had them castrated; eunuchism was a favored path to political,

Mosaic pulpit in the Cathedral at Ravello, near Amalfi, Italy.

ecclesiastic or military advancement. Some imperial families had their sons unsexed, particularly those of illegitimate birth, thus removing the danger of usurpation by future heirs.

The Patriarch, head of the church, was generally a eunuch; swelling the ranks of the bureaucracy, eunuchs served to offset the threat of a hereditary nobility. Castration was not deemed a stigma but an opportunity; eunuchs were never employed as guardians of a harem, as the custom was in Moslem society.

The government supervised all industry: manufacturers and merchants were subject to minute regulations on accumulating stockpiles, exporting goods, the location of retail shops. Artisans and craftsmen were restricted to their specialized vocations. Silk was a state monopoly; the manufacture and sale of silk materials were hemmed in by elaborate economic strictures. All prices were fixed to conform with tariffs established by the state. Prescribed one edict: "Bakers will visit the prefect each time there is a rise in the price of wheat so that the weight of loaves may be adjusted."

A universal institution was chariot racing; every Byzantine town had its arena, racing events kept the public at a high fever of excitement; Constantinople's Hippodrome could accommodate 100,000 spectators, who frequently plunged into bloody combats over their favorite charioteers.[5]

Social life revolved around the Hippodrome, where the emperor offered his subjects chariot races, hunts, battles between men and wild beasts, acrobats, and clowns. In the vast arena were held parades of victorious generals, abominably cruel tortures and executions, festivals and displays. Here the people expressed their feelings, acclaimed an emperor or dethroned and slaughtered him.

Byzantine society was almost from the first racked by class warfare. A feudal system grew out of the need of humble people for protection in times of trouble; this gave birth to a class of powerful landowners who defied imperial edicts, ravaged the countryside, and oppressed the people. Noted a famous Byzantine historian: "All these great men ... civilians and soldiers, laymen and ecclesiastics ... flouted the law and strove by every means to enlarge their estates at the expense of the poor."

At the head of the wealthy class stood the senatorial aristocracy and mercantile princes. Unlike the Romans, Byzantine nobles were restrained in their eating, drinking, and amorous exercises; dancing was condemned, the Byzantine theatre showed suggestive but not outrageous mimes.

Fathers were not absolute masters in their families; husbands and wives owned property jointly; before children married the parents' permission was required. Divorces were made difficult to obtain: at one time there were possible only four different reasons for divorce, one of which was attempted murder.

Feasts and parties were a Byzantine enthusiasm, but historian Cecaumenus reported that guests came merely to criticize the housekeeping or to seduce other men's wives. The emperor's kitchens served appetizers with game and poultry, caviar, cakes, sweets, and fruits. When the emperor traveled, 100 horses transported his silverware, utensils, and food.

THE STATE. While Western Europe fell into fragments, Byzantium developed a strong central power in which the emperors were absolute monarchs over church and state, military and judiciary establishments. The emperor was also the Chosen of God, the Anointed of the Lord, the Vicar of God on earth; he was the *isapostolos*, or prince equal to the apostles. Paradoxically this power was not hereditary, nor was there any orderly succession prescribed by law. An aspirant to the high office of *basileus* required the approval of the Senate, the support of the army, and the acclamation of the populace.

Emperors were not necessarily of noble blood: a butcher, swineherd, soldier, horse trader, farmer, petty naval officer, dockworker took turns in donning the diadem. Three women ascended the throne: a circus girl, a cook, a tavern keeper's daughter.

The mainstay of the state were its officials who inherited many of Rome's administrative skills. These included secretaries of the treasury, army, navy, flocks and herds, police, interior. Government officials were well paid, were also free to accept bribes or gratuities.

The Byzantine army relied heavily on cavalry: the heavy *cataphracts* wore caps, gauntlets, shoes, and breastplates all made of steel; their weapons were the broadsword, dagger, bow and arrow; a light cavalry (*trapezitae*) carried lesser equipment. Ground troops were divided into heavy infantry armed with a short battle-ax and dagger, a light infantry with long-range bows.

The army was built for speed; strategy was carefully planned, based on a knowledge of the enemy's fighting habits. Military leaders were trained in a wide repertory of deceptions and decoys: officers carrying a flag of truce were often spies sent ahead as a delaying action.

Soldiers were well paid and well treated; a general received forty pounds of gold a year. The ranks were issued beans, cheese, wine, were expected to take plunder from the country; they were allowed to possess slaves and servants.

Army units were provided with a surgeon, stretcher-bearer, and ambulance; the stretcher-bearers were paid a fee for every man they carried from the field.

The fleet was a powerful element in the empire,[6]

Preceding pages: *Scene shown is a cave hospital near Caesarea Mazaca (now Kayseri, Turkey). In foreground two physician-priests are treating a patient. Attendants are seen bringing victuals and herbs. On walls and ceiling are symbols believed to possess curative powers. Painted by Hans Guggenheim from sketches made on the spot.*

dominating the Eastern seas for centuries before the Arabs appeared. Byzantine shipbuilders developed the powerful *dromons,* manned by 300 men; lighter craft were frequently manned by Russian seamen.

Naval armament included "Greek fire" invented in the seventh century, an inflammable mixture pumped from siphons or thrown in grenades. The Russian duke Igor who attacked Constantinople in 941 was routed by this chemical warfare.

CULTURAL LIFE. Books in Byzantium contained either "divine wisdom" or "profane wisdom" depending on whether they were Christian or pagan. Despite the threat of proscription scholars prodigiously studied, copied, translated, and annotated the Greek classics.

The four great centers of learning were Alexandria, Antioch, Athens, and Constantinople, comprising a vast treasury of Greek poetry, prose, drama and the works of the Hellenic philosophers, scientists, and historians.

State, church, and private libraries abounded with works by Pindar, Sophocles, Aristophanes, Thucydides, Plato, Aristotle.

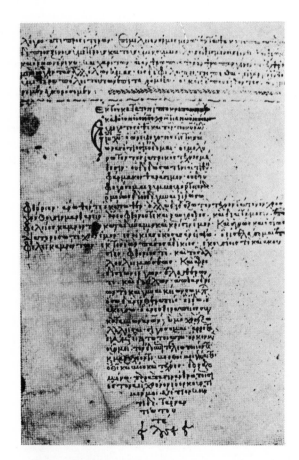

Oath of Hippocrates written in form of cross in a Byzantine manuscript of the Twelth century. In Vatican Library.

Byzantium's own literary output included countless devotional poems, dialogues, essays, epigrams for special occasions, chronicles, stories, and bestiaries;[7] a most impressive single work was the eleventh century epic poem *Digenis Akritas.* While no towering literary talent appeared, there were many creditable historians and theologic writers.

Byzantine art followed the path of literature, borrowing heavily from the classic forms. The Hellenist traditions were combined with Asian elements to produce splendor, ornate ornamentation, brilliant colors, and an atmosphere of pomp.

In the golden age (ninth to eleventh centuries), Byzantine art flourished in sober simplicity, producing magnificent churches and public buildings, exquisite works in ivory, mosaic, and illuminated manuscripts. Its weakness was an exaggerated devotion to traditional forms, an excessive preoccupation with formulas and theologic iconography.

MEDICINE AND HEALTH. Byzantine medicine was essentially dogmatic, based on a Christian faith that appealed powerfully to broken, despairing spirits, to the sick, the sinful, and the disinherited of the world. The afflicted were welcomed into the Christian community, were promised healing and redemption.

The Church officially controlled medical practice in Byzantium, but beyond this flourished sorcerers, thaumaturges, professional poisoners, and dealers in amulets, spells, and enchantments.

The earliest Christian physicians are generally accepted as the Arabian twins Cosmas and Damian, martyred by the Roman Emperor Diocletian in the fourth century; they were later beatified and honored by a shrine erected in Constantinople.[8]

Saints were believed to possess the power to cure specific diseases, e.g., St. Artemis for genital afflictions, St. Sebastian against pestilence, St. Job against leprosy. Also reputed as healers were the Stylite hermits who spent their lives on platforms atop pillars.

In a society that believed neither in drugs nor in the study of the sick patient, there was small opportunity for the physician. When one Byzantine physician dared to ascribe a raging epidemic to the city's airless dwellings he was accused of blasphemy. Sickness and death were considered strictly a divine visitation.

The devout had no need for hygiene or exercise; care of the body, its anointment with oil or refreshment with baths, seemed to them superfluous. Later it was believed a dishonor to the soul to neglect the body, thereby restoring the prestige of the physicians.

The Byzantine state established numerous welfare institutions such as Constantinople's combined military hospital, orphanage, and home for the blind which housed 7000 persons. Attached to the Pantocrator Monastery was a hospital with a staff of eleven physicians and numerous assistants and servants.

Widespread also were public and privately supported leprosaria, foundling hospitals, homes for the aged. The Empress Eudoxia built hospitals in Jerusalem; the Empress Theodora established a home for the rehabilitation of prostitutes.

Huge bathing establishments were built in military camps; emperors when they traveled were seldom without a portable Turkish bath.

COMPILATIONS. Best known of Byzantine physicians was Oribasius, a patrician born in Pergamum (Galen's birthplace) in 325 and a pupil of Zeno of Cyprus. He served as palace physician to the Emperor Julian, who had enforced strict licensing requirements for the practice of medicine.

Among the seventy works of Oribasius were writings on diet in pregnancy, contraception, the choice of nurses, diseases of children; his *Euporista* was a manual of practical instructions on accidents and diseases that might afflict travelers beyond the reach of a physician's aid.

Physician to Emperor Justinian was Aëtius of Amida (sixth century), born on the Tigris and educated in Alexandria. He wrote a resumé of all medical knowledge until the sixth century in his *Tetrabiblos,* compiled a total of 16 books quoting many Greek writers on medicine.

Aëtius' method mingled Christian mysticism with pagan superstition, recommended amulets and incantations; one of the contraceptive devices he recommended was a child's tooth suspended over the woman's anus.

Brother of an architect who designed the Hagia Sophia, Alexander of Tralles (sixth century) was a physician with a rare independence of mind. Reminded that he once departed from Galenic prin-

ciples in one of his works, he retorted: "I love Galen, but I also love the truth and so, if a choice must be made between them, I give preference to the truth."

A practitioner of wide experience, Alexander enjoyed wide fame during his lifetime; his twelve books included a pathology and therapy of internal diseases. They were translated into Arabic and Latin.

For hemoptysis, he suggested rest, vinegar potions, cold compresses on the chest, bleeding for plethoric patients. His descriptions of the stomach and the intestines were based on observation. He studied the nervous system, considered phrenitis a cerebral disease to be treated with narcotics, bleeding, warm baths, and wine.

Last of the great Byzantine physicians was the remarkable surgeon and gynecologist-obstetrician Paul of Aegina whose work on medicine appeared in seven volumes. He mentioned the ligature, described nasal polyps; he excised tonsils, detected synovial fluid in the joints. He gave directions for irrigation of the bladder with an ox bladder attached to a catheter, resected ribs for empyema, used an expanding rectal and vaginal speculum.

When the Byzantine Empire crumbled in the fifteenth century, European medicine was already well on the road to glory. The golden age of the schools of Salerno, Bologna, Montpellier, and Oxford had flowered and the Renaissance was in full swing.

A thousand years before the empire's end, the exiled Patriarch of Constantinople, Nestorius, and his disciples had already sowed the seeds of medicine in Syria and Persia. Byzantium preserved the best of Greek and Roman medical knowledge, but it required a theologic controversy over heresy to plant medicine in the Arabian soil where it was to flourish mightily.

EWING GALLOWAY

Ruins of the great walls of Constantinople showing breach through which Turks entered city.

HERITAGE OF AN EMPIRE

After the fall of Constantinople in 1453 the Byzantine Empire as such ceased to exist. Its destruction opened the way to the aggrandizement of the Ottoman Empire, ruled by the Osmanli Turks, an astonishing people who only a century before had been a primitive nomadic horde.

In short order the new rulers captured Serbia, Walachia, and Bosnia. Albania was overrun, the Venetians were forced to cede Scutari, and the Crimea was conquered.

A century after the fall of Constantinople, the empire was ruled by Suleiman I (the Magnificent, 1520-1566) who proceeded to conquer most of Hungary, the islands of Rhodes and Cos (the alleged birthplace of Hippocrates) and to offer a serious threat to Austria and Western Europe.

Under Suleiman I, the empire's administration was reorganized and consolidated. The new Turkish system was considerably influenced by the earlier Byzantine form of government, being a strong combination of military might and religious fervor, but equally weakened by court intrigues and all-pervading corruption and bribery.

During the eighteenth and nineteenth centuries the Ottoman Empire was steadily sapped by wars with Russia, until it came to be known in diplomatic circles as the Sick Man of Europe. The Crimean War (1854-1856) was fought by Britain and France to save Turkey from the Russians. But disintegration continued and the Ottoman Empire finally passed out of history in 1923 when a republic was declared by Mustafa Kemal Pasha (later called Atatürk), the father of modern Turkey.

GEORGE PICKOW

Streamlined modern building is in international fair at Smyrna (Turkish, Izmir).

113

UPI

An operating room in a Turkish hospital, with attending students.

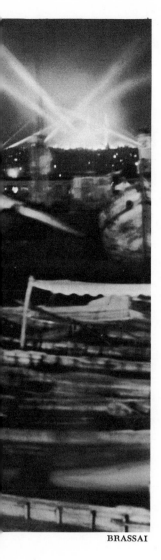

*Istanbul formerly Constantinople
seen from the Bosporus.
At left is Suleiman Mosque.*

BRASSAI

WHO

Ankara mothers are shown how to mix powdered milk.

115

Avicenna surrounded by his students. From a seventeenth century Persian miniature.

VI

While Scheherazade Tells Her Tales

Aᴺᴰ on the 436th night, Scheherazade began the tale of Abu al-Husn and his slave girl, the fair Tawaddud.

A "rose of crystal and silver, scented with sandalwood and nutmeg . . . with eyes like gazelles' eyne . . . cheeks like anemones of blood-red shine . . . and hind parts heavier than two hills of sand," Tawaddud prevailed upon her impoverished master to sell her to the caliph Harun-al-Rashid. Once in the presence of the caliph, Tawaddud offered to answer all questions on "syntax, poetry, jurisprudence, exegesis, philosophy, the divine ordinances, arithmetic, geodesy, geometry, ancient fables, the Koran, the exact sciences, medicine, logic, rhetoric and composition, the lute, dancing and fashions." The answers of this fabulous creature to the questions on medicine, anatomy, and physiology afford a revealing picture of Arabian medicine in its golden age.

Arabian medicine was Persian and, indirectly, Hellenic in origin. Long before the Arabian conquest there lived in Constantinople one Nestorius, an eloquent Aramaic priest who was banished to the Libyan Desert, because he dared maintain that the Virgin Mary was the mother of Christ, not of God. In a distant oasis, in the green shades of the towering palm trees, Nestorius and his followers, having paid dearly for their aspirations to heal man's soul, turned to healing man's body. Disillusioned with their own times, the Nestorians cast their eyes back to classical Greece and drank avidly of the medicophilosophical waters of the Greco-Roman school. Later, generous with their new knowledge, they poured the ancient Hellenic nectars into Syrian vessels, translating Greek medical works into Syrian and establishing the famous medical school at Jundishapur and others in various Persian towns. Thus the Nestorians revived in Persia the lost luminous Hippocratic-Latin tradition. Later, when the Arabs conquered Persia, they suddenly found their shepherds' pouches filled with the medico-philosophical treasures of the Greeks recorded on old Nestorian parchments.

A young and ardent Semitic people, the Arabs, who for centuries had been content to roam the burning sands of Arabia, spurred on by the monotheistic preachings of Mohammed, set out in the seventh century on a fabulous historical cavalcade, in the course of which their scimitars carved out an empire that stretched from China to Spain, including northern Africa. Centering their power in the caliphates of Baghdad and Córdoba, they created the mighty Saracen civilization, which was to perish in the thirteenth century with the sack of Baghdad by the Tartars and the expulsion of the Arabs by the Turks in the East and by the Spaniards in the West.

The Arabs never forced their religion on the peoples they conquered; they only required that the Koran be recognized as the vehicle for the divine word, and since the sacred book was written in Arabic, the conquered peoples had to learn the tongue of the victorious invaders. Thus the vast Moslem empire came to be united by one single language. Before Arabic became the official language among learned men, Greek, and later Syriac in western Asia, had been the preferred language. But from the ninth century on, both the humble rug vendor in the public market and the haughty physician at the caliphs' courts spoke in Arabic.

The only other term imposed by the Arabs upon the conquered people was the surrender of old Greek manuscripts. What splendorous times, when even beneath the warrior's mail beat a heart avid for culture! When Michael III of Constantinople was defeated, the penalty imposed on him was that he send a caravan of camels loaded with ancient manuscripts to Baghdad. The pen was mightier than the sword.

The Abbaside Caliphs wisely recognized the importance of translating into Arabic their vast Greek cultural war booty. Never in history have translators played as important a part as they did at the beginning of Islamic expansion. Heroes of this period were the famous Syrian and Coptic families of translators, the Bakhtîshû and the Mehsues, and that prince of translators, Hunain, also called Joannitius. Thanks to these men, the Arabs, whose total knowledge at the end of the eighth century consisted of a translation of a Greek medical book and a handful of alchemy books, before the end

Sheherazade and Sultan Harun al-Rashid. From a Persian miniature.

of the ninth century had become acquainted with all the Greek sciences.

The glory of Greece vanished and the might of Rome destroyed, there remained only the work of these Arabian translators and that of the Byzantine copyists to span a bridge of light across the thousand dismal years that elapsed between the fall of the Roman Empire and the jubilant explosion of the Renaissance.

Schools of medicine flourished in Samarkand and Baghdad, Isfahan and Alexandria, Córdoba, Seville, Toledo, Granada, and Saragossa. Through almost the whole of the ninth century, medical practice in Baghdad was in the hands of foreign Christians, whose skill was considered superior to that of the Arabs.

The Eastern Caliphate, or Caliphate of Baghdad, was illuminated by the presence of four Persian luminaries: al-Tabarî, Rhazes, Haly Abbas, and Avicenna.

Al-Tabarî wrote *The Paradise of Wisdom*, a paper chest scented with Arabian vegetable drugs—tamarind and sandalwood, nux vomica, Persian vetch, gum arabic. For, more than by any other branch of medicine, the Arabs were fascinated by pharmacology.

Rhazes, "the Experimenter," who alternately cultivated the gusla and medicine, head of the great hospital of Baghdad, physician to caliphs, proponent of a meager therapeutic arsenal in contrast to the abundant pharmacological fare served at the banquets of Arabian chemistry, was also a great compiler. His *Liber continens* gained him much fame. It also lost him his sight. It is said that a hierarch whom he had offended ordered that he be beaten on the head with his own book until one or the other broke. Rhazes' head broke first.

To Haly Abbas, a Zoroastrian magician, we owe *The Perfect Book of the Art of Medicine,* perhaps the best and most lucid of all Arabian medical works and the first to be translated into Latin.

With even greater brilliance shone Avicenna, the Persian Aristotle, prince of Arabian physicians, devourer of libraries, unparalleled dialectician in Moorish, Arabic, and Latinity, statesman by day, ready at night to forsake deep philosophizing for light-hearted feasts, well versed in old wines, chaser of fresh maidens, now wielding the vizier's staff, now turning to the guitar, the gusla, and the pen. Avicenna wrote the *Canon medicinaa,* the most famous medical book in history, a medical Bible whose million words made its author world dictator of medicine until Vesalius, supplanting for six centuries the medical dictatorship of Galen. In the *Canon,* epitome and summary of Greco-Latin medicine, the thorns of dogma bristle on the roses of science. The backbone of Arabian medical thought, it recommended the cautery instead of the surgeon's knife, for the Arabs had a horror of dissecting the human body. Today, a thousand years later, the principles of Avicenna's *Canon* still continue to heal the sick of Persia.

In the Western, or Córdoban, Caliphate the arts and sciences flourished, but except in mathematics and literature the Arabs were compilers and transmitters, rather than creators. Their architecture, rich in domes and ornate surfaces, derived from Byzantium; their cloistered patios, from Rome; their medicine, from Greece by way of Syria and Persia. Above all, the Arabs catered to the pleasures and comforts of the body, to which they subordinated even the soul. Their cities boasted glass windows and street lamps—reflections of their yearning for clarity and light—and abounded in enchanting gardens, redolent of exotic flowers and resonant with the murmuring of brightly tiled fountains.

The caliphs were generous patrons to scholars, and next to their deep-in-sensuous-shadowed seraglios, stood their libraries, lined wall to wall with yellowing parchments. Córdoba alone had fifty hospitals, seventy public libraries, and the most renowned university in Europe in the tenth century. In the library of al-Hakam II alone there were nearly three hundred thousand volumes, bound in leather and gold, containing in the sinewy and virile Arabic language the whole of Arabian knowledge. The Arabs assiduously cultivated astrology and alchemy, the mother of Arabian polypharmacy. There were numerous families of physicians, such as that of Avenzoar, which followed the medical tradition for three centuries. Next to sandalwood-scented mansions, the Arabs built hospitals, which, in Andalusia as in Baghdad, were also refuges for the insane and the destitute. And everywhere water, so prized by them, spurted and spun

View of a famous Fourteenth century Lions Court in the Alhambra of Granada, a typical Hispano-Arabian construction.

into braids of crystal for the baths and ablutions that were as indispensable as prayers. They led an indolent life in their flower-laden gardens, sipping fruit- and rose-flavored drinks, watching the golden dance of the bees from flower to flower, while deep in myrtle and basil, rosebays and gilly flowers, the water gurgled in the tiled fountains.

Medicine was taught privately; a general education was acquired at the *medressen*, a cultural center attached to the mosques. Medical students learned first the art

Acupuncture technique illustrated in a Turkish text on surgery. In Bibliotheque Nationale, Paris.

of mortar and pestle from an apothecary, then sought to enter the service of an experienced physician with an extensive library.

They considered the heart the sovereign of the body; the lungs, its fan; the liver, its guardian and the seat of the soul; the pit of the stomach, the seat of pleasure. They combined alchemy with ancient Chaldean magic, establishing "correspondences" between stars, spirits, metals, and the anima mundi. Seeking the elixir of life and eternal youth, they founded medicopharmaceutical chemistry; searching for potable gold, they discovered aqua regia. Led astray by Galenic polypharmacy and by Aristotelian dialectics, the Arabs also believed that it was sinful to open the human body and so halted progress in anatomy.

The giants of the Córdoban caliphate were four. The Córdoban Albucasis the surgeon, the Arabian Vesalius, wrote *al-Tasrif*, beacon light of European surgery until the time of Paré. Defying tradition and the Koran, he illustrated his texts himself. He adopted the iron cautery, tied arteries, described the position for lithotomy, practiced transverse tracheotomy, and differentiated between goiter and thyroid cancer. The Sevillian Avenzoar, an anti-Galenist, a ladies' man, physician to Almohad caliphs, was perhaps the greatest clinician of this period. He despised Avicenna's *Canon* and was the most Hippocratic among the Arabian physicians. The Córdoban Averroës, Aristotelian and pantheistic philosopher, perhaps the initiator of medieval scholasticism, physician to a caliph in Marrakech, influenced even his opponents with his subtle heterodox philosophies. The wandering Córdoban Maimonides, the greatest Jewish humanist and philosopher of the Middle Ages, whose services Richard Coeur de Lion tried in vain to secure, physician to the Sultan Saladin, practiced medicine in Egypt, whither the intolerance of the Almohades had forced him to flee. By basing theological principles on reason, he did for Judaism what Averroës had done for Islamism and St. Thomas would do for Christianity. Devoted to medicine as an art, he studied patients, not diseases, reconciling reason and faith, rejecting astrology, and left as heritage his wisdom-permeated *Guide to the Perplexed* and his priceless axiom: "Teach thy tongue to say I know not, and thou wilt progress."

The Arabian legacy to civilization was vast and varied, comprising fireworks, as colorful and explosive as the Arabian temperament, exquisite gardens and palaces that have endured to this day, geology and algebra, ceramics, textiles, botany, medical chemistry, and the first materia medica. The Arabs discovered various acids, nitrate of silver, benzoin, camphor, saffron, sublimate of laudanum, and anesthetics; developed the alchemical techniques of crystallization, distillation, and sublimation; and created the first pharmacies, which displayed their vast polypharmacy and their medical panacea: the melliti, together with numerous vials containing all sorts of weird things, from fetuses to frogs and scorpions. These pharmacies served also as meeting centers where all sorts of information and news were exchanged and discussed. The Arabs enriched man's language with such words as "drug," "alkali," "alcohol," "sugar," and many others. Their search for the philosopher's stone led them to advance laboratory methods and to invent the art of compounding prescriptions, sirups, juleps, poultices, electuaries, pills, powders, and alcoholates, which they kept in majolica jars, magnificent examples of pottery, embellished with fruits and leaves because at first they were used for preserves.

Above all, the Arabs built splendid hospitals, such as al-Mansur in Cairo, equipped with wards for both sexes, murmuring fountains to cool feverish limbs or soothe restless minds, libraries, dispensaries, reciters of the Koran, music for the sleepless, singers, and storytellers. Discharged patients were provided with money so that they need not go to work immediately. Their high rate of blindness from trachoma led the Arabs to make a thorough study of the human eye, and to progress markedly in optics and the removal of cataracts, the latter operation being symbolic of their thirst for more light.

Arabian medicine, reflecting the Hellenic sun on the Arabian crescent, illuminated the medieval darkness until the dawn of the Renaissance.

F.M.I.

Hispano-Arabian astrolabe made in Cordoba, ca. 1055.
Latin engraving was added in fourteenth century.

A camel caravan wends its way from China bringing Eastern luxuries and herbs to the Moslem world.

VI
ARABIAN MEDICINE

Aт the dawn of the seventh century the regions from the North Sea to the Persian Gulf were engulfed in strife or crumbling in decay.

The Byzantine Empire was fighting for its very existence against Persians and Avars while at home it was torn by theologic controversy; Rome under Pope Gregory strove to shake loose the oppressive hand of the Byzantine exarchs; Gaul was rent by the fratricidal war of two Frankish chieftains; England was parceled into warring kingdoms of Angles, Saxons, Jutes; once mighty Egypt had fallen under Persian domination.

Amid such chaos the civilized heritage of Greece was in danger of perishing: historic towns were sacked, precious libraries destroyed, scholars were killed or hounded from place to place.

Into this falling darkness a ray of light penetrated from the wilderness borne by an ancient Semitic people. From the sandy plateau of Arabia spread a new force that was to build a mighty bridge between the classic and the modern worlds.

ORIGINS. The Arabian peninsula is generally accepted as the home of the Semites, a people traditionally descended from Noah's son, Shem. Inscriptions show that the area was the home of a great civilization some 1000 years before the Christian era, divided into at least four kingdoms of which the Minaean and Sabaean[1] were apparently the most powerful.

The Arabian Semites who wandered north came in contact with the Sumerians established in the fertile Mesopotamian river regions, conquered or merged with them to help form the mighty Babylonian state founded by Hammurabi around 2000 B.C.

At the turn of the seventh century, Arabia was peopled by a few towns and communities along the coasts, but mostly by nomadic tribes living a pastoral life; several precarious kingdoms depended on more powerful neighbors such as Persia, Abyssinia, Byzantium.

Religious life was fragmentary and confused: the majority of tribes believed in a pantheon of some 300 gods; in southern Arabia a kingdom that accepted Judaism had warred with Abyssinian Christians, while in the northeastern kingdom of Hira flourished a large and prosperous Christian community, most of them Nestorians; from Persia permeated fragments of Zoroastrianism, while throughout the peninsula a few scattered Jewish communities disseminated monotheistic Judaism. Arabia was overly ripe for political and religious unification.

ISLAM. Mohammed was born around 570 of parents who belonged to the ruling tribe of Mecca, then a prosperous town and a place of pilgrimage to the pagan Arabs who came to worship at the Kaaba, the shrine enclosing the mystic Black Stone.

In his youth he married a wealthy widow and became a prosperous merchant. When he was 40 he had a vision in which God chose him to be the Arab prophet of a true religion, the first of many revelations later collected into the Koran, sacred book of Islam. Mohammed considered himself the successor of Jesus Christ and the last of the prophets.

Mohammed at first made few converts and many enemies in Mecca. In 622 a plot to assassinate him caused him to flee to Yathrib (later named Medina)[2] where he established a theocratic state. A blend of proselytizing and warfare during the next years overcame his enemies and made numerous converts; when Mohammed died in 632 he had unified Arabia politically and spiritually.

The next three centuries saw one of the most astounding growths of an empire known to history. Starting from the small walled town of Medina, Moslem rule was extended some 4000 miles: to the west over Egypt, North Africa, and most of Spain; to the north were held Syria, Armenia, and the Caucasus; northeastern conquests included Mesopotamia, Persia, and Afghanistan; further east the empire extended to parts of India. And the spiritual center of this vast domain was then (as today) the holy city of Mecca to which every good Moslem hopes to make a pilgrimage at least once in his life.

Unlike the later Mongol invasions that sowed only misery and chaos in their wake, the conquering Moslems left intact the seats of learning along their victorious path.

One such brilliant intellectual center was Jundishapur, founded in the fourth century by the Persian King Shapur.[3] Its academy and hospital attracted physicians and philosophers from many lands.

A serious rift in the Eastern Church of Byzantium was caused in 428 by Nestorius, Patriarch of Constantinople, when he propounded the doctrine that the divine and human natures of Jesus were separate. He and his followers were condemned as heretics in 431, fled first to Edessa (now Urfa, Turkey), eventually settled in Jundishapur.

Here they mingled with Platonic philosophers who had abandoned Athens when Justinian closed their schools in 529, Jewish scholars with a command of languages, Syrian scribes and translators, Chinese and Indian sages.

When the Arabs overran Persia they made the academy of Jundishapur the scholastic nucleus of the Islamic empire. A Christian priest-physician named Sergius translated some Greek medical literature into Syriac; this was later translated into Arabic by the Persian Jew, Masawayh. As Arabic proved to be a most flexible language it gradually supplanted all others in the world of learning.

MEDICINE AND THE KORAN. In the Moslem religion the cause of all things is Allah, and by transgressing against the divine will man can bring on disease. Diseases might also be the work of malignant spirits, through possession by disease demons (*madshunun*), or the effect of the evil eye. Catastrophes that wiped out nations, such as plagues, were attributed to the wrath of Allah, as punishment for sins.[4]

The Koran accepted the ancient concept that a *pneuma* supplied the body with life, reaching the heart via the nostrils and trachea; the heart was the seat of the soul; in death the soul returned to Allah via the breath. In physiology, the coarse elements of food were seen as passing out through the kidneys and rectum, while the more delicate ones were turned into milk and the finest became blood.

Procreation was a mixture of the male seed and female blood in the uterus, there to form a clot out of which was formed a skeleton and a covering of muscles and flesh; the source of the seminal fluid was the head, reaching the testicles through the spinal column.[5]

The Koran prescribed strict rules of personal hygiene: frequent washing of the body (especially after excretion) and clean clothes; water was regarded as a spiritual as well as physical cleanser. All foods were permitted except the flesh of pig; honey was regarded as a remedy for many ailments. Milk was highly valued ("It is a fluid reserved for the believers in Paradise") except that of the ass; which was forbidden.

There is no reference to surgery in the Koran, although circumcision was an obligatory rite. Later religious regulations strictly forbade anatomic dissection.

THE ARAB WORLD. As remarkable as the swift military conquests of the Arabs was their conversion from rugged nomads to luxury loving city dwellers, a gigantic leap that spanned several thousand years of culture.

When the soldiers of Mohammed burst out of their desert peninsula they wore homespun cloth, subsisted on a lean diet of meat, milk, and cheese. Their military development was primitive, except in their skill in besieging and storming fortified points. They scorned farmers and townspeople.

Noted a ninth century Moslem scholar: "As for the desert Arabs, they had never been merchants, tradesmen, or physicians nor had they any aptitude for mathematics or agriculture. On the other hand, when they gave their minds to poetry and oratory, to horses, weapons, and implements of war, or to the recording of traditions and annals, they were unexcelled."

These restless poet-warriors in a few years found themselves masters of vast territories that had to be administered, were forced to borrow from the Persians their systems of taxation, local administration, centralized government, absolute power in the hands of the ruler.

These same hardy cameleers brusquely emerged among Persians who had for centuries enjoyed a settled existence, whose leading families lived in an atmosphere of luxurious refinement and exquisite artistry.

Within a few years Arabian courtiers at the Omayyad caliphate in Damascus had replaced homespun wool by brocaded silk, had discarded camel milk for Persian delicacies, had adopted Persian table manners in place of the communal *kuskus* bowl. Those Arabians who penetrated into eastern Persia learned to wear trousers instead of skirts, drank wine (against the Koran's injunction), celebrated many Persian feast days.

Facing page: *In the School of Toledo, scholars translate classic medical texts. Man with broadbrimmed hat at left is a Jew, turbaned man is Arab, others are Christian monks and scholars. Through typical Mauresque arch can be seen outline of Toledo on its hill. Painted by Hans Guggenheim.*

BAGHDAD. In the thousand years of Sumerian glory, a small town called Baghdad huddled between the Tigris and Euphrates, overshadowed by the mighty cities of Kish and Babylon. On this strategic site, in the year 762, the Caliph al-Mansur ordered some 100,000 laborers to build him a new capital for the Moslem empire.

In four years there emerged a circular city, about a mile and a half in diameter, ringed by three lines of walls, some of them containing bricks weighing 200 pounds. In the center of the circle rose the caliph's palace, surrounded by walled-in gardens and cool fountains, ornamented with novel arches and domes, porticoes and balustrades.

Rich villas were built along the river banks, tall minareted mosques jostled cupolaed Christian churches; the dark noisy streets were lined with shops: silk weavers, booksellers, money-changers, perfumers, basket weavers. The poorer people clustered in flat-roofed brick hovels, yet bore themselves with a natural dignity. In the streets they gathered around a storyteller or a street singer, or fished in the river, or gaped at the magnificence of a rich man's cortege.

This was the Baghdad of Caliph Harun al-Rashid, whose wife served meals in gold and jeweled vessels and spent 3 million dinars on a pilgrimage to Mecca. The rich dressed in colored silks brought by caravan from China, perfumed their hair and beards, repelled the stench of the city by burning frankincense, paid huge fees to musicians and dancers.

For entertainment besides singing and dancing there were the games of chess and polo, both favorites of Harun al-Rashid.[6] Although learned Moslems condemned works of fiction as unworthy of serious attention, Arabians throughout the empire were addicted to listening to stories.

The second Abbasid Caliph (al-Mansur) lured many learned men from Jundishapur, established them in schools of medicine, astrology, chemistry, mathematics.[7] The traditions of the medical school were thus described by contemporary scholar al-Qifti:

"They made rapid progress in science, developing new methods in the treatment of disease along pharmacologic lines so that their therapy was judged superior to that of the Greeks and the Hindus. Furthermore, their physicians adopted the scientific methods of other peoples and modified them by their own discoveries. They elaborated medical laws and recorded the work they had done."

Baghdad's best-known hospital was founded by Vizier Abud al-Daula in 970: it contained a pharmacy stocked with drugs from all parts of the world, a system akin to the modern in and outpatient, a division of physicians into the equivalents of interns and externs, a primitive nursing system, and an almoner's office.[8] p 279

During the twenty years under Caliph al-Mamun (son of Harun al-Rashid, 813-833), Baghdad flowered into the second largest and most opulent city west of the Indus (Constantinople was the first). Its center of learning was a splendid academy called the House of Wisdom, and the city itself earned the gentle surname of the Abode of Peace.

CORDOBA. At the western end of the empire flourished another mighty center of civilization, firmly anchored in the Spanish city of Córdoba. At a period when London and Paris were mere conglomerations of mud-and-wattle houses, Córdoba was the most civilized city in Europe, the wonder of northern barbarians.[9]

Under the Omayyad Caliphs in the tenth century, the city contained some million inhabitants, over 300 mosques (each housing a school), 70 libraries, 900 public baths, 50 hospitals, a university that became renowned throughout Europe.

The caliph's summer residence (Medina Zahara) about three miles west of Córdoba was a fabulous dream palace, grouping spacious patios, lattice-windowed harems, fountained courtyards, mosques, buildings-within-buildings shimmering white, blue, and gold amid groves of figs, almonds, and pomegranates.

Above the crooked, narrow streets towered the great mosque with its nineteen bronze gateways, 4700 lamps of perfumed oil, a roof supported by 1200 columns of porphyry, jasper, and multicolored marbles, surrounded by a massive buttressed wall, and reputed to contain some of the bones of the Prophet.

The city became a wealthy trading center, terminus for caravans from as far as China. Around the city walls, merchants' tents displayed carpets from Bukhara, muslin from Mosul, pearls from the Persian Gulf, damask from Damascus, glassware, pottery, dried fruit, and sweetmeats.

Moslems brought to Spain all the arts and crafts they had gleaned along their route of conquest: new and exotic food plants from Asia and Africa, the construction of roads and canals, the manufacture of silk and ceramics, the tanning of hides.

Córdoba became renowned for its ivory carvings, pottery embodying a unique shimmering luster, especially its soft leather and bookbinding. Moslems had introduced the Chinese art of papermaking to the West; Spanish Moslems raised the making of books to a great art.

While Córdoba with its palaces and gigantic mosque remained for centuries the seat of the Western Caliphate (sometimes termed the Baghdad of the West), Hispano-Arabian culture also flowered in Seville, Granada, and Toledo; after Córdoba was de-

Mosque lamp with sacred inscriptions. Islamic art of the Fourteenth century.

stroyed by Berbers at the beginning of the eleventh century, Toledo became the center of Spanish-Moslem learning, attracting scholars from all Europe.[10]

Arabian culture and science thus flourished between its two great centers in Baghdad and Córdoba,[11] fertilizing barbarian communities, ringing Europe with a southern belt of graceful architecture, fine crafts, lyric poetry, music, and dancing, and the medical art inherited from the disciples of Hippocrates and Galen.

THE TRANSMUTERS. In the schools of medicine and academies of general learning established in all the main centers of the Moslem empire the first task of scholars was to translate texts preserved from the Greco-Roman civilization.

One of the earliest Arabian physicians of the sixth century was Al-Harith: he studied medicine at Jundishapur, flourished as a wealthy practitioner in Persia, returned to Mecca, and became a friend of Mohammed.[12]

The first of a remarkable dynasty of physicians, a Nestorian named Jurjis (Georgeus) Bakhtishu,[13] chief physician of the hospital at Jundishapur, was called upon to treat the Caliph al-Mansur in Baghdad around 770; his son Jabril (Gabriel) became the personal physician of Caliph Harun al-Rashid.

Under the Caliph al-Mansur a school of translators was established in Baghdad, directed by the Christian physician Yuhanna (Johannes) Masawayh (777-

857).[14] Their task was to translate Greek manuscripts acquired in Asia Minor and Egypt.

Masawayh's greatest pupil was Hunain ibn Ishaq (809-877?),[15] a Nestorian who enriched Arabic with many scientific terms. His school translated the greatest part of the Hippocratic and Galenic writings into Syriac and Arabic.

Hunain himself translated most of Galen, the great *Synopsis of Oribasius*, the important *Materia Medica* of Dioscorides; his own works included a question-and-answer manual on medicine, the first textbook on ophthalmology (*Ten Treatises on the Eye*).

The search for classic manuscripts went on intensely throughout the Moslem world: Hunain described how he personally hunted for a work of Galen throughout Mesopotamia, Syria, Palestine, and Egypt, finally tracking down only half of it in Damascus. When Moslem forces defeated the debauched Byzantine emperor Michael III in battle, his penalty was to send to Baghdad a camel caravan laden with manuscripts from Constantinople's libraries.

THE PHYSICIANS. Unlike their status in the Roman Empire, physicians in the lands under Moslem rule enjoyed high esteem. Many of them were not only trained in Greek and Galenic medicine but were also adept in philosophy, mathematics, astronomy, and theology.

In *A Thousand and One Nights* a physician tells how he cured a member of the governor's household, was rewarded with a handsome dress of honor and the post of superintendent of the hospital in Damascus.

Physicians-in-ordinary in rich households and court physicians received high salaries and numerous gifts, often became tremendously wealthy.[16] But when treatment failed or when a physician fell out of favor, the penalty was often imprisonment, flogging, or death.

Even the most reputable physicians were not above indulging in some mysterious practices, as in writing out prescriptions with purgative ink (possibly colocynth) or calling on astrology for a diagnosis. The richer physicians usually treated the poor without charge.

Quacks abounded, using the same tricks that were to persist on the fringe of European medicine for centuries. A favorite device was to hire confederates who posed as patients, went about praising a charlatan's miraculous cures.

One of Islam's greatest physicians was Persian born Al-Razi (Rhazes, 865-925) who first studied at Baghdad university, then became chief physician of its renowned hospital; he also traveled in Africa, visited Jerusalem, attended at the academies of Córdoba.

Application of a clyster or acupuncture by Arabian physician.

His teaching characteristically began: "According to my experience..." His capacity for observation and bold treatment earned him the title of the "experimenter."

He deplored dishonest medical practices, entered a plea for a frank relationship between physician and patient, criticized laymen for expecting a physician to know everything from a mere examination of a patient's urine and pulse.

Rhazes assembled most of the medical knowledge of his time in a monumental work of some twenty volumes called *al-Hawi*, meaning "Comprehensive Book."[17] It included medical lore culled from Greek, Syrian, Persian, and Indian authors, plus his own opinions and experiences.

Some of his other medical treatises dealt with renal and vesical calculi, anatomy (in which he described the recurrent laryngeal nerve), a description of spina ventosa and bifida, the use of animal gut in sutures, the introduction of a mercurial ointment.[18]

Another important work was a collection of ten medical treatises (*Liber medicinalis ad Almansorem*), of which the ninth dealing with general medicine, was widely published in Western universities. This work contained these two aphorisms:

"Truth in medicine is an unattainable goal, and the healing art described in books is much inferior to the experience of a thoughtful physician.

"He who interrogates many physicians will commit many errors."

Rhazes' most celebrated work, which was reprinted innumerable times as late as the nineteenth century, was his treatise on smallpox and measles (translated as *Liber de pestilentia*), containing the first clear account of these two diseases; his therapy was purification of the blood.

His treatment of fever was cold water applications; for inflammation of the chest he recommended wine, for phthisis the use of milk and sugar; indigestion would be benefited by buttermilk and cold water; constipation would yield to mercury; for cases of melancholia, chess and music were salutary measures; for over-all hygiene, diet and bathing.

Discovered only some thirty years ago was Rhazes' great book on the art of alchemy in which he classified substances concisely into vegetable, animal, and mineral, distinguished between volatile and non-volatile bodies.

An important contemporary of Rhazes was Isaac Israeli (?880–932), Egyptian-born Jewish physician known in the West as Isaac Judaeus, whose practical works on fevers, elements, drugs, and urine dominated Western medicine for centuries.[19]

His tract *The Guide of Physicians* demonstrated a high ethical concept of the medical profession. Among its precepts: Let thine own skill exalt thee and seek not honor in another's shame; Neglect not to visit and treat the poor, for there is no nobler work; Comfort the sufferer by the promise of healing, even when thou art in doubt, for thus thou doth assist his natural powers.[20]

A shining light in the Eastern Caliphate was the Persian Moslem known to the West as Haly Abbas (died 994), author of a twenty volume encyclopedia called *Kitabal-Malik* (Latin: *Liber regius*) dealing with the theory and practice of medicine.

Haly Abbas advised young physicians to devote time to practical medical teaching in hospitals, combine this with a good grounding in theory. One authority has claimed that he was the first to suggest the existence of the blood capillary system. The *Liber regius* remained the standard textbook of Arabian medicine until it was displaced by the *Canon* of Avicenna a century later.

A prominent physician at the Caliph's court in Córdoba was Abulcasis (Abu al-Qasim, ca. 936-1013), born of Spanish parents and the greatest surgeon of that period. In his thirty-sectioned *al-Tasrif* (Latin *Vade mecum*, largely borrowed from Paul of Aegina) he described the use of cautery, lithotomy, herniotomy, trephining, amputations, operations for fistula, goiter, aneurysm, and arrow wounds. He recommended artificial teeth made of beef bone, the use of silver catheters for bladder disorders.

Abulcasis advised aspiring surgeons: "He who would devote himself to surgery must be versed in the science of anatomy which Galen has transmitted." But he admitted that his own knowledge of anatomy was derived from books and not from dissection. His surgical text containing numerous sketches of surgical instruments dominated European teaching until the advent of Ambroise Paré in the sixteenth century.

In his obstetric and gynecologic work, Abulcasis

was prevented by custom from examining virtuous women directly, was obliged to rely on female operators who worked under his guidance. Nevertheless the *Vade mecum* describes several procedures for treating abnormal presentations, including instrument deliveries.

The most famous of Arabian physicians whose influence extended for centuries over the Islamic world and Europe was Abu Ali al-Husayn ibn Sina (980-1037) known as Avicenna. He was born near Bukhara, son of a Persian tax collector.

He was reputed to have memorized the entire Koran and much Arabian poetry by the age of ten; by sixteen he claimed to know medical theory; two years later he was appointed physician to the Emir whom he had cured of a dangerous illness. He spent some years wandering from town to town, finally established himself as a physician in Hamadan where the Emir appointed him as his physician and vizier.

Avicenna was a scholar who loved the pleasures of life; his physical vigor enabled him to combine study with a passion for wine and women. Wrote he autobiographically: "When I found a difficulty, I referred to my notes and prayed to the Creator. At night, when weak or sleepy, I strengthened myself with a glass of wine."[21]

The *Canon* consists of five books covering physiology, hygiene, therapy, materia medica. The material is heavily borrowed from Hippocrates and Galen, adopts the ancient Greek humoral theory of disease. Although lacking in originality it presents with admirable clarity a synthesis of the medical knowledge of that time.

Some of Avicenna's contemporaries thought little of him: Avenzoar used the margins of the *Canon* as scribbling paper; Arnold of Villanova dubbed Avicenna a "professional scrivener." Nevertheless the work remained the foremost medical treatise of European universities for centuries, was used as late as 1650 in the medical schools of Louvain and Montpellier.

The twelfth century in Moslem Spain produced three great physician-philosophers, Avenzoar, Averroës, and Maimonides, who exercised an enormous influence not only on contemporary medicine but also on thought.

The Sevillian Abu Mervan ibn Zuhr (Avenzoar, ca. 1113-1162) was a wealthy aristocrat descended from generations of physicians, a foe of quackery, and a believer in independent thought even if it opposed Galen.

His chief work was *al-Taysir* (Latin: *Theisir*), rich in personal experiences, independent observation, and judgments based on rational practices. He distinguished between primary and secondary heart disease, described pericarditis, paralysis of the phar-

Avenzoar engaged in study. Woodcut from an edition of Averroës, Venice, 1530.

ynx, otitis media; he opposed purgatives, strongly advocated venesection, firmly believed in the virtues of the bezoar allegedly produced by the eyes of a deer.

His friend and pupil was the Córdoban Abu Walid ibn Rushd (Averroës, 1126-1198) who became famous (or infamous) as an Aristotelian philosopher.[22] His seven-volume medical work, *Kitab al-Kullyat* (Latin: *Colliget*), was largely a commentary on Avicenna's *Canon*, adding little from his own experience.

The celebrated pupil of Averroës was another Córdoban, Abu Imram ibn Maimun (Maimonides, 1135-1204), better known as a philosopher and a Talmudist than as a physician. He became personal physician in Egypt to the great Sultan Saladin, mighty opponent of the Crusaders and chivalric foe of England's King Richard I, called the Lion-Hearted.

His best-known medical work was *Fusul Musa* (Latin: *Aphorisms*), a collection of 1500 aphorisms extracted from Galen's writings, combined with some forty of his own critical remarks. He also wrote a treatise on hemorrhoids, a book on poisons and antidotes, a discourse on asthma, and a widely renowned treatise on sexual intercourse (Latin: *Ars Coeundi*) comprising nineteen chapters.

For the melancholic eldest son of Saladin who complained of bad digestion and dejection, Maimonides wrote a treatise on dietetics, hygiene, and climatology that remained a classic for centuries.

Maimonides' most lasting fame is based on his philosophic work *Guide to the Perplexed* which profoundly influenced Thomas Aquinas, the development of Christian thought, and the rise of scholasticism. His basic tenet in all studies: "Employ your reason and you will be able to discern that which is said figuratively, hyperbolically, and what is meant literally." In his age this appeal to the individual intellect was crass heresy that drew the fire of orthodox Christians and Moslems.

Averroës. Ink drawing by Raphael.

*Portrait of Maimonides, not regarded
as a faithful likeness.*

Maimonides was the last great medical figure produced by the Hispano-Moslem culture, marking the decline of Islamic medicine. A mere eight years after his death Alphonso VIII of Castille expelled the Moslems from most of Spain (1212); two decades later Mongolian hordes swept over much of the Moslem Empire.

PHARMACOLOGY. The Arabian schools introduced into medicine a large number of drugs, herbal and chemical, also developed the art of pharmacy. In the works of the mysterious Jabir (Geber)[23] are contained improved methods for evaporation, filtration, sublimation, distillation, crystallization, also methods for producing mercury, sulfide, and arsenious oxide, vitriols, alums, lead acetate, crude sulfuric and nitric acids (combined as *aqua regia*).

The most complete medieval work on botany and materia medica was the *Corpus of Simples* of Ibn al-Baitar (1197-1248), an eminent botanist from Málaga who collected plants and drugs along the Mediterranean, from Spain to Syria, described more than 1500 medicinal drugs. In the middle of the thirteenth century the textbook on the art of pharmacy was that of the Jew Kohen al-Attar, which established professional standards for all pharmacists.

Among the medicines introduced by the Arabs were amber, musk, cloves, peppers, Chinese ginger, betel nut, sandalwood, rhubarb, nutmeg, camphor, senna, cassis, nux vomica.

A rich trade in such drugs or simples developed between Arabian pharmacies and European countries. At one time this commerce formed an important part of the wealth of the Italian maritime republics such as Venice.

Pharmacies adorned by blue-tiled fountains became centers for gossip, exchange of alchemic lore, horoscope readings. They dispensed herbs, simples, honey, syrups, essence of flowers (favored by physicians for washing their hands), poultices, plasters, and aromatic waters.[24] Arabian pharmacies contributed to art through their exquisite ceramic drug jars and bottles.[25]

HOSPITALS. A feature of Arabian medicine that profoundly influenced the development of medicine in medieval Europe was the hospital, both in the treatment of the sick and the teaching of medicine.

Islamic hospitals became models of humane kindness, especially in the treatment of the insane. Cairo's Mansur hospital cooled its fever wards by fountains, contained lecture halls, a library, chapels, dispensary, nurses of both sexes. It employed reciters of the Koran, musicians to lull patients to sleep, storytellers for their distraction; discharged patients were given money to tide them over convalescence.

Arabian hospitals impressed Christian pilgrims to the Holy Land, led to the creation in the eleventh century of a hospital in Jersualem. This was later expanded by the Crusaders, formed the kernel of the religious Order of the Hospital of St. John of Jerusalem, the famous Knights Hospitalers who played a major role in the Crusades.

THE HERITAGE. Arabian medicine saved for the

130

Entrance to hospital at Kayseri, dated 1205, showing typical Arabian arch.

West the treasury of medicine amassed by the Greeks, enriched it with its own advances in chemistry, pharmacy, botany, hospital administration. Profound minds in Moslem Spain added subtlety to the physician's art, deepened the roots of practical medicine.

Of vital importance to the growth of medicine was the fact that for more than a thousand years two parallel systems developed side by side, both basically drawn from the common fount of Greek medicine.

Although Latin became the language of medicine in Europe, Arabic remained for long centuries the language of science in countries as far apart as Spain and India. The great contribution of Arabian scholars and physicians was to make medicine truly international and to build bridges between East and West.

The clash between the Christian and Moslem worlds during the two centuries of the Crusades further enriched the cultural, medical, and pharmacologic links between the growing centers of learning.

The physicians and alchemists who flourished under Islam came from many ethnic sources, drew their inspiration from Greece, Rome, Syria, China, India. By the time Islamic medicine and science floundered to a standstill in the thirteenth century, the seeds had been transmitted and planted in medieval European soil, waiting for the fructifying rain of the Renaissance.

Following pages: *Scene is the Al-Mansur hospital in Cairo, showing alcoved couches in background. Patient is being treated by a Jewish physician (yellow turban) according to Maimonides prescription, a pigeon applied to the afflicted part. Man next to him with black turban is a Copt. Agitated patients were soothed by lute player in foreground; fever wards were cooled by fountains such as one seen at right. Painted by Hans Guggenheim.*

Bench in Seville, with azuelejos *type of ornamentation.*

HISPANO-MOORISH WORLD TODAY

The last Moors were driven out of Spain in the same year that Columbus discovered America, but their influence can still be seen everywhere.

What was once the unified empire of the Arabs has in five centuries split up into fragments, some of them separated by a thousand years of civilization. Parts of Arabia are today much the same as they were in Mohammed's time, suffering from the same diseases and the same blights of nature. The incorporation of some of these lands in the modern system of oil production and air transport has hardly begun to change the old ways.

At the other end of the once-flourishing empire is Spain, a modern country that has kept pace with its European neighbors in industrial and commercial development. Yet from Mecca to Madrid runs a cultural thread that recalls the fallen empire: in architecture, customs, language, music.

Arab countries today face the sometimes intolerable stress of adapting ancient ways and modes of thought to a high speed electronic world.

Moreover, twentieth century medical services are slowly but surely conquering the age-old diseases such as malaria and trachoma, thereby increasing the pressure of populations in sparse regions. The unstable political conditions in most of the former Arabian lands is partly the outcome of the great physical and mental stress of an impact between two cultures.

Above, University city in Madrid.

At right, reception in the court of the Al Hambra at Riyadh (Saudi Arabia).

Cathedral at Seville, showing Moorish influence.

*Bloodletting through cupping
is done by a street barber
at Ouarzazate in Morocco.*

Following page: *Conquest of Jerusalem in July, 1099, by soldiers of First Crusade. In foreground, physicians and monks minister to wounded on the battlefield. Painted by Hans Guggenheim.*

VII

The Cross and the Eagle

Through the bloody dust stirred up by the medieval wars, over which still hovered the shadows of the Christian cross and the old pagan eagle-like symbols of conflicting civilizations, a new type of man was emerging—a man forever on the defensive, eternally tortured by the terrors of the beyond, by the fear of God in heaven and of devils and plagues on earth.

For a thousand years medieval man had lived in perpetual conflict with God, with the world, and with himself. Ravenous for knowledge, he crowded into the public squares to listen to the golden words of Albertus Magnus, Abelard, Duns Scotus, or St. Thomas Aquinas. Obsessed with saving his soul, he neglected his malodorous body, concealing it with voluminous garments, heavy perfumes, and architectonic wigs. Burning with sexual desire, brutal and gluttonous in his pleasures, mystical and romantic in his deeds, rebellious against the law and enslaved to classical dogma, believing, under the spell of astrology and alchemy, that invisible zodiacal-magical filaments connected men, stars, and matter, fear and faith were the opposite poles of his soul. He sought refuge in the love of God, in the collective security of medieval cities—where everything, including disease, was collective—and in the perpetual imperative of action, from tournaments and single combats to the gigantic collective adventure of the Crusades. He exchanged the celestial bodies of astronomy for the cabalistic signs and symbols of astrology, and the test tube of the chemist for the crucible of the alchemist. But he also created masterpieces. He built the Gothic cathedrals, soaring hymns in stone, skyrockets of granite and glass, with rainbowed windows, illuminated missals, and statues and paintings that extolled, to literate and illiterate alike, his world of allegory and symbolism. He wrote the *Divina Commedia*, immortalizing through Dante's lips his own spirit and deeds. And—perhaps his greatest claim to glory—he was the first to create, on a vast scale, universities, a public health system, and hospitals. From such as he sprang the modern European man.

The medieval cathedrals were, so to speak, centers of entertainment and instruction, whither flocked the pilgrims to pass long days huddled around the still time-untouched dazzling white walls, gazing in wonder at the stained glass windows (their equivalent to our electronic newsboards, just as the religious processions with their pomp and pageantry were their cinema and television), whereon were recorded in jewel-toned colors the news, stories, biographies, and even technical advances of the period.

In an age that was collective, medicine was faced with the problem of "collective" diseases (plagues, leprosy, dancing mania), just as it was faced with "individual" diseases (syphilis) in the individualistic Renaissance. Symbolically, the Middle Ages began and ended with terrible pandemics: leprosy, which made its victims, with their gray sackcloth, peaked hood, and sinister rattle, the most dreaded of phantoms; and the Black Death, which killed the majority of lepers but also a quarter of the population of Europe, causing some forty-three million deaths, spreading over the entire planet

137

through maritime and caravan routes. Among its social consequences, it dealt the death-blow to feudalism, increased the value of labor by making laborers scarce, and caused loss of faith in the Church and priests by showing that they died like anyone else, which helped to spread the Reformation. Ironically enough, the Black Death inspired a cynical and irreverent Florentine to write the immortal *Decameron*.

The collectivistic characteristics of the Middle Ages partly determined the monastic nature of medieval medicine. Medieval man sought protection and safety in the anonymity of either huge armies, like the Crusades, or monastaries. Located on the main routes traversed either by foot or on horseback by all travelers, the monasteries were at once inn, refuge, hospital, news agency, and nerve center of medieval life. Here a handful of dedicated men toiled to learn the new universal language, Latin, which for a thousand years would replace Greek, already supplanted by Arabic in the Islamic world. In these monasteries study and calligraphy were made paths to heaven. Knowledge became for the Church the means of consolidating its power and authority. Thus clerics came to study, among other things, medicine. Sickness became a divine punishment, and repentance a prerequisite for its cure, with the medical arsenal including relics, rituals, scapulars, and prayers. Medical aid was free until the High Middle Ages, when medicine for the first time became a profession commanding remuneration.

Monastic medicine coincided with Romanesque art, man being the subservient to the Church militant, even as, later, the medicine of Salerno coincided with Gothic art, and the birth of nationalities at this time, together with the rise in the universities, threatened the Church's medical monopoly. The state of mind of the peoples of both periods was reflected in their architecture: in the former, it comprised fortress-like—squat and square and windowless—granite carapaces that provided collective shelter against individual fears, while in the latter period it soared into spiraling towers, symbol of alertness and power.

The monk-physicians accepted the Hippocratic doctrine of the four humors and the correlation between the macro- and the microcosm. Therapy was based on the polypharmacy, bloodletting, cupping, baths, emetics, purgatives, and diuretics described in the antidotaries and herbals, basis of all monastic medical knowledge. To be a physician one first had to be ordained a priest, though monks practiced medicine only in the monastaries.

Theurgic therapy, based on saints' miracles and magic herbs, had its first center in the monastery of Monte Cassino, founded in 529 by St. Benedict of Nursia on the ruins of a temple of Apollo, and the model for future "cathedral-schools." The monks at Monte Cassino practiced religious psychotherapy and physiotherapy, and devoted much time to copying classical medical texts. There the monk Cassiodorus combined classical Greco-Latin and Christian thought, and Greek formularies and compilations were translated into Latin. More a vast medical library and general teaching center than a genuine medical school, Monte Cassino was the cradle of western *religious* medicine. A mass of stone atop a hill near Naples, often sacked during the centuries and finally destroyed in World War II, Monte Cassino had its golden age in the eleventh century. The moving spirit of its medicine was Constantine the African, a mysterious physician disguised as a Benedictine monk, who studied medicine and magic in Babylon. He translated into Latin the works of the Arabian, Jewish, and Greco-Roman physicians, especially Galen, and his translations initiated the lay emancipation of medicine and formed a bridge between Monte Cassino and Salerno.

Some one hundred and twenty-five miles from Monte Cassino, on the azure Tyrrhenian Sea, was Salerno, an ancient Greek colony. The School of Salerno, created as a *civitas Hippocratica*, three centuries after Monte Cassino, by a group of students organized in a *universitas*, and a group of physicians composing a faculty, was the oldest center of *lay* medical instruction and the first school to confer diplomas and the title of doctor.

Supported by neighboring Benedictine monastaries, Salerno combined Greek, Latin, Jewish and Arabian cultures. In Salerno, though most of the teachers were clerics, medicine was taught freely, even by women physicians like Trotula, the "Dame Trot" of popular tales, and became emancipated from the clergy. There anatomy was taught, though only pigs were dissected; there the first medieval pharmacopoeia was compiled, and surgery, practiced often on the mangled bodies of returning Crusaders, made progress. In Salerno was written the most famous hexameter poem of popular medicine in history, the *Regimen sanitatis Salernitanum*, later attributed to Arnold of Villanova.

Nearly a thousand editions were published of this work, which recommended diet, exercise, herbs, drugs, rest, and recreation. And in Salerno, disease was regarded as arising from natural causes and not as a result of divine punishment, astrology and magic were rejected, and the path was opened that would lead to the medieval universities.

The universities crystallized the passionate desire for knowledge that permeated medieval Europe. The center of knowledge shifted with political power, passing successively from Salerno to Bologna, Paris, Montpellier, Oxford, Cambridge, and Padua. Physicians were still "book doctors," more philosophers than clinicians, for their clinic was the library, although already in the fourteenth century genuine clinical histories were being written, such as the famous *consilia* of Padua and Bologna. Horror of blood made the Church abandon surgery to barbers, executioners, and quacks. The *universitates,* or free associations of students, attired either in full cloaks and tabards or clerical habit and tonsure, finally originated more than eighty universities in Europe. Students led a hard and difficult life, constantly threatened by hunger, cold, and other discomforts, but at the same time they were gay and given to wild pranks that often ended in bloodshed.

The University of Bologna was governed by lay students (whereas Paris University was governed by the masters), and the streets of Bologna often rang with festive graduation processions, with much beating of drums and waving of banners. Luminaries at Bologna were: the surgeon of the Crusades, Ugo Borgognoui de Lucca: his son Theodoric, who used a soporific sponge soaked in opium and mandragora; William of Saliceto, who substituted the knife for coutery; Taddeo Alderotti, immortalized by Dante and creator of the *consilia*; and the astronomer Copernicus, whose thinking revolutionized the whole universe. Bologna witnessed perhaps the first autopsy in history (1281), and made great advances in anatomy under Mondino, the first man to dissect a human body in public, whose *Anathomia* was the basic anatomy textbook for three centuries.

Physicians of Salerno with patients. Extreme right: *examination of urine, frequently used by Salernitans for diagnosis.*

A group of students from Bologna founded the school of Montpellier (1208), whose roster of students included such illustrious names as Arnold of Villanova, physician to popes and kings, the most extraordinary figure in medieval medicine, possibly the author of some of the first hundred medical books printed in Europe, advocate of wine in therapeutics, and defender of naturalistic observation against the magic and dogma of the Inquisition; the Franciscan Ramón Lull, who in the shade of the tortured olive trees of Majorca wove his immortal philosophies; Bernard de Gordon, whose work made perhaps the earliest mention of reading glasses; and the magnificent Guy de Chauliac, whose textbook on surgery was the most authoritative until the eighteenth century.

The school of Paris was founded by Peter Abelard. Its students had to remain unmarried on pain of losing their title of doctor. Paris was illumined by the greatest genius of the thirteenth century, Albertus Magnus, *Doctor Universalis,* the most learned man of the Middle Ages, master to St. Thomas Aquinas, to Roger Bacon, and to the only physician to become Pope, Petrus Hispanus. Such was the fame of Albertus Magnus that he had to teach in the open in order to accommodate the thousands of students who flocked to listen to him. His work marked the beginning of experimental medicine. Outstanding too were the surgeons Lanfranchi of Milan, Jan Yperman, father of Flemish surgery, and Henri de Mondeville, whose observations on the qualitative change in the humors added a new dimension to the humoral doctrine.

The school of Oxford sprang from that of Paris. A school of clerics governed by masters, mother of the liberal and naturalistic school of Cambridge, it sheltered the mysterious Michael Scot, physician and magician; the Franciscan Bartholomaeus Anglicus, author of the most popular encyclopedia of medieval medicine; the *doctor mirabilis*, Roger Bacon, the first modern scientist, defender of experimentation against dogma, who described the magnetic needle, gunpowder, and reading glasses, and predicted radiology, the discovery of America, the airplane, the steamship, and television; and John of Gaddesden, author of the *Rosa anglica*, a book divided into five parts, like the petals of a rose, and immortalized in Chaucer's *Canterbury Tales*.

Daughter of Bologna, the school of Padua, where the student was lord and master, was an isle of liberalism under the protection of the fair Venice. In Padua, the illustrious Pietro d'Abano, an Averroist philosopher, used the "dry" aseptic technique to treat wounds and reconciled Arabian medicine and speculative philosophy. Accused of practicing magic, d'Abano was burned at the stake.

All the universities, especially that of Montpellier; were fertilized by the cultural stream from Toledo's school of translators, where Christians and Jews happily fraternized and a new type of medieval scholastic physician was born, a doctor-cleric crammed with book knowledge and dialectic and highly versed in Latin, the *lingua franca* of educated men.

Set by their office above all manual labor, physicians eschewed surgery, which was practiced chiefly by barber-surgeons, with scarcely any preliminary technical training, and by empirical barbers, bloodletters, and executioners. This occasioned countless conflicts between the "long-robed" surgeons (schoolmen and clerics) and the "short-robed" empirics. Surgery used tampons, cautery, sutures, and the soporific sponge.

The lord at dinner.

Medieval art attained its highest form of expression in illuminated medical manuscripts and miniatures of daily life. Animals and flowers gradually replaced the earlier figures of kings and emperors. Herbals, luminous with colored pigments and gold, supplemented the popular botanical gardens of the friars, whose herbs Charlemagne called "friends of the physician and the cook."

Other healing practices coexisted with university medicine, such as the healing miracles of patron saints, like St. Sebastian and St. Roch, and the "Royal Touch," healing performed by a mere touch from the hand of a king. Medieval medical concepts were Galenic; the dominant pathology was humoral and pneumatic; diagnosis was based on the symptomatology and examination of the patient, especially of his pulse and urine. At the same time *pronoia*, the art of divining disease without questioning the patient, was practiced, and dreams were studied. Uroscopy, immortalized in medieval paintings, was the supreme diagnostic tool, for the golden liquid, believed to be filtered from the four organic humors, was revered; it was sent to the physician in flasks cradled in straw baskets like a noble old wine, and the physician, as portrayed in paintings, studied it with pensive eyes. Therapy employed phlebotomy, exutories, cathartic treatments by means of clysters, cupping, emetics and purgatives, symptomatic polypharmacy, and many fantastic remedies.

The medical man, who was first *physicus* and then doctor, became a professional when his services were at last remunerated, but hospitals continued to be little more than refuges for invalids.

Weird diseases prevailed, such as the epidemic of flagellants, who scourged themselves to the sound of bells, and the dancing mania, exorcised by the church and depicted on canvas by Brueghel, called in Italy tarantism, collective social phenomena revealing of the prevailing psychic contagion.

Belief in magic and demons flourished, and so did the use of amulets, gems, bezoars, and saints' relics, the doctrine of astrological signatures, and miraculous nostrums, the belief in incubi and succubi, fairies and gnomes, flying witches, demonic possession, and visions of the witches' sabbath, Ptolemaic astrology, and the signs of the zodiac. The addition of faith and prayers to these "curative" resources marked the change from natural to Christian magic.

Medieval medicine, via Arabian medicine and the European universities, preserved and passed down Greek medical thought. Worthy of admiration are the men who, though surrounded by a hostile and violent world, strove indefatigably to kindle the dawn in the medieval night. It was night, but night illuminated by Gothic cathedrals, musical with the verses of Dante and the discourses of Albertus Magnus, tempestuous with students at the universities, ablaze with the passionate adventure of the Crusades, and redeemed by medieval man's longing to set the barren desert of his soul abloom with the roses of his faith in the future.

F.M.I.

French or Flemish tapestry. (ca. 1500) shows unicorn at bay. Ground horn was thought to be a panacea.

VII
MEDIEVAL MEDICINE

For a thousand years peoples of many origins and tongues strove to survive in a Europe tortured by strife and pestilence, forging out of barbarism a society of men based on order, charity, and the love of God.

To the Western Church was vouchsafed the immense task of building a Christian society out of warring pagans, imbuing fierce warriors with the spirit of charitableness, forcing unruly princes to recognize the supremacy of one God and the authority of His vicars on earth.

These were the medieval centuries in which the political and spiritual foundations of Western culture were laid, an amalgam of barbarian customs, remnants of Roman law, Church theology and organization.

THE SOCIETY. During the earlier centuries of the Middle Ages were established the barbarian kingdoms of the Celts, Goths, Vandals and Franks, sharing these common traits: a fierce attachment among kinsmen, the custom of making tribal decisions through assemblies of freemen, the powerful institution of lordship. The Celtic strains contributed a gift for lyric expression, a passion for hyperbole, mystic sensuousness. The Teutons (Anglo-Saxon, Germanic, Norse) brought a fierce love of warfare, bravery, stubbornness, an insatiable thirst for adventure.

In these earlier centuries before Charlemagne founded the new Western Empire (800 A.D.), the barbarian kingdoms were a loosely formed society as yet not fettered by feudal rules, unhampered by massive castles and crowded towns.

The usual grouping was a number of villages, sometimes protected by earthworks or wood and wattle palisades; a king's "palace" might be no more than a group of wooden buildings surrounded by a wall. If stone was used it quite possibly was carted from shattered Roman villas and temples, or dug out of the disused Roman roads.

In seventh century England the lowest social class was the slave, usually a captive of war; above him came the half-freeman *(laet)*, the freeman *(ceorl, churl)*, the noble *(eorl)*, and the king, in most cases merely a tribal or clan chieftain, surrounded by warriors.

In the next three centuries, the barbarian kingdoms were transformed into the characteristic medieval feudal society, an intricate hierarchy of orders, estates, and rights. Innumerable codes and forms governed the behavior of nobles, knights, monks, clergy, vassals, burghers, peasants, and slaves. Laws distinguished the privileges of lords, overlords, and lord kings; at royal courts even the kitchen help were divided into four estates: breadmasters, cupbearers, carvers, and cooks.

The general scheme of cultivation in a village community was the open field principle of strips, giving each peasant a fair share of the good and bad land.

On this democracy of peasant cultivators the Norman Conquest in the eleventh century imposed the feudal power of the manor lord. Although peasants were a self-governing community in relation to one another, in relation to the lord they were serfs bound to the soil.

They were obliged to grind their corn at the lord's mill; they owed him field service for a specified number of days every year; they could not give their children in marriage without his consent.[1]

In the earlier medieval centuries relations between men and women were coarse and often rough-handed, although women generally enjoyed a measure of equality with men.

143

Monte Cassino, founded by St. Benedict, was Europe's first monastic infirmary.

Under feudalism the leisured and cultivated lady developed the *amour courtois*, encouraged troubadours who sang the despair of a lover sighing for an ideal mistress.[2] The high point of this form of worship of the unattainable was reached in Dante Alighieri's *La vita nuova* (1292) in which he told the story of his love for Beatrice, the ideal woman who later appeared in his immortal *Divine Comedy*.

The two strongest social forces of the Middle Ages from the eleventh century onward were the Crusades and the rise of knighthood and chivalry.

The first Crusades, beginning in 1095, were inspired by a genuine zeal to protect the Holy Places in Palestine from defilement by the Moslems. But as one expedition followed another, religious devotion was mixed with the desire for territorial expansion, greed for loot, and the ambition of the rising Italian mercantile city-states for trade with the East.

Although these immense undertakings failed in their primary objective of conquering the Holy Lands they exercised an incalculable effect on Western civilization by cross-fertilizing the relatively barbarous West with the luxurious and cultured East, by increasing the knowledge of geography, and by instilling the spirit of adventure that flowered in the great voyages of discovery at the end of the Middle Ages.

The Crusades also stimulated the growth of knight-

hood and chivalry which upheld the ideals of courage, loyalty, courtesy, honesty and fidelity, opposed to the feudal vices of cruelty, impiousness, and treachery.

Knighthood was allied with medicine in the Knights Hospitalers,[3] a military celibate order devoted to the care of sick pilgrims to the Holy Land. Although it gradually acquired the character of a combatant crusading order (thereby engendering rivalry with the Knights Templar), it never lost its function as a nursing brotherhood.

A rule in a Hospitaler establishment was that the sick were entitled to give orders, the serving brethren must obey. Food and clothing were provided free to all. The brethren engaged only in nursing; attached to a Hospitaler establishment were physicians and surgeons who enjoyed the privilege of eating with the Knights.[4]

THE MONASTERY. In the sixth century, at Monte Cassino (between Rome and Naples), a highborn Italian named Benedict of Nursia founded a monastic community; ultimately some 40,000 such institutions of various orders were built throughout Europe.

Members of the Benedictine order took vows of poverty, chastity, and obedience; Roman and Goth, noble and peasant, worked and worshiped together, lived an orderly pious life. They perfected the craft of calligraphy and illumination, transcribing surviving Latin and Greek texts.

Over the centuries, Monte Cassino's granite mass was increased; added were a cathedral, a huge library, schools, infirmaries. Established from the first was a combined tradition of learning and medicine, derived from St. Benedict's friend and contemporary, the Roman statesman-historian Cassiodorus.

In Monte Cassino, as elsewhere in Europe, the early medieval physician was a priest attached to a religious order. Classical Greek medicine lay dormant; the only translations made were those of prescriptions, short compilations and formularies, dietary rules, monographs on phlebotomy, uroscopy, fever, pulse, often couched in the form of catechisms and letters.

A monastic infirmary was in no sense a hospital such as those launched in European towns in the thirteenth century. It was primarily intended for old or sick monks, also for those who underwent their periodical bloodletting; occasionally sick travelers were admitted.

Infirmarians might have some training in medicine (e.g., Walter of Langston at St. Swithin's), but most likely they were simple monks who practiced folk medicine, drawing remedies from the monastery's medicinal herb garden. Yet many monasteries were repositories of medical books: over 200 volumes of medical interest were listed in the monastery of

Christ Church, Canterbury, in the thirteenth and fourteenth centuries, almost as many in the neighboring monastery of St. Augustine.[5]

From Monte Cassino the teaching of medicine was spread by Benedictines to other establishments of the order. In the cathedral schools founded by Charlemagne in the ninth century, medicine (called physics) was added to the curriculum in 805.

Monastic medical treatises included the encyclopedic *Origines* of the Hispano-Roman Bishop Isidore of Seville, which for a long while served as a medical textbook in monasteries, and some of the writings of the Venerable Bede, Anglo-Saxon prior at Wearmouth.[6]

The decline of monastic medicine came in the twelfth century when the Church authorities feared that monks were being drawn too far from their vows by their healing duties. Medical activities were finally entirely banned at the beginning of the thirteenth century. By this time the body of medical learning preserved in the monasteries had been passed on to lay schools and universities.

By this time also monasteries were entering into contracts with lay physicians for regular medical attendance. In 1320 Master Robert of St. Albans was described as *Medicus conventus*, receiving the yearly salary of £2.13s.4d. (worth about $150 today); John de Bosco, physician to Worcester Convent in 1329 was, in addition to a similar salary, paid in victuals and beer, plus provision for horse and groom.[7]

THE TOWN. In the first five centuries of the Middle Ages the usual groupings of people were villages clustered around a manor house, castle, abbey, or monastery. There were no towns that could even remotely compare with the magnificent cities of the Byzantine and Moslem empires.

After the two centuries of turmoil that followed the breakup of Charlemagne's empire, trade slowly revived throughout Europe, beginning in the Italian communities that lay astride the great mercantile routes between West and East.

At the turn of the twelfth century appeared the first Italian self-governing town, forerunner of the mighty city-republics such as Florence, Venice, Genoa. Throughout that turbulent century, one community after another in Europe rebelled against the heavy hand of feudalism to found communal town governments. Feudal lords in time realized that they had much to gain by the sale of charters to the *villes neuves*, and in revenues from prosperous trade. From 1100 onward the face of Europe was changed, so was the fabric of medieval social life and culture.

The typical European town[8] was usually built around a castle or a religious establishment, contained within stone walls for protection against rival lords or marauders.

Before 1200 most town buildings were made of

Thirteenth century mss. shows physician examining inflamed jaw, couching a cataract, giving inhalation, diagnosing a rash, incising scalp, extracting foreign object.

wood, and fires were frequent. As the number of inhabitants grew, houses had to be erected on bridges, town walls, above moats. Thus the upper stories overhung narrow streets, the houses almost touching.

Life in the market place was gaudy and boisterous, a mele of religious processions, traders' caravans, beggars, pilgrims, peddlers. Entertainment was offered by jugglers, or public executions of malefactors who were hanged, decapitated, or drawn and quartered according to their social rank and crime. People danced in the streets, or attended cockfights, bull-baiting, wrestling contests.[9]

Itinerant predicant friars, scholars, and theologians, among them Thomas Aquinas, Albertus Magnus, Peter Abelard, Duns Scotus, preached in front of churches or in fields outside the town walls. Fiery reformers thundered against vice and luxury, persuaded repentant people to heap their playing cards, finery, and ornaments on street bonfires.

All through the day town criers bellowed their news, shopkeepers and peddlers yelled out their wares, ironbound cartwheels and horses' hoofs clattered on cobblestones, jugglers clashed their cymbals, minstrels played on rebec or flute. And at regular Church hours the great bells of church or monastery pealed, in antiphony at Angelus, in concert when a peace was concluded or a new pope elected, in terrifying medley when danger threatened the town.

Each town gradually became a "collective seignory" with its own constitution and laws, its mayor and burgesses who could, when the need arose, defy a powerful lord and even a king. The strength of a town rested on its merchants and artisans; its most turbulent elements were the boisterous apprentices and students.

site near Notre Dame cathedral and considerably enlarged; St. Bartholomew's Hospital in London was expanded; St. Thomas' Hospital was founded in that city in 1213.

The medieval town's enduring contribution to culture was the cathedral. Church architecture followed the squat rounded-arch Romanesque style until in 1140 the first Gothic structure arose, the choir of St. Denis Abbey near Paris. Thereafter builders elaborated the new structural inventions of the flying buttress, rib vault, and pointed arch; in the cathedrals

Midwives attending a mother after childbirth. Flemish painting in State Museum, Munich.

The medieval towns' greatest contribution to medicine and public health were their hospitals, many of which survive in the great cities. Hospitals flourished throughout the Byzantine and Moslem empires, also at Salerno and Montpellier, but it was not until Pope Innocent III took a personal interest in founding a hospital in Rome in the thirteenth century that the movement spread throughout Christian Europe.

Hospitals of the Holy Spirit (modeled on the one founded in Rome in 1204) sprang up in scores of towns:[10] in Paris the Hôtel-Dieu was moved to a new

of Chartres, Amiens, Lincoln, and Salisbury they erected medieval man's soaring sacraments in stone and glass.

Countless unnamed craftsmen devoted lifetime skills to the glorification of God in stone carvings, rose windows, altars, choirs. The cathedral also became the mother of music: Notre Dame was at one time the greatest music center in Europe; in it was developed the earliest polyphonic music.

A cathedral was like a great stone and stained glass book for the illiterate to read: scenes from the

Scriptures, the legends of saints, the work done in each season, illustrious personages, animals and plants, the joys of heaven and tortures of hell, especially moral allegories rich in symbolism.

A colorful feature of medieval life were the innumerable pilgrimages made to famous cathedrals, immortally recounted in Chaucer's *Canterbury Tales*. The towns thus served as centers of communication between outlying communities.

SALERNO. The first medieval center of lay medicine appeared by the blue Tyrrhenian Sea in a health resort famed since Horace's time. In Salerno (south of Naples) during the tenth century gathered a community of physicians, teachers, students, translators, the first medical faculty in the West and a true *Civitas Hippocratica*.

Because it bore the stamp of Latin, Greek, Arabic, and Jewish culture, the legend grew that Salerno was founded by four physicians, one of each culture. It enjoyed intervals of independence between domination by Normans, Lombards, and Germans, became a resting place for wounded and exhausted Crusaders. Within its boundaries were a Benedictine monastery and its infirmaries, a cathedral believed to contain healing relics, and the famous medical schools.

Its faculty of physicians, professors, nuns, monks, apothecaries was the first of medieval times; ten physicians of the *Collegium Hippocraticum* were paid by students. Women also taught, among them Trotula,[11] a noble physician who wrote on women's and skin diseases.

Emperor Frederick II, patron of science and medicine, decreed in 1231 that the curriculum of the Salerno School should include three years of logic, five of medicine, and one year of practice, ending in a diploma.

The director of the school was Nicolaus Praepositus, author of the *Antidotarium*, first medieval pharmacopeia; other works of its Salernitan teachers were the *Passionarius galeni* of Gariopontus; the *Circa instans* of Matheaus Platearius; the *Anatomia porci* of Copho; Roger of Palermo's standard text on surgery, the first to describe hernia pulmonis and anastomosis of the intestine over a hollow cylinder.

The most circulated (1500 editions), translated, adapted popular book in medieval medical history was the *Regimen sanitatis Salernitanum*[12] (or the *Flower of Medicine*), a handbook of hygiene in Latin hexameters, discussing diet, sleep, exercise, work, and play. Noteworthy was its freedom from superstition, its Galenic, Hippocratic, pseudo-Aristotelian sources.

The *Regimen* dealt with anatomy, physiology, pathology, therapeutics, venesection, enemas, laxatives; recommended were moderation in eating and drinking, breakfasting on bread dipped in wine, eating cheese at the end of a meal, chopped onions for growing hair, prunes as laxatives. It suggested that sexual intercourse and bathing might be harmful. Not originally intended as a popular work, the book anathematized physicians who indiscriminately revealed secrets of the healing art.

Salerno nurtured a rebirth of Hippocratic tradition, inspired fresh medical literature by the publication of over fifty new works; it advanced the knowledge of surgery and sketched the outline of university life.

One of the most famous teachers at Salerno in the eleventh century was Constantine the African who brought a vast collection of Arabian manuscripts. Later, as a Benedictine monk at Monte Cassino, he spent his life translating a prodigious body of medical works by classical Arabian and Jewish physicians, including Hippocrates, Galen, Isaac Judaeus, and Haly Abbas. Thus opened to the West were new vistas of medical learning: the stream of medicine, once running from west to east, now flowed from east to west.

THE UNIVERSITY. During the eleventh century the cathedral schools founded by Charlemagne awakened from the torpor caused by two centuries of anarchy, began to organize themselves as self-governing associations, following the pattern set by the burgeoning towns.

These were at first known as *studia generalia*, i.e., schools frequented from all parts; they formed guilds for the protection and regulation of the craft of learning; these in time established the customs and rules of the universities.[13]

Two distinct types of establishments then emerged: south of the Alps the universities were ruled by the students; in northern Europe they were directed by the masters. Example: in the University of Bologna in the twelfth century the rector was elected by the scholars, the masters were paid individually by the students; their movements were restricted and they were regarded as traitors if they went to teach elsewhere.

Bologna first won fame for its law school; at its zenith it had 10,000 students living in national groups. Medical students studied surgery, considered a minor subject, and astrology; Copernicus began his calculations at Bologna. At graduation, scholars formed processions ablaze with pageantry.

To Bologna in the early thirteenth century came Dominican friar Theodoric of Lucca (1205–1298), son of Ugo Borgognoni, who was a surgeon during the Crusades. He maintained that the formation of pus was not necessary and that wounds were prevented from healing by all the substances applied to them.[14]

In surgery he advocated the use of sponges

SCENES IN LIFE OF MEDIEVAL CRAFTSMEN
From left to right: *(top)* a painter; an organ builder; *(center)* at a tavern;
a sculptor; *(bottom)* clockmakers; a scribe.
15th century Italian miniatures attributed to Cristoforo de Predis.

drenched with a narcotic such as opium or mandragora, applied to the patient's nose; cutting was not to begin until the patient was asleep. For skin diseases he recommended mercurial ointments.

A noted surgeon of the Bologna school was Guglielmi Saliceti (William of Salicet, 1219–1277), who preferred the knife to the Arabian cautery, favored the ligature of wounds and styptic powders, learned to suture nerves. Celebrated for the wealth he attained as physician to popes and nobles was Taddeo Alderotti (1223–1303), father of medical dialectics; from practical observation he accumulated a large body of clinical case histories called *consilia,* introducing a new form of medical literature.

The first European anatomist to supervise publicly the systematic dissection of the human body was Mondino de Luzzi (Mundinus, ca. 1275–1326), who in 1315 demonstrated before his students the abdominal organs, thorax, head, and extremities. His *Anathomia* was the first manual based on practical dissection, but it contained no advances over Galenic anatomy. Dissection declined after Pope Boniface VIII forbade the boiling of Crusaders' cadavers and sending home their skeletons for burial, or any similar abuse of dead bodies.

Devoted to the teaching of medicine was the University of Montpellier, in southern France (where Rabelais later studied), second oldest medical school in western Europe. One of its famous figures was visionary Arnold of Villanova (1240–1313): an extraordinary scholar of medicine, physician to numerous kings; friend of popes, he often clashed with the Church, advocated truth based on experiment, questioned the authority of Hippocrates and Galen; he wrote prolifically, including a famous treatise on medicinal wines.

Others prominent at Montpellier were Raimundo Lulio (1235–1315), missionary monk of Majorca, composer of 150 books of medicine, poetry, religion, who led three expeditions to Africa; Bernard de Gordon (d. 1320), practitioner of rational and empiric therapy despite a belief in astrology and magic, who made the first observation on reading spectacles.

Guy de Chauliac (1300–1370), considered the father of surgery, developed the treatment of fractures by slings and extension weights, operated on hernias and cataracts, excised superficial growths, believed that pus from wounds served to release the *materia peccans*; his *Chirurgia* became a standard surgery textbook.

At the University of Paris taught one of the most learned men of the Middle Ages, Albertus Magnus (1192–1280), called *Doctor Universalis*: botanist, astronomer, philosopher, geographer, zoologist, and author of numerous 1000-page volumes. His renown was so great that his classes had to be held outdoors to accommodate the crowds of scholars. Albertus was the teacher of Thomas Aquinas, Roger Bacon, and the physician Petrus Hispanus who later became Pope John XXI, the only physician to attain that office.

Other Paris scholars: Guido Lanfranchi (d. 1314) of Milan brought surgery to high estate in France, deplored the work of barber-surgeons, and insisted that no one could perform operations unless he knew medicine; Henri de Mondeville (1260–1320), who wrote the first French treatise on surgery, believed in cleansing wounds rather than encouraging pus, and advocated cheering patients with viola music.

Oxford University (a school since the ninth century) began to flourish in the thirteenth century when the conflicts between England and France

Prominent in the school of Montpellier were (left) *Arnold of Villanova, author of* Parabolae medicationis *and* (right) *Raimundo Lulio, author of* Ars major.

Portrait of Albertus Magnus. Palazzo Ducale, Venice.

forced many English students to abandon Paris University and return home. The University of Cambridge was formed in 1217; it was augmented by many Oxford students forced to flee after a particularly murderous town-and-gown fracas.[15]

One of the most celebrated teachers at Oxford was Dominican Friar Roger Bacon (ca., 1214–1294), called *doctor mirabilis*. He was profoundly discontented with the existing state of knowledge, repudiated popular beliefs, and was convinced that no progress could be made without an intellectual return to nature.

He advocated applying mathematics to physics, maintained that experiment was the only means of verifying truth.[16] He has at various times been credited with the invention of the telescope, microscope, spectacles, and gunpowder, for which evidence is not conclusive.

One of the most remarkable figures in the Middle Ages was Pietro d'Abano (Petrus Aponensis, 1250–1316), whose fame as a teacher helped to build the illustrious reputation of the University of Padua.

D'Abano was a follower of Averroës, but he was also an original thinker who attempted to reconcile contradictions between Arabian medicine and speculative philosophy.

In medicine he was a disciple of Avicenna, a physician who believed in simple therapeutic measures, hostile to charlatan complications.

His originality and daring brought him in conflict with the Inquisition; the Dominicans at one time accused him of heresy because of fifty-five passages in his writings that clashed with Church dogma. The Inquisition accused him of heresy in 1315, but he died before the trial could be held.[17]

Between the thirteenth and fifteenth centuries, the zenith of the Middle Ages, some eighty universities were founded in Europe. Medical texts and teachers multiplied rapidly, replenished from the centers of Arabian medicine in Spain. The torch of Hippocratic teaching now burned brightly throughout Europe.

THE STUDENT. Students at medieval universities led strenuous, often violent lives; they frequently wandered from one city to another in search of some distinguished master; eight years were required for a bachelor-of-arts degree, from twelve to fifteen years for a doctorate.

Fees were low, poor students received tuition free. Even when rented, books were expensive; it was cheaper to travel from Oxford to Paris to hear a lecture than to buy a published work. In unheated halls, without benches or desks, students and masters sat on straw on the floor.

Mornings were devoted to logic, metaphysics, ethics, natural sciences; evenings to rhetoric, history, poetry, the classics. Examinations were oral and difficult; some universities had rules against stabbing examiners. Bizarre questions were asked: Is happiness a volitive, intellectual, or virtuous act? Is woman an imperfect product of nature? Is it healthful to get drunk once a month? Does a libertine's life cause baldness?

The exuberance of youth frequently burst out in rioting and uproar, in drinking, gambling, lovemaking, molesting women, and fighting the authorities. A common practice on the eve of an examination was to get the masters drunk.

St. Thomas Aquinas. From fresco by Fra Angelico.

Most of the students were sons of gentlemen, merchants, and artisans; some were wards of church officials or supported by friends. Housing was in private hostels in familial groups that included chaplains and tutors; the poorer students acted as servants to wealthier companions.

A fourteenth century student at the University of Orleans in a letter to his father writes:

"Wines are dear, and hostels, and other good things; I owe in every street, and am hard bested to free myself from such snares. Dear father, deign to help me! I fear to be excommunicated. Well-beloved father, to ease my debts contracted at the tavern, at the baker's, with the doctor and the bedells [beadles] and to pay my subscription to the laundress and the barber, I send you word of greetings and of money."

Classes began at six o'clock in the morning after mass. Dinner, solemnly eaten, usually consisted of salt fish, beef, or mutton. Rich students shopped at markets for pigeons, geese, beef, pork, or mutton roasted on spits and seasoned with sauce; cheaper fare were tripe and sausages.

Students wore long cloaks or tabards; at the University of Paris they wore the tonsure and monkish gown. Black gowns were compulsory at Oxford; prohibited were long hair, lace, or ornaments.

New arrivals were hazed: in German universities they were compelled to wear costumes depicting animals, confess their faults publicly, take an oath not to bribe their masters; hazings frequently degenerated into brawls or orgies.

THE PHYSICIAN. The spread of medical schools and the rise of powerful medical guilds greatly enhanced the social and financial status of physicians. Those in private practice owned land, fine homes, sometimes art collections. The celebrated ones amassed fortunes: Taddeo Alderotti, summoned to attend the Pope, demanded 100 gold pieces per day, received a total of 10,000 gold pieces after the pontiff was cured.

Family physicians were paid by the visit, at monthly or annual rates. Town physicians, employed to treat the poor, to investigate epidemics and supervise pharmacies, might receive an annual salary of the equivalent of $4000; some physicians found security in the household of a nobleman.

Physicians wore fur-trimmed coats, velour hats, sparkling rings, gilded spurs. Wrote Petrarch to Boccaccio: "Tell me where there is an eye . . . which can defend itself against such dazzling magnificence."[18]

Surgeons were for a long time in a lower rank than physicians; frequently they were barbers who performed phlebotomies and cuppings, drew teeth, treated ulcerations, fractures, luxations, flesh wounds.

Here is a contemporary account of the duties and recompenses of physicians and surgeons in the service of England's King Edward III in the first half of the fourteenth century:

"And muche he should talke with the steward, chamberlayn, assewer, and the maister cooke, to devyse by counsayle what metes and drinkes is best according with the Kinge. . . . Also hym ought to espie if any of this courte be infected with leperiz or pestylence, and to warn the soveraynes of hym, till he be purged clene, to keepe hym oute of courte."

Roger de Heyton, the king's first surgeon, received numerous grants of land and died a rich man, as did two other royal physicians whose records have survived.[19]

DIAGNOSIS. Early Christian belief held that disease was either punishment for sin or the result of witch-

Following pages: *Scene shows patient attended by faculty of medical college at Salerno. In background, physician examines urine flask. Seated woman (in green) is semilegendary physician Trotula compiling notes on women's diseases. Women attendants carry water and towels. Boy in foreground prepares cautery instruments. Painted by Hans Guggenheim.*

craft or possession. Diagnosis as such was superfluous; the basic therapy was prayer, penitence, and invocation of saints. Lay medicine based diagnosis on symptoms, examination, pulse, palpitation, percussion, inspection of excreta and sometimes semen.

Diagnosis by watercasting (uroscopy) was universally practiced: the urine flask became the emblem of medieval medical usage; under the Jerusalem Code of 1090, failure to examine the urine exposed a physician to public scourging.

Patients carried their urine to physicians in handsome flasks cradled in wicker baskets; since urine could be shipped, diagnosis at long distance was common. Constantine the African translated the *Book of Urine* of Isaac Judaeus giving detailed directions for examining color, density, quality, and sediment.

This story is told about a monastic physician named Notker in the tenth century:

"In medicine he wrought marvelous and amazing cures, for he was singularly learned in medical aphorisms and spices and antidotes, and in Hippocratean prognostics, as appeared in that matter of Duke Henry [I of Bavaria] who sought craftily to deceive him. The duke sent to Notker, as his own urine, that of a lady at his court; which when our brother had inspected, he said: God is now about to work a portentous and unheard-of-miracle, that a man should give birth to a child. . . . The duke blushed to find himself discovered."

Chastity belt.
Illustration from medieval manuscript.

The interpretation of dreams could aid diagnosis: repeated dreams of floods indicated an excess of humors that required evacuation; dreams of flight signified excessive evaporation of humors. But there were also many medieval physicians who interrogated patients in the tradition of Rufus of Ephesus, who believed in the clinical history as an indispensable first step in diagnosis.

THEORY. Apart from the curative powers of saints or holy relics, the foundation of medieval therapy was the expulsion of corrupt humors by purges, emetics, cupping, bleeding, enemas. John of Arderne wrote a famous treatise on clysters, prescribing the use of lard, butter, soap, and herbs. Bleeding was universal: controversies arose whether phlebotomy should be near or far from the afflicted organ.

A school of astrologic medicine ruled late medieval therapeutics: Bologna University maintained a chair in astrology; the moon was believed to be most influential during venesection; the value of emetics and purgatives depended on zodiacal conditions; plague was thought to arise from a malign conjunction of stars.

On a vaguely defined principle of *similia similibus*, thistles were used to treat slashes, scorpion stings were treated with heliotrope which was thought to resemble the animal.

Amulets, bezoars, and magic concoctions were standard elements of the medieval pharmacopeia. Precious stones were symbols: the emerald repressed sexual impulses, the sapphire strengthened sight and other senses, gold in electuaries was used against melancholia, gold flakes suspended in wine were believed to promote longevity. A prized aphrodisiac was mandragora, the roots of which resembled a human figure.

Organs and excreta of various animals were concocted into potions and medicines, also the milk, blood, urine of humans; powdered pearls were used against plague.

In medieval surgery, dressings were soaked in old wine, operators were forbidden to eat food that might foul the air or to consort with menstruating women. The narcotic sponge was used; hemorrhages were inhibited by cold, cautery, and plugging.

Surgical practice included extirpation of nasal polyps, tonsillectomy, trepanning, tracheotomy; in abdominal operations a small animal was cut open as a magic device to inhibit bleeding. In suturing abdominal injuries, the patient's pelvis was raised to keep intestines free of the wound.

Midwives managed childbirth; surgeons practiced embryotomy when necessary. Special parturition chairs were in use; shaking the mother was thought to facilitate birth. Cesarean section was known from the texts but not practiced.

THE EPIDEMICS. By a curious concatenation, the Middle Ages began and ended with two of the most catastrophic plagues that ever ravaged Europe: that of the sixth century and the devastating Black Death of the fourteenth century that killed almost half the population.

The outbreak of bubonic plague that spelled the end of feudalism in many parts of Europe began in the Crimean grain port of Caffa,[20] spread via rats in the mercantile ships to Constantinople, Sicily, and

Genoa. In 1348 it reached England; within two years it had crossed Germany and Scandinavia into Poland. Here is the eyewitness account of surgeon Guy de Chauliac who bravely remained in Auvergne while many physicians fled:

"The visitation came in two forms. The first lasted two months, manifesting itself as an intermittent fever accompanied by spitting of blood from which people died usually in three days. The second type lasted the remainder of the time, manifesting itself in high fever, abscesses and carbuncles, chiefly in the axillae and groin. People died from this in five days. So contagious was the disease, especially that with blood-spitting [pneumonic] that no one could approach or even see a patient without taking the disease. The father did not visit the son nor the son the father. Charity was dead and hope abandoned."

This eminent surgeon's primary recommendation was to flee the region. Failing that, one should purge with aloes, let blood, purify the air with fire, comfort the heart with senna and things of good odor, soothe the humors with Armenian bole and resist putrefaction with acid things; carbuncles should be cupped and scarified.

The Black Death is estimated to have killed from one quarter to three quarters of the population of Europe; Germany was one of the hardest hit countries.

The social effect of the plague was an economic revolution that spelled the end of the feudal system. The tremendous shortage of farm labor now meant that the surviving peasants had the whip hand of the lord and his bailiff. Instead of a hunger for land there was now a desperate need for hands to guide the plow. Serfs who ran away from a tyrannic master could now obtain work on other estates, and no questions asked.[21]

Plague reappeared in various parts of Europe about every ten years. It forced communities to take a number of public health measures: in Italy suspected disease carriers were isolated for forty days (*quarantenaria*, hence quarantine); suspected houses were aired and fumigated; in Belgium corpses had to be removed to some distance from towns.

Next in severity to the plague was leprosy, which came from the Near East via Sicily, and in the twelfth century became pandemic. Clerical and lay authorities ordered lepers segregated. Christendom built some 19,000 leprosaria. When nobles were stricken they were forced to remain in their homes; quarantine measures finally brought the disease under control.

Two forms of leprosy were identified; the nodular and the mutilating. Franciscan monk Bartholomaeus Anglicus in 1246 recognized its contagious nature; he believed it was hereditary, also that it was brought on by eating hot food, pepper, garlic, and the meat of diseased hogs.

An ulcerative skin inflammation[22] became known as St. Anthony's fire, gout as St. Maur's evil, dropsy as St. Eutropius' disease. The veneration of saints formed numerous cults, until the Church took steps to halt the drift toward pagan forms of worship.

Another epidemic was the cult of Flagellants who whipped each other with iron-barbed scourges in repentance for sin. For defying the authority of priests they were stoned, burned at the stake, excommunicated.

Following the Black Death came another mass contagion in Germany: the dancing mania. To the tune of wind instruments, shawms and sackbuts, thousands danced through the streets until exhausted; victims were eventually exorcised in the chapel of St. Vitus. In Italy, the dancing phenomenon was called tarantism, in the belief that victims had been bitten by the tarantula spider.

HYGIENE. The lavish use of baths in Rome, Byzantium, and Islamic societies found no counterpart in medieval society.

Powerful stenches pervaded towns, villages, baronial castles; Moslem travelers in Europe often complained of "infidel smells."

Water conduits consisted mainly of hollowed logs placed end to end. Homes with water supply were rare; some German burgher dwellings had well water piped into kitchens. As towns grew, refuse on streets waited for scavenging pigs, birds, or cleansing rain.

Wealthy homes, castles, and monasteries built latrines that emptied into cesspools; a dozen ordinary homes often shared one outhouse. Thirteenth cen-

CULVER

Among the most popular forms of treatment was the bath, consisting of tubs in which patients stood or sat. After a miniature in L'Histoire de Gérard de Nevers, *Bibliothèque Royale.*

tury Parisians emptied chamberpots from windows with the warning cry, *Gare l'eau!* Paris depended on the overflow of the Seine to purge its streets.

Charlemagne briefly revived the lost interest in bathing when in the ninth century he built a *therma* on his palace grounds; returning Crusaders later brought reports of luxurious Saracen baths. The custom of hot baths gradually spread: a travel-stained knight, taking respite in an aristocratic home, was scrubbed in his bath by ladies of the manor.

By the twelfth century, bathing became the enthusiastic diversion of both common folk and nobles; the vogue ended by evading both hygiene and morality. The sexes bathed together in public baths with only a rail to separate them, while spectators watched from above. These baths became little more than brothels.

Before the Middle Ages ended, public officials were supervising street cleaning, the sanitary state of fish and meat markets, bakeries, groceries, apothecaries, and brothels.

The Middle Ages ended with the fifteenth century: the fall of Constantinople in 1453, the expulsion of the last of the Moors from Spain in 1492, the discovery of America, and the vast changes brought by the age of navigation.

Medieval medicine rediscovered the Greek tradition, assimilated Arabian medical practices and pharmacology, built hospitals on a vast scale, developed medical teaching in universities, and established public health measures. It built the pillars of modern medicine, and the stage was now set for the Renaissance and the beginning of science.

MODERN MIDDLE AGES

BLACK STAR

Sea battle recreates twelfth century victory of Milan over Como.

Contrary to the general trend of life in this highly technologic world when old ways are daily superseded by new methods, tradition and pageantry born in medieval Europe are still extant. They seem to grip the imagination tighter, and some have become part of daily life.

Commonest carry-over from the Middle Ages are fairy tales compiled from middle-European folklore by German anthropologists, the brothers Grimm. Londoners are treated to the daily sight of the procession of Yeomen of the Guard, the Beefeaters, founded in the fifteenth century, standing their watch at the Tower. Every first of May, the Morris, a rustic dance re-enacting the deeds of Robin Hood, is performed in northern England.

Most performances of pageants today are in celebration of freedom from tyranny or to give thanks for a special beneficence. Revived in gratitude for the cessation of seventeenth century attack of Black Death is the Oberammergau Passion Play, most important survivor of miracle plays popular in medieval times. The *Palio* in Siena commemorates a twelfth century victory over the Florentines.

By latest accounts, the scores of current medieval pageants show no signs of lessening.

Good Friday procession in Perpignon, France, dating from 1416, reminds faithful of the story of Calvary.

FRENCH GOVERNMENT TOURIST OFFICE

ITALIAN STATE TOURIST OFFICE

In Arezzo jousting games dating from First Crusade, rotating figure representing the Saracen is hit and passed before suspended weight strikes rider.

Contemporary view of Henry VIII sailing to meet Francis I on field of cloth of gold. At Hampton Court.

VIII

In a Sunlit Garden

A Belgian youth twenty-two years of age was the central figure in the brilliant procession that, one December morning in the year 1537, slowly advanced through the narrow gray streets of Padua toward the Bishop's palace. The masters of the University at the head of the procession wore sumptuous gowns; the soldiers' halberds glittered in the sun; poor students shivered with cold in their threadbare capes; plumes like cocks' combs fluttered atop the great hats of rich students; knights and clerics wore a sober mien; a band sounded the gold of its trumpets; nobles looked arrogant in beribboned uniforms; and at the tail of the procession the populace added a note of gaiety. At the Bishop's palace, the youth named Andreas Vesalius was to be granted the title of Doctor of Medicine.

Born in Brussels of a family of physicians, Vesalius had studied in Louvain and Paris, where, still under the Galenic tyranny, anatomy was taught by a master who read Galen while the *ostensor* and the *demonstrator*, usually barbers or executioners, dissected a corpse and exhibited its parts in time with the monotonous reading. The students were never allowed to approach the corpse. Rebel and visionary, Vesalius felt that anatomy could not be learned in such fashion. *Seeing* rather than listening was the only way. This visual nature of his mind, which made him oppose his masters, was the key to Vesalius' secret.

Determined to learn anatomy the right way, Vesalius even stole corpses from the Cemetery of the Innocents in Paris. In the dead of night, stealthily seeking his way through the dark tombs, he carried off under his cape the limbs and other members from the corpses of executed criminals. Back in his room, after soaking the parts in vinegar to disguise the terrible stench, he would by candlelight dissect them until all hours in the morning. Thus was anatomy learned by one who later became professor of surgery at Padua, wrote the greatest book in medicine, the *Fabrica*, and ushered physicians into the sunlit garden of Renaissance medicine.

Vesalius lived in a glorious period. The air was electrified by a new historical climate. Various historical forces had been set in motion. More than a revival of classic culture, this was a period of *rebirth*, which is more important than birth, for it involves the consciousness of being born. With the disappearance of empires, nationalities began to spring up in Europe. In Spain the Catholic kings had created the modern concept of the state as a *nation*. Everywhere new faiths replaced the uniform creed previously imposed at the point of swords. By preaching a return to earlier religious simplicity, the Reformation unleashed wars of religion. Gunpowder destroyed castles, and with them the feudal system, and created the new problem of firearm wounds. A new social condition confronted man. The static medieval societies and orders (clergy, nobility, corporations) were replaced by a dynamic society. The action of the bourgeois class, the use of money, the appearance of capitalism—these turned the spatial medieval economy into a *dynamic* one.

In vibrant response to the prevailing dissatisfaction with the present, Humanism arose, the longing to return to the classical past, to the clear springs of Greco-Latin wisdom. Learning Greek, the humanists launched a crusade against Arabianism. They sought to restore classical wisdom. This was the dawn of the artistic Renaissance. The rediscovery of the beauty of the naked human body aroused interest not only in its form but in its structure or internal machinery, stimulating progress in anatomy and medicine.

The discovery of the compass stimulated daring transoceanic explorations, which culminated in the discovery of America. The craving to know what lay beyond the ocean paralleled the craving to know man's inner anatomical space. The adventure of navigators and conquistadors had its parallel in that of anatomists and surgeons, who for the first time dared probe into the *terra incognita* of the human body.

Palazzo Ducale. Woodcut. View of Venice in the fifteenth century from Supplementum Chronicarum *of Filippo da Bergamo, 1490.*

The invention of printing and the manufacture of paper facilitated human intercommunication. The cosmography of earth, sea, and sky progressed. Academies and universities flourished, and Humanism advanced with Petrarch, Erasmus, and Boccaccio. Among the humanist luminaries of the Renaissance were physicians and botanists (intrigued by nature, almost all of the humanists were botanists): Konrad von Gesner; Thomas Linacre; Copernicus; Geronimo Cardano, physician, gambler and mathematician, who with his description of moral insanity introduced "modern" psychiatry; von Andernach; Andrés de Laguna; the Valencian Juan Luis Vives, father of modern psychology, voluntary exile in Brussels, where he wove philosophies as subtle as the lace his wife wove in their shop; Jean Fernel, humanist and physiologist, author of the *Universa medicina;* and the Spanish martyr Michael Servetus, discoverer of the pulmonary circulation of the blood, who for his heretical disputes with Calvin was in Geneva burned alive over green wood to prolong his death, a crown of sulfured thorns on his brow.

Solitary scholars began to flourish, Robinson Crusoes on the islands of their endeavor, contemners of the Arabs and devotees of classical Greek learning. New instruments, such as optical lenses and Galileo's telescope and microscope, exemplified the Renaissance thirst for novelties, as did new mercurial remedies and necropsy methods. But medical innovations came late in this period, following in the wake of discoveries in art, philosophy, and religion. Medical innovators were few, isolated, late to appear, and, except for Paracelsus, were all still to some extent Galenists. Nature was conceived as architecture by Vesalius, as an organism by Fracastoro and Paracelsus. The greatest triumphs of the Renaissance were Vesalius' new architectonic approach to anatomy; Paracelsus' and Fracastoro's new concept of medicine as dynamic pathology; and the new approach to surgery, as an empirical and conservative art, by Ambroise Paré.

Clinical histories progressed, developing from the medieval *consilia* to *observationes*

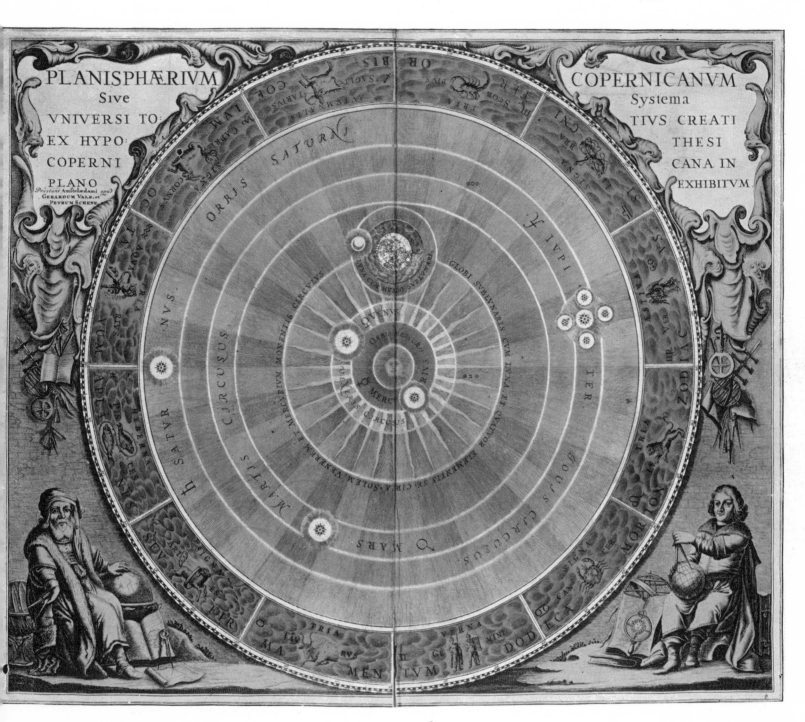

Plane view of Copernicus' system of the created world. Engraving from a 17th-century Atlas.

of a biographical nature. In contrast to the "collective" medieval diseases typical of communal life under feudalism and in monasteries, new *individual* diseases appeared, such as exanthematous typhus and syphilis. Syphilis, which probably already existed in Europe, was aggravated by the new and more virulent American strains brought back in Columbus' ships and disseminated during the siege of Naples. Its nature and that of infectious diseases and their contagiousness were studied by Fracastoro, humanist, physician, and poet, who, a solitary figure amid the golden vineyards near Verona, created a dynamic epidemiology and established the fact that infection passes from one person to another either directly or indirectly. Fracastoro gave the "malady of love" the poetic name of syphilis after the shepherd hero of his beautiful poem *Syphilis sive morbus Gallicus.*

Four great Renaissance rebels started the revolution in medicine, surgery, anatomy, and psychiatry. Paracelsus was born near Zurich, among forests of pines and firs. Itinerant and adventurous physician, drunkard and wrangler, he studied the book of the world and nature and dramatized his iconoclastic scorn for classic dogmas by publicly making a huge bonfire with the works of Galen and Avicenna. He died prematurely, worn out by his bitter career of rebellion. Paracelsus bequeathed to medicine a dynamic pathology, establishing the fact that diseases often came "from without." He rejected the dominant polypharmacy in favor of simple medicaments, and introduced in therapy metals, tinctures, and essences, which made him the forerunner of medical chemistry. His concept of disease was a weakening of the vital principle or *archaeus*, and his therapy was based on the curative power of nature, each malady having its specific remedy (*arcanum*) in the surrounding world. He left as legacy not a system but a rebellion like a flaming sword.

Beside the conquistador and the *condottiere* there stands out in the Renaissance the surgeon, whose great adventure was in exploring the human body. The importance of the barber in surgery had then increased, intensifying the conflict with the "long-robed" or licensed surgeons. At the same time there was an increase in the new problems created by firearm lesions. The ambition of Parisian Ambroise Paré, a good and humble man, was to be a "short-robed" barber-surgeon. He attained fame when, having exhausted his supply of boiling alder oil for treating "infected" gunpowder wounds, he improvised a compound of egg yolks, oil of roses, and turpentine, thus breaking the tradition that such wounds were infected and ending the terrible trauma produced by the brutal boiling oil treatment. Later, Paré completed his contribution to *conservative* surgery by using onion poultices (rich in bactericidal principles) on infected burns; by replacing cautery by arterial ligature; and by practicing both herniotomy without castration and podalic version. Paré summed up his creed in the modest and beautiful words: "I dressed him and God healed him."

Plastic surgery progressed with Gasparo di Tagliacozzi; the new respect for women inspired by Erasmus, Luis Vives, and Sir Thomas More helped obstetrics; and ophthalmology advanced through the new visual attitude, the respect for the *saper vedere* recommended by that great visual genius Leonardo da Vinci.

The revolution in anatomy was accomplished by Vesalius. But interest in the human body was spurred by other things as well. Violence, stirred by families like the Borgias and by the *condottieri,* required one to learn the art of killing in order to survive. The spring and power of the muscles, the strength and weakness of every part of the body had to be known, for such knowledge was vital in fighting an enemy or safeguarding life. This inspired the new pictorial approach in art, best exemplified in Michelangelo's "Last Judgment" and particularly in his magnificent "Moses," which Sigmund Freud would later psychoanalyze.

Forerunner of Vesalius and the greatest genius in the history of mankind, Leonardo da Vinci, "physician," engineer, architect, poet, musician, and painter, performed numerous dissections, leaving 1500 anatomical sketches and 7000 pages of notes. He united science and art, an endeavor made glorious by the brilliant anatomical artists of the Renaissance: Verrocchio, Pollaiuolo, Cellini, Raphael, Donatello.

Before Vesalius' interest was focused on the *origin* of the bodily ogans; with him it became focused on their *design*. For Vesalius each part of the organism was, as the title of his *magnum opus* indicates, the *fabrica*, the structure and architecture of the human body. Not only did Vesalius know more anatomy than anyone else; he knew a different anatomy, correcting certain Galenic errors and introducing the concept of *living* anatomy, in opposition to the static anatomy of the past. With the help of Titian and his pupil Calcar, Vesalius sketched the corpses he dissected in "living" positions, using the lush Paduan landscape as background. The wood engravings completed, Vesalius sent the three hundred printing blocks on muleback, across the Alps, to be printed at the famous Oporinus press in Basel. The violent criticism aroused by his colossal and incomparably beautiful book, *De humani corporis fabrica*, made him flee to Spain, where he became physician to Charles V. Returning from a pilgrimage to the Holy Land, he died on the island of Zante. With his new architectonic anatomy (his physiology was Galenic), Vesalius launched the concept of the body as the *fabrica* and statue of man, later developed by his followers Fallopius and Fabricius ab Aquapendente, who dissected the venous valves. Vesalius revolutionized medical teaching with his beautiful illustrations of dissected men, who, endowed in death with a strange beauty and a supreme dignity, appear to be pleadingly revealing their anatomical structure to an invisible deity.

The fourth revolution—after that of the concept of the human body as *fabrica* and architecture by Vesalius, that of the humane conservative approach to surgery by Paré, and that of internal medicine as dynamic pathology by Paracelsus—occurred in psychiatry, when the Swiss physician, Johann Weyer, regarded "witches" as unfortunate mental patients with hallucinations. Belief in witches was then universal. Almost a million were burned in Europe, especially after the inquisitors Sprenger and Krämer published their infamous *Malleus maleficarum*, a penal code regulating the unmasking and punishment of practitioners of witchcraft, a book that caused countless mental patients to be tortured and burned. The quixotic crusade against the hunting and burning of witches was started by Johann Weyer in his book *De praestigiis daemonum et incantationibus ac veneficiis*; his thesis was later reinforced by Juan Luis Vives.

The smile of Vesalius, depicted in the frontispiece to the *Fabrica*, is that of the rebel who, in the Renaissance, defied a thousand years of medical tradition and dogma, tyranny and superstition. The other famous Renaissance smile is that of the Mona Lisa, who exemplifies the defiance in art of that other great rebel, Leonardo. Da Vinci symbolized in his "Gioconda" the attitude of men who, loving truth and beauty, fought dauntlessly to master them. They were men with sun in their hearts, who illuminated the flowerbed of beauty that is Art, and the flowerbed of truth that is Science, in the sunlit garden of the Renaissance.

F.M.I.

Following page: *Johann Weyer, known under the Latin name Wierus, accompanied by a skeptical ecclesiastic, examines a women imprisoned for witchcraft. After careful studies of condemned witches, he promulgated a psychiatric interpretation of their behavior, attacked their condemnation.*

VIII

RENAISSANCE MEDICINE

THE two centuries that built the bridge between the medieval and modern worlds produced a fabulously rich age, an era of stupendous contrasts: spiritual grandeur and petty despotism, superb artistry and despicable politics, awakening minds and decaying morals, the colorful exciting Renaissance.[1]

Beginning on the sunny shores of the Mediterranean and Adriatic seas, the new concept of man and his enjoyment of life spread to the colder northern countries, bursting the shackles of a medieval collective order to release the rich capabilities of individual man.

In this era of creative chaos emerged new classes of men and women: statesmen, merchants, scholars, patrons of the arts, artists, and craftsmen. The boisterous and often brutal manners of the Middle Ages slowly gave way to the refined etiquette of the gentleman.

THE SOCIETY. The heart of the Renaissance first beat in Italy, whose great cities (Venice, Milan, Florence) sprawled astride the natural trade routes between the Orient and Europe.

It was born out of total political confusion: a host of petty city-states independent of emperor or pope, torn by hostile factions, fighting one another for trade routes or commercial gain, a boiling maelstrom of despots and bands of professional soldiers, bound by no law except that of cynical personal advantage. Their unethical code was exemplified in Niccolo Machiavelli's *Il Principe* (The Prince), the handbook of unscrupulous Renaissance rulers.

In northern Europe and Spain the transitional centuries marked a constant conflict between kings and their powerful princely subjects, a struggle to establish the type of strong central government that Italy did not possess.

England was torn by the Wars of the Roses, a bloody contest for the crown by the houses of Lancaster and York; Louis XI of France spent years in reducing the powerful duchies to vassalage; the house of Aragon unified Spain against the Moslems and introduced the modern concept of the state; Germany saw the phenomenal growth of the house of Hapsburg. Europe began to develop the new notion of nationality which has persisted to this day.

Simultaneously the gradual disintegration of medieval institutions[2] and the great pandemics caused widespread unrest among the peasants and urban workers: royal power in England was almost overthrown in the fourteenth century by the ragged bands of Wat Tyler; France witnessed the first *Jacquerie* revolt in 1358; the first decades of the sixteenth century unleashed the atrocities of the Peasants' War in Germany and the furious revolt of the *comuneros* in Spain.

Also at war sporadically were kings and princes against the papacy. The heavy weight of papal taxation led to open opposition in England; the subservience of several popes to France reduced their prestige. More serious still was the popular discontent stirred by the demoralization of the clergy, laying the foundations for the first "heresies" of John Wyclif in England and John Huss in Bohemia.

Throughout the Renaissance the economic structure of the Middle Ages was totally transformed: whereas the medieval tradesman operated in a small field, the Italian merchants of the fourteenth century developed the techniques of credit, exchange, and large-scale enterprises in a vast network reaching to the fabulous East, thereby laying the foundation of modern capitalism. Thus a new dynamic economy based on money replaced the static medieval system founded on the ownership of land.

The new forms of trade and industry spread

throughout northern Europe, bringing the growth and power of the Netherlands, the development of England's commerce through the wool trade, the great Hanseatic League merchants of northern Germany, and the rise of such famous international bankers as the Fugger family, with branches in Venice, Rome, Antwerp, and Lisbon.

As the new merchants rose in wealth and power, so the medieval landowners declined. The tremendous labor shortage caused by the ravages of the Black Death in the fourteenth century gave peasants the strength to oppose and in most cases destroy the old manorial system of serfdom. During the Renaissance the peasants and merchant-burghers profited at the expense of the manor lords, thereby dealing the final death blow to the medieval structure of society.

One of the most powerful forces of change at work during the Renaissance was the restless urge of man to explore new lands and sail uncharted seas. The improvement of the astrolabe and the introduction of mechanical clocks extended enormously the range of navigation; the changes in ship design broadened the variety of vessels. In these daring two centuries, ships were sailed to the Americas, to the Orient, around the globe.

The other great force that revolutionized man's life and thought was the invention of printing in the middle of the fifteenth century, thereby transferring literature from the monasteries to the homes and universities. Humanism and the revival of classic learning owed its glorious flowering to a German printer whose identity is in doubt.[3]

Townsfolk and peasants released from the rigid structure of the medieval manorial system were now able to give vent to their boisterous nature: the Renaissance centuries witnessed innumerable gay and colorful festivals, dazzling balls, glittering regattas, popular frolics.

This change was greatly encouraged by the new design of towns; the medieval town of mean alleys cramped within protective walls gave way to open *piazzas*, graceful fountains, broad avenues, large and spaciously colonnaded public buildings, streets with shops under shady arcades, a new and vastly expanded theatre of life.

For amusement there were bearbaiting, bullfighting, cockfights, football, bowling, boxing, wrestling. Dancing was the most popular pastime, open to all in the broad squares or public gardens.

As trade routes were opened up with the Indies, food became more plentiful, varied, and spicy. Newly introduced was the potato, brought by Spanish navigators from the Andes. Slowly accepted were such novelties as cabbage, lima beans, carrots, rhubarb, and strawberries. The poor drank ale and wine; the rich indulged in exotic liquors.

San Lorenzo de El Escorial (1563-1584), by Juan Bautista de Toledo and Juan de Herrera. Somber and massive, it is the epitome of Spanish Renaissance architecture.

Italy led all countries in the development of the graces of genteel society, also in creating the ideal image of Renaissance man. The most widely read book in the early sixteenth century was Count Baldassare Castiglione's *Libro del cortigiano* (The Book of Courtiers), which established the etiquette and intellectual accomplishments of the well-bred person.

The ideal of the well-rounded personality required the man of culture to acquire knowledge in all branches of human activity, to develop grace, tact, good manners, and personal charm, to be proficient in gymnastics, fencing, riding, music, dancing, hunting, the courtly arts, and the delicate art of lovemaking. The moving forces of his conduct were to be *l'onore* and *virtu*.

At the same time the Renaissance was an age of individual violence never equaled before or after. Brigands roamed the country, robbing and killing in broad daylight; assassins were for hire everywhere; bands of *condottieri* in Italy were available for any act of violence or private warfare between powerful princes.

Wives poisoned their husbands; lovers stabbed their mistresses; princes poisoned or had assassinated anyone who stood in their way, even bishops.[4] Witches and magicians were hired to cast deadly spells *(maleficii)* or concoct secret poisons. The autobiography of artist Benvenuto Cellini is a horrific tale of brawls, ambushes, stabbings, in which police forces seem to be useless puppets.

This unbridled passion and violence was the inevitable product of the Renaissance man's intense individualism. In states that were for the most part tyrannical and unjust, man learned to rely for his survival on his own right arm.

THE HUMANISTS. The most striking aspect of the Renaissance was the humanist movement[5] which revived the spirit of classic antiquity through the reverent study of Greek and Latin authors. It began in the fourteenth century with poet Francisco Petrarca (Petrarch) and satirist Giovanni Boccaccio, ultimately became an intellectual communion of educated minds throughout Europe.

The return to classicism was an attempt to simplify thought which was just emerging from the incredibly complicated forms of the Middle Ages. Knowledge and natural perception replaced the medieval faith and scholasticism.

The men of the Renaissance felt that the old medieval order was disintegrating; they were plunged in a profound uneasiness until the dawn of the seventeenth century and the birth of intellectualism. Until the future became somewhat clearer, Renaissance thinkers preferred to take refuge in the security of classic masterpieces.

The humanistic ferment also altered the medieval cast of literature and art, stirred rebellion against the

Leonardo da Vinci was obsessed with anatomy, made thousands of anatomic drawings.

dominance of Arabism. Humanists bravely sought to put down the still prevailing dogmatic dictatorship of Galen, Aristotle, and Avicenna.

Humanist scholars played active roles in politics and society, became secretaries to dukes, popes, and the senates of city-states: for example, Desiderius Erasmus was simultaneously wooed by Henry VIII and Pope Leo X.

A sense of beauty pervaded wealthy and wellborn Italians: in architecture and décor, style dominated function; each humble utensil was expected to be a work of art. Out of the emphasis on beauty of form grew a cult of the classics which captured Renaissance Italy.

The anonymity of collective labor in cathedrals disappeared: many painters now worked in their own ateliers and signed their paintings, developed schools of painting. The faces of monks, kings, saints, beggars, and bandits, all approximately alike in medieval art, now also showed individuality. Scholars labored in solitary concentration instead of serving as members of a monastic team. At universities the pedantic reading of masters was replaced by the personal discourses of such teachers as Vesalius and Fallopius.

During the sixteenth century the Italian, French,

and German universities gradually released themselves from ecclesiastic bonds; the Venetian senate was the first to open the doors of learning without regard for creed or nationality.

Among the medical humanists were many profound Greek and Latin scholars who toiled to disengage medical teaching from inaccurate Arabic texts. Famous for his wrathful attacks on Hippocratic and Galenic inaccuracies was Niccolo da Lonigo (Leonicenus, 1428-1524) who performed the monumental labor of correcting botanic errors in Pliny's *Natural History*. He was also the author of one of the earliest medical texts to give a clinical picture of syphilis; as the creator of a school at Ferrara, he was an outstanding clinician of the time.

Another medical humanist was Geronimo Cardano (1501-1576), physician, mathematician, astrologer, musician, gambler, and author of one of the great Renaissance autobiographies, *De vita propria*. He earned disfavor among fellow physicians by publishing a diatribe called *The Bad Practice of Healing Among Modern Doctors*.

BETTMANN ARCHIVE

Geronimo Cardano (1501-1576) helped to free medicine and thought from a rigid Aristotelian scholasticism.

A brilliant intellect, Cardano can be termed a pioneer in psychiatry: after his son was beheaded for poisoning his wife, Cardano wrote *De utilitate ex ad-*

versis capienda in which he described immorality as a disease of the spirit; in true Renaissance fashion he distinguished between the truly wicked (perverse) and those who do wrong only through the vehemence of their passion (*perfidi*).

CULVER

Thomas Linacre,
founder of the Royal College of Physicians.

Thomas Linacre (1461-1524) carried the torch of humanism from Italy to Oxford and Cambridge where he established chairs of the new philosophy; he also founded the Royal College of Physicians of London. As physician to Henry VIII he treated Cardinal Wolsey; he translated numerous Galenic texts, was a devoted friend of Erasmus, the prince of humanists.

Also a physician to royalty was the greatest of the French medical humanists, Jean François Fernel (1497-1558), who served both Henry II and Catherine de' Medici. Fernel was an avowed anti-Galenist: he taught that physicians must not become enslaved by tradition; among his beliefs was that the cause of an illness lay in the body itself and not in the fluids produced by the malady. Widely read for more than a century was his masterpiece *Universa medicina*.

Humanism enlivened Renaissance scholarship, removed much dogmatic debris, but barely refreshed scientific thought. Printing made quantitative progress but perpetuated nonsense as readily as knowledge.

In spite of the growth of humanism, the centuries of the Renaissance continued to nurture all manner of superstitions, some left over from the Middle Ages, others created by the new conditions.

Most powerful of all superstitions in this age was

astrology. Princes, free cities, popes, universities, all had their entourage of astrologers. A few brave spirits could say *Vir sapiens dominabitur astris* ("the wise man is master of the stars") but the vast majority passionately embraced the delusion.

A leading opponent of astrologers was the renowned humanist Pico della Mirandola[6] who considered astrology to be handmaid to geomancy, chiromancy, and every form of disreputable magic, as well as the root of all impiety and immorality.

Another prevalent superstition was the fervent belief in omens derived from any unusual occurrence of astronomic phenomenon. Most of the humanists, even the brilliant ones, were believers in auguries and prodigies recounted in the classics.

Against this, the spirit of scientific inquiry was strengthened in one remarkable year (1543) which saw the publication of both Andreas Vesalius' *Fabrica* and Nicholas Copernicus' *De revolutionibus orbium cœlestium.*

Mikolaj Kopernik (1473-1543) of Thorn in Prussian Poland, mathematician and astronomer, studied canon law at Bologna and medicine at Padua; at Frauenberg in East Prussia he practiced medicine at the same time as he discharged his religious duties as canon of the cathedral. He received on his deathbed the first published copy of the work which demolished the Ptolemaic notion that the universe was centered on the earth.

The humanist passion for a comprehensive knowledge of nature advanced the study of botany, a science founded on observation and organization of data. The collection and classification of plants already had a long tradition, kept alive from antiquity by the medieval medicinal and kitchen herb gardens. Distinguished botanists of the Renaissance were Konrad von Gesner (1516-1565), physician and naturalist, famed for his description of the canary, and Leonhard Fuchs[7] (1501–1566), who set a standard for beautiful plant illustration, was also professor of medicine for many years.

THE DISEASES. In the summer of 1485, shortly before Henry Tudor slew Richard III on Bosworth Field and ended the Wars of the Roses, a mysterious disease known as the sweating sickness appeared on the Welsh coast and spread to London.

As later described by the court physician John Caius, the onset of the disease came suddenly, with apprehensiveness, cold shivers, giddiness, neck pains, and prostration. In its acute stage victims suffered heat, profuse sweating, intense thirst, miliary eruptions; death frequently came within 24 hours; recovery took 8 to 14 days. Five major epidemics of this *sudor anglicus* occurred in the next six decades; one of them reduced by half the populations of Oxford and Cambridge.[8]

A still more devastating scourge was typhus fever,[9]

CULVER

Nicholas Copernicus.

first accurately described by Gerolamo Fracastoro. The Spanish named it *tabardillo,* lost 17,000 lives to it during the siege of Granada; in 1529 it all but wiped out a French army besieging Naples. Prisoners contracted typhus fever in jail, then infected judges at their trial, hence the English name of jail fever.

Renaissance children suffered from rickets: Ambroise Paré in the sixteenth century described valgus and varus deformities of the legs. Scurvy plagued sailors on long sea voyages; it had been observed in the Middle Ages when besieged towns were cut off from food supplies.

CULVER

Konrad von Gesner whose Historia Animalium *compiled all of the known material about animals.*

*Guy Patin, of the Faculty of Paris opposed all inno-
vation, declared Harvey's theory false and absurd.*

A brochure written by Ulrich Ellenbog in 1472 discussed the prevention of "poisonous, evil vapors and
fumes of metals." The German physician and father
of mineralogy, Georg Agricola, described the diseases and accidents of miners. Smallpox and malaria,
prevalent in the Middle Ages, continued in sporadic
outbreaks through the Renaissance centuries.

The great pox, or syphilis, made its dramatic entry
on the Renaissance scene while Charles VIII of
France was laying siege to Naples in 1493; it became
as widespread a scourge as the Black Death. Mercenary armies and their camp followers spread the disease through the whole of Europe.

Within a few decades the sexual nature of the
"love sickness" was fully recognized; a campaign of
control began against brothels and prostitutes. Some
cities sought to expel prostitutes; others passed stat-
utes requiring physical examination. Special hospitals were established; some communities gave free
medical treatment, usually generous inunctions of
mercury. Quacks, called "greasers of pox," smeared
their patients from head to foot with so-called Sara-
cenic ointment, subjected them to sweat baths; sali-
vation and diaphoresis were thought to eliminate
syphilitic poisons.

A common belief was that the disease came from
America; a Sevillian physician, Ruy Díaz de la Isla,
treated Columbus' diseased sailors in 1493, concluded that they had contracted it in Haiti. Yet some
Renaissance documents referred to the disease as
early as 1440; a typically syphilitic crural ulcer was
depicted in a 1461 painting.

Some ascribed to the new ailment a divine, astral
origin; rising national pride also made it an inter-

national taunt: the French named it *mal napolitain*,
the Italians *mal francese*. Other terms for it were
morbus gallicus, mal lusitano, mal spagnole. Syphilis
became the scourge and riddle of the Renaissance.

THE EPIDEMIOLOGIST. At the humanist center, the
University of Padua, a fellow student of Copernicus
in the early years of the sixteenth century was a
young gentleman of Verona, Gerolamo Fracastoro
(1483-1553). His family had wealth and property: he
owned a villa on Lake Garda, a country estate near
Verona. Here he spent most of his life, a country
squire, poet, playwright, affable host, and practicing
physician who carried a volume of the classics to
read as he made his leisurely rounds on muleback.

Fracastoro practiced medicine in Verona for some
twenty years, then in 1534 retired to devote himself
to writing. Among his terrestrial globes, astrolabes,
and a notable library, he produced discourses on
poetry, geography, astronomy, also two major medical works.

Epidemic disease held his interest, in particular
the "love pestilence" moved him both as poet and
physician: in polished Latin hexameters modeled on
Virgil's *Georgics* he wrote three volumes, published
in 1525 and 1530, describing the disease, its origin
and its treatment. His poem entitled the *Syphilis sive
morbus Gallicus* became the most widely known
medical poem since the *Regimen* of Salerno.

The poem tells the adventures of a rich and beautiful shepherd Syphilus who insulted Apollo and was
afflicted with a terrible disease: limbs were stripped
of flesh, teeth fell out, the breath became fetid, and
the voice was reduced to a whisper.[10]

Fracastoro's second and greatest contribution, *De
contagionibus et contagiosis morbis*, appeared in
1546; here he laid the groundwork for the future
understanding of contagion. He described it as oc-
curring by way of seeds of disease, *seminaria*, generated in the corrupted humors, communicated from
one person to another by direct contact, indirectly by
way of clothing and utensils (fomites), or at a distance through the air.

He was the first to describe typhus as a disease
distinct from plague; he also re-established tuberculosis, neglected since Plato's time, as an infectious
disease.

THE ICONOCLAST. University medicine, slavishly
following classic teaching, met a formidable enemy
in Philippus Theophrastus Bombastus von Hohen-
heim. This truculent opponent of bigotry and tradi-
tionalism in science took for himself the name of
Paracelsus to suggest that he was superior to Celsus,
Rome's aristocratic medical writer.

During a brief tenure as city physician and teacher
in Basel he horrified the University by denouncing
the doctrine of humors and casting into a bonfire the
works of Avicenna and Galen.

170

He was a good example of the violent opinionated individualist of the Renaissance, a law unto himself. His coarse character and habitual drunkenness alienated many friends; he was restless and unpredictable. He wandered from country to country, talking everywhere with barbers, bathkeepers, quacks, alchemists, common people. He compounded his own medicines, wrote medico-religious works, arrogantly defied the official views of his day.[11]

The healing art, according to Paracelsus, was built on philosophy, which embraced the study of nature and man, astronomy, from which a medical ecology could be derived, alchemy, or the search for effective drugs through the study of nature's own chemistry, and virtue, which encompasses love. He urged the value of sulfur, lead, antimony, mercury, iron, copper, and their compounds, rejected Arabian polypharmacy; he never hesitated to prescribe large toxic doses.

Paracelsian nosology regarded diseases as real entities, classified them as tartaric or caused by deposition of sediments, syphilitic and industrial. Among mental diseases he included lunacy, insanity, mental derangement, melancholia, mania, and changes of character.

He based his therapy above all else on the curative power of nature, thought of the universe as a pharmacy with God as its chief apothecary.

He saw the material world as composed of four elements inhabited by beings best suited to that element: man lived between earth and heaven in the air; the earth was inhabited by gnomes; water was the element of nymphs; fire was the habitat of salamanders. For him these elemental beings were God's own creatures, possessing an elemental and astral body, though without a soul. They were the guardians of the treasures of nature; nymphs could give birth to sirens, sylphs to giants, gnomes to dwarfs, salamanders to will-o-the-wisps.

Paracelsus founded no school but he re-examined the basic problems of the healing art, contributed a dynamic concept of disease as a living process. He made a distinction between physicians who cured through medicine and those who cured through miracles. He replaced the ancient polychemical preparations with simple essences and tinctures such as laudanum and turpentine, also preparations of metals. He was in this respect a great experimenter, constantly searching for new substances to effect cures. He helped to raise the ethical standards of the medical profession with his famous dictum: "The most precious thing we physicians possess is our art, and next comes love for our patients, hope being the keystone of both."

THE SURGEONS. The invention of firearms and cannon during the Renaissance made wars bloodier, wounds more mutilating.[12] The first work on gunshot

CULVER

Ambroise Paré revolutionized the treatment of wounds, advocated humane procedures in surgery.

wounds, published in 1497, held that the only treatment for gunpowder poisoning was cautery with hot irons, pitch, or boiling oil of elder.

Suppuration was deemed essential since many wounds did heal afterward; the causal relationship between "laudable pus" and recovery was accepted in Renaissance medical doctrine.

Continued during the Renaissance was the schism between surgery and medicine: the surgeons' craft, practiced on the battlefield or in public places, was denigrated by the university-trained physicians who had been awarded diplomas, dignity, and office. Itinerant ("short robe") surgeons, barbers, bloodletters, and quacks set up booths and tents; some specialized in extracting bloodstained pebbles from the crania of the mentally deranged, using sleight of hand.

Other nonacademic surgeons specialized in hernia and gallstones, sprains, dislocations, fractures, amputations; barbers, bath attendants, even butchers and executioners, attended to cupping, bleeding, and tooth extraction.

The ambivalent status of the surgeon was raised by Ambroise Paré, a kindly French barber-surgeon who revolutionized the treatment of gunshot wounds, introduced vascular ligation of arteries to arrest hemorrhage. He first performed a herniotomy without castration, reintroduced podalic version to correct dystocic deliveries.

Following pages: *Andreas Vesalius dissecting one of his famous muscular cadavers and lecturing to students at the University of Padua where, from 1537 to 1544, he held the Chair of Surgery with care of Anatomy. Painted by Federico Castellon.*

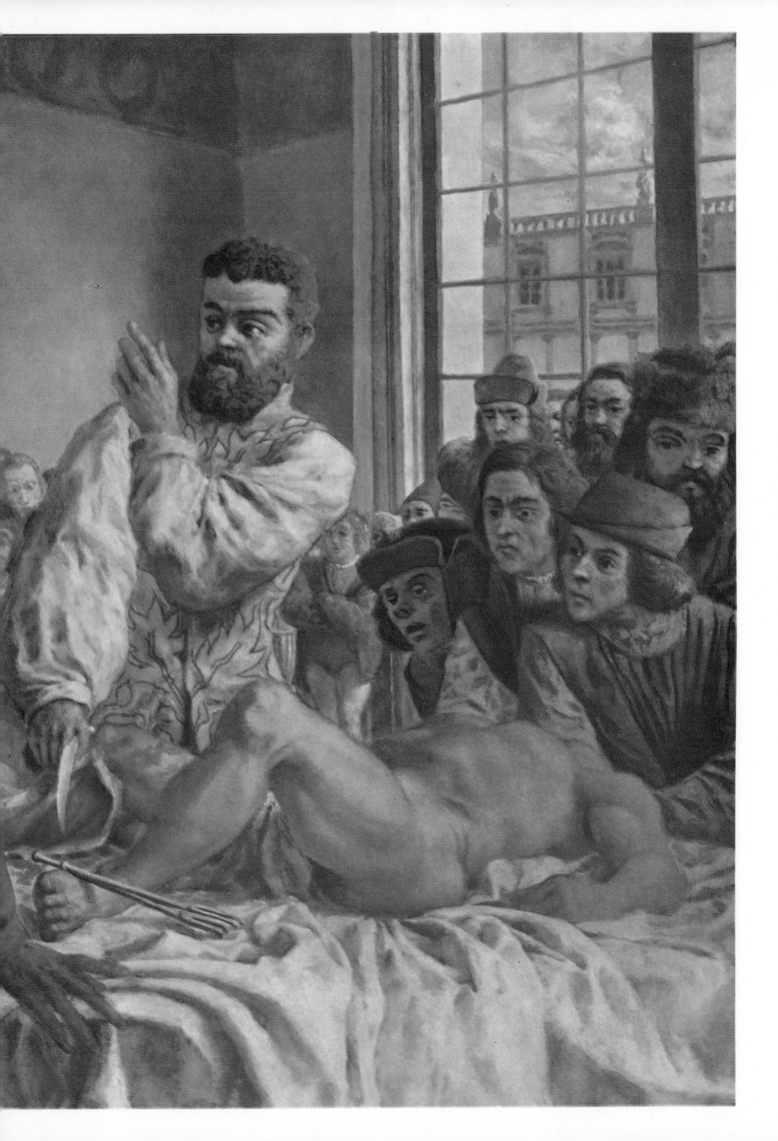

Girolamo Fracastoro (1483 — 1553), father of modern pathology, was the foremost epidemiologist of his time.

Paracelsus (1493?-1541). Behind the bombast, a student of psychology, founder of medicinal chemistry.

Besides demolishing the stubborn belief that gunshot wounds were necessarily infected, Paré ridiculed cures by unicorn horns and similar superstitions.

In that age of violence, Paré was an unusually humane character who tried to inflict as little pain as possible. During the French campaigns in Italy he used instead of boiling oil on wounds a salve made of eggyolk, attar of roses, and turpentine, then worried all night about this innovation; in the morning those treated with the salve were comfortable, those who had been scalded with oil were feverish, in pain, with their wounds inflamed.

Paré was also a physician who had a profound faith in the healing powers of nature. One day when he was congratulated on a cure, he made the historic remark: *Je le pansay, et Dieu le guérit*, I dressed him, and God healed him.

Renaissance surgeons learned the use of the skin flap, advanced lithotomy with a technique of perineal incision and catheterization. Rhinoplasty was practiced; an interest in ophthalmology revived after Leonardo da Vinci lauded the human eye's excellence.

ART AND ANATOMY. The course of anatomy changed when an Italian artist, seeking to carve a crucifix for a church, obtained the prior's permission to flay a cadaver and study its muscular structure.

Renaissance artists endowed medicine with a quickened perception of biologic man, stimulated studious minds to observe the form and function of the human organism.

By contrast with the stylized imaginative figures of pre-Renaissance art, the new masters found the greatest beauty in faithful representations of man in all his complex, vigorous, and beautiful nudity.

Silversmith Benvenuto Cellini wrote of the admirable bones of the head and the shoulder blades which, when the arm is raised, produce magnificent effects; he also admired the floating ribs which formed marvelous projections about the navel.

Painters and physicians often fraternized in apothecary shops where pigments were bought; the artists Lucas Cranach, Cosimo Rosselli, and Masolino da Panicale were once apothecaries' apprentices; physicians were among the close friends of Giotto, della Robbia, and da Vinci; some surgeons studied paintings before opening the veins of patients.

One of the first Renaissance artists to reveal a magic exactness in line and form, with a singular control of air, light, and scenery, was Andrea del Verrocchio (1435-1488) who had Leonardo da Vinci as a pupil. The fierce emotions of the time were expressed by Luca Signorelli; he was also a pioneer in introducing powerful elements of anatomy into his figures. Perugino advanced the art of perspective; his pupil Raphael added an intricate study of anatomy to his contours to become one of the greatest artists

174

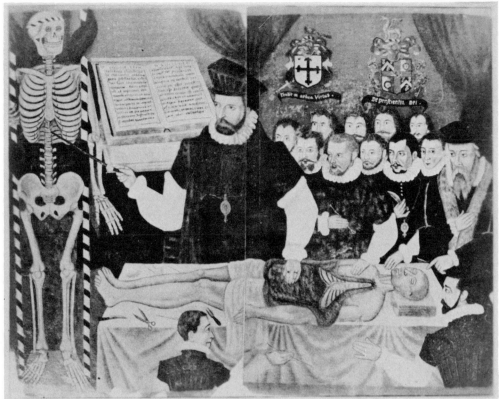

Dr. John Banister delivering the Visceral Lecture at Barber-Surgeon's Hall, London, 1581.

of the period. He made some admirable medical observations in his "Saint Peter and the Lame Man" and the portrait of Tomasso Inghirami.

THE UNIVERSAL MAN. In Leonardo da Vinci art and science joined in a mighty confluence of anatomy, physiology, medicine, physics, engineering, astronomy, philosophy, geology, painting, sculpture, poetry, music, and literature.

Da Vinci believed that anatomic verity in art could be attained only on the dissection table; with his own hands he probed anatomic structure, measured with a goniometer, calculated the proportions of the organism, and reduced them to mathematic formula.

Of the 6000 closely written pages of his diary, da Vinci devoted 190 pages to anatomy (750 drawings), fifty of these being about the heart. In refutation of Galenic belief he demonstrated that the heart was a muscle, described two new cavities, the auricles. He watched Tuscan farmers slaughter pigs by driving a spike into the heart, observed its contraction and dilatation and thus identified cardiac systole and diastole.

For his projected 120 volume treatise on anatomy, da Vinci dissected more than thirty corpses. He studied muscular antagonisms, ascertained the points of insertion and outlet of muscles. To study the cerebral ventricles he injected them with liquid wax; he described the pleura and lungs but did not probe the circulation of the blood.

Unbounded strength and dynamism of the human body reached their zenith with Michelangelo Buonarroti, poet, painter, architect. His figures, caught in bronze or canvas, were robust, tormented giants bursting from their titanic musculature; his Virgins were fiercely naked; his muscular captives strained against their bonds.

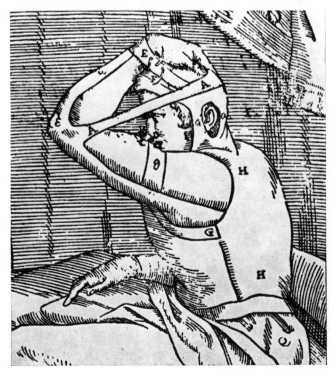

Rhinoplasty, using graft from the arm. From Chirurgia curtorum per insitionem *of Gaspare Tagliacozzi, Venice, 1597.*

Michelangelo used live models to capture reality; in a cell in the monastery of Santo Spirito, he dissected cadavers obtained from gravediggers in exchange for his statuettes. By the light of a candle inserted in the navel of the corpse he studied muscles, tendons, ligaments. All the postures of the human body were known to him; he could make them eloquently express deep emotions.

His sculpture of "David" is a masterpiece of anatomy, in the "Virgin and Child" can almost be seen the trembling of the Madonna's figures, the "Moses" sculpture is a titanic work of powerful anatomy, the figures on the ceiling of the Sistine Chapel are stupendous but anatomicaly correct.

THE ANATOMIST. Renaissance man witnessed the beginning of a drastic revision in concepts of his own anatomy when Andreas Vesalius (1514-1564), a young Flemish firebrand, published *De humani corporis fabrica*.

Vesalius was born in Brussels, the son of Emperor Charles V's apothecary; a family tradition of distinguished physicians early spurred his interest in medicine. At the University of Paris he led his fellow students on night raids to cemeteries and gallows to obtain cadavers, smuggled home specimens piece by piece.

At Padua he received his medical degree "with highest distinction" on one day, on the next he was made professor of surgery, and on the third he began his anatomy course.

The spectacle of a professor performing his own dissection and sketching as he lectured drew students, teachers, clergy, courtiers, and soldiers. In 1538 were published his *Tabulae anatomicae sex*, six anatomic plates for his students' use.

Inspired by a controversy on bleeding between Arabic and Hippocratic schools was his *Venesection Letter*, published the following year; in it he described his investigations of the endothoracic venous system, his discovery of the greater azygous vein and its outlet in the vena cava. The Giunta press of Venice meanwhile commissioned him to prepare Galen's work on anatomy, revised in the light of new discoveries.

His studies of Galen had shown him the errors into which the master had fallen by dissecting only monkeys; he was thus inspired to write his own work on anatomy, the monumental and epoch-making *De humani corporis fabrica libri septem*, known universally as the *Fabrica*, published in 1543.

The plates for the *Fabrica* were drawn by van Calkar and other pupils of the Titian schools (some possibly by Titian himself), were sent on muleback across the Alps to a Basel master printer, Johannes Oporinus. The book was to become one of the greatest works ever published in the history of medicine.

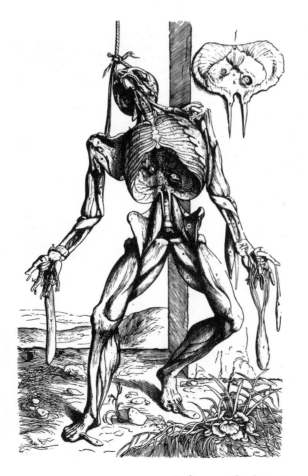

Left, *seventh plate of muscles from Vesalius'* Fabrica.
Right, *title page of Vesalius' famous work.*

Vesalius had discovered that many of Galen's descriptions did not accord with observed fact: he found no curvature of thigh and upper arm bones, no general muscle of the skin, no *os intermaxillare* in adults, no opening between the two ventricles of the heart. The *Fabrica* corrected some 200 Galenic errors.

The *Fabrica* and the six *Tabulae Anatomicae*, published five years earlier aroused tempests of unprecedented violence. Attacked by scholars and fearful of the authority of the Church, Vesalius left Padua and took refuge with the Emperor Charles V.

Vesalius became wealthy at the emperor's court but he had no further opportunity to pursue his anatomic work. He was considerably embittered by the attacks on his *Fabrica*, and in 1563 decided to undertake the pilgrimage to Jerusalem.[13] On the return voyage his boat was wrecked on the Ionian island of Zante where he died, probably of typhoid, in 1564.

The inestimable value of the *Fabrica* lay not only in the vast breach it made in the Galenic ramparts but also in the fact that it opened the way for the new and scientific approach of a later age. It relied not on dogma but on observation, not on doctrine but on experimentation. Although it still contained Galenic errors, notably in physiology, it was a gigantic step from medieval darkness to the age of enlightenment.

An odd figure at the close of the Renaissance was the Spaniard Michael Servetus (1511-1553), a disputatious theologian who was also a man of medicine. His first work on digestion criticized Galenic and Arabic pharmacologic practices; he also suggested that medicine need not be offensive and could be administered in pleasing vehicles.

Interpolated in a theologic treatise (*Christianismi restitutio*, 1553) were some remarks on the circulation of the blood, indicating that he was familiar with (or brilliantly surmised) the mechanism of the pulmonary circulation. He was also the first to deny that the ventricular septum was perforated.[14]

THE PHYSICIANS. The status of physicians steadily rose during the Renaissance as they became disentangled from the superstitions and hocus-pocus of medieval medicine. Outmoded concepts of disease were shed; once sacrosanct Galenic and Arabian doctrines were challenged; the old rigidity of scholasticism was shattered beyond repair.

Rewards were high: Fabricius, teacher of William Harvey, left his niece 200,000 ducats; Henry II's chief physician received 1200 livres annually; Fernel was paid 10,000 *écus* for each of the ten pregnancies of Catherine de' Medici; France's Louis XII kept a medical retinue of one physician at 800 livres annually, five more at 500, five surgeons at 180, two barbers, an apothecary, and an astrologer.

Michael Servetus (1511-1553) described the pulmonary circulation in his Christianismi restitutio.

While astrology still played a role in medical practice, it was during the Renaissance that the physician climbed to the eminence of scholarship. Many of the great physicians were humanists, men of letters, art collectors, deeply appreciative of classical literature.

Therapy was based on evacuation of "phlegm" by bleeding, laxatives, emetics, and enemas. Hot baths were prescribed so that harmful humors could be expelled through the pores; wrinkling of the fingertips indicated successful expulsion. Jets of hot water played on the patient's head were thought to treat the cold mucosity of the brain, seat of all affliction.

New remedies were discovered: mercurial salves, pomades, ointments, and fumigations for venereal disease, also lignum vitae or guaiacum, Peruvian balsam, sarsaparilla, jalap, and sassafras.

Moderation in diet, drinking, and sex was championed by Luigi Cornaro, Venetian nobleman and friend of Fracastoro, who wrote four books on the art of living a long and sober life.

The most memorable champion of truth in the closing decades of the Renaissance was Johann Weyer, who in 1563 published his *De praestigiis daemonum* in which he maintained that witches were merely miserable people whose minds were distorted; in the many cases he examined he showed that what was called witchery was either sickness or rascality.

It was an antidote to the infamous *Malleus maleficarum*, published by two Inquisitors in 1489, a brutal and sordid handbook of witch-hunting. Weyer's book was a pioneering treatise in psychiatry and it undoubtedly saved countless lives of mentally ill men and women who would otherwise have died in shackles or been burned.

In spite of the persistence of astrology and demonology, the bonds of the Middle Ages were irretrievably broken during the Renaissance and the way was opened toward objectivity and scientific observation. The next period, which saw the birth of modern rationalism, was to advance medicine along the road outlined by the courageous men of the Renaissance.

Illustration for Don Quixote *by Gustave Doré. Cervantes'*
satiric novel is a great prose work of the Renaissance.

Europe's playground, Venice has accepted a small amount of modernization.

RENAISSANCE HERITAGE TODAY

Controversial in Italy today is contemporary architecture, as Italians, proud of their cultural traditions, face the problems of adapting the great Renaissance cities to the necessities of a technologic world.

Loath to see the economic lines of glass and steel rising beside time-honored edifices built by Brunelleschi, Michelangelo, Palladio and decorated by Donatello and the della Robbias, many Italians are actively resistant to twentieth century esthetics. Typical are the Florentines who recently spent years and millions of dollars rebuilding the Ponte Santa Trinita, destroyed during World War II, according to its sixteenth century design. Where once the Medici and Strozzi armies marched, Fiats and Vespa motorscooters now race across the Arno. A few years ago, Venetian authorities announced that Frank Lloyd Wright would design a building on the Grand Canal; when the plans were shown, opposition was so intense that the project was indefinitely postponed.

The Renaissance here is surveyed as it continues to impose itself on the descendants of the men who made it.

Florence's pride is Brunelleschi's dome of the Cathedral, built 1421-1434, with double walls independent of each other without scaffolding or staging.

Franz Hals contrasted lust and refinement of the seventeenth century in the proximity of lace with saus ages and onions in "The Merry Company."

IX

Whirlwind in the Soul

Four candelabra and eight candles illuminated with their ballet of light and shadows the anatomical theatre of Padua, a small cylindrical structure of wood on whose tiers restless students from all Europe stood, packed closely together like matches in a box.

The door squeaked like a soul in torment, heralding the entrance of the teacher, Fabricius ab Aquapendente. The air suddenly became electrified. All eyes focused at once on the dissecting table, on which there lay a corpse. The flickering light from the candles, like the pale tongue of a compassionate dog, licked the naked flesh. The master's hands, bejeweled with the rubies of gout, promptly and deftly laid bare the intimate mysteries of man's anatomy. Among the youths watching the great master was a dark-haired, dark-eyed English student named William Harvey.

In the seventeenth century Galen's theories were still accepted, but the way was already being paved for momentous changes. The Spaniard Michael Servetus had already discovered the pulmonary circulation, and Realdo Colombo had clearly described it; Fabricius ab Aquapendente had dissected the venous valves; Cesalpino had shown that the blood flows and that the heart is the central organ of the circulatory system. But it was William Harvey who was to revolutionize medical science.

The mind of a scientist mirrors the atmosphere of his times. Perhaps the seed of Harvey's work was already beginning to grow as he watched, through Galileo's telescope, the motion of the heavenly bodies in the glittering sky of Padua; perhaps it was nourished further by the whirling motion that characterized the triumphant baroque art, and even further by the literature of the time, particularly Shakespeare's plays and John Donne's poems and sermons, which often rang with the mention of the words "blood" and "heart." In any case, Harvey dedicated his life to studying the two basic *motions* of the human body—pulse and respiration—and finally demonstrated that the blood flows and that it flows in a circle. With this animate anatomy, Harvey set in motion the static anatomy created by Vesalius, and with his concept of local motion in the human body, he ushered in modern physiology.

Other investigators completed Harvey's work. Leeuwenhoek, a Dutch lens grinder, with his homemade lenses materialized the invisible world of animalculae, infusoria, and living organisms contained in a drop of water. (It is noteworthy that, while Leeuwenhoek was dedicated to investigating the world of minute living creatures, his neighbor, the painter Jan Vermeer, in a significant coincidence of interests, was himself dedicated to immortalizing in his paintings the minute details in the world around him.)

Marcello Malpighi, pioneer in microscopic anatomy, described the delicate network of the capillaries and their circulation, thus unraveling the riddle left unsolved by Harvey of how arteries and veins communicate; Jean Pecquet and Olat Rudbeck confirmed the white mystery of the lymphatic circulation, already foreseen by Gaspar

Aselli; with the discovery of the circulation of the blood and the lymph—the two main fluids of the human body—and of the fact that the lymph does not travel to the liver, this organ was stripped of the supreme hierarchial rank conferred on it by Galen.

This work was supplemented in other fields by the search for the basic structure of the human body, which both the French humanist Jean Fernel and the Italian anatomist Gabriel Fallopius situated in a *solid* entity—the "fiber"—thus displacing Galen's humoral physiology. And Harvey, with his embryology, established *anatomia animata* in time, just as earlier, with his new physiology, he had established *anatomia animata* in space.

The atmosphere at that time was electrified by the prevailing thirst for motion and emotion, two characteristics that found expression particularly in art and gave the baroque age its name. For this was the period when, in rebellion against the pure, austere, classic Greek style, the dynamic curve was preferred to the rigid straight line in art. The world was rediscovered in its infinite mobility, and all this motion was celebrated with profound emotion. Greatest among the great exponents of this trend were fantastic El Greco, emotional Bernini, dramatic Caravaggio, photographic Veláz-quez, realistic Zurbarán, sentimental Murillo, joyful Rubens, and perceptive Rembrandt. They gave meaning and glory to the baroque age.

Medicine, too, strongly reflected the trend. The static Vesalian structures of the human body were set in motion and were even infused with emotion and embellished with decorations in the work of those miniaturists of the circulatory apparatus, "water-color painters," as it were, of the capillaries and the lymphatics.

In a parallel development, the baroque age saw the new religious movements flourishing at the same time that new horizons were opening across the seas and that printing and the stagecoach were shortening distances between minds and between cities. The compass had already dispelled the mystery of what lay beyond the ocean; gunpowder had put an end to the tyranny of the feudal system; the concept of state evolved; great scientific societies were born, and the first periodical of any kind, *La Gazette* (later *La Gazette de France*), made its appearance. Published at first as a weekly political and civic newspaper by Théophraste Renaudot—physician to Louis XIII and founder of the first pawnshop in France—and later changed into a medical journal, the motto of *La Gazette* is still of value today, 330 years after its creation: "*Le journal tient de la nature des torrents—qu'il se grossit par la résistance.*" ("A journal is like a torrent—its power increases with resistance.")

Individual endeavor, the rise of a middle class, and increasing industrialization were changing the face of Europe, and while the power of Spain was undergoing its sunset of grandeur, that of England and Russia was ascending. The incredible voyage of the *Mayflower* planted the first seed of American democracy. The French philoso-pher, René Descartes, who died, coughing and shivering, at the court of Christina of Sweden, and whose medical ideas followed the iatrophysical system, established the scientific value of doubt, the mechanistic concept of the "human machine," and the dichotomy between soma and psyche; and the philosophers Francis Bacon and John Locke emphasized the value of the experimental method in science.

The dynamic universe of Kepler, Galileo, and Newton replaced the somewhat static universe of Copernicus. The qualitative impression of nature was replaced by quantitative measurement. Science became mensural and rational. General motion in space was replaced by local physiological motion; the torch of learning passed from Padua in the sunlit south to Leyden in the misted north of Europe; illustrious physicians investigated the mysterious structure of the organs of the body—Francis Glisson, the lining of the liver; Johann Georg Wirsung, the pancreatic duct; Niels Stensen, the parotid gland.

Clinical medicine in the baroque was illuminated by the multicolored lamps of three new medical systems: the iatrophysical, the iatrochemical, and the systematist. The iatrophysicists—philosophical heirs of Vesalius and Galileo in Italy, of Harvey in England—regarded the body as a machine and sought to explain all its workings accordingly. Outstanding exponents of the school were Redi, Borelli, Baglivi, and Sanc-torius. The last named spent thirty years of his life seated in a huge scale weighing him-self while in different emotional or physical states, such as sleep, anger, sexual excite-ment, sadness, thus initiating the way to the modern concept of metabolism. He con-sidered pathology a matter of the "tensional state of the fibers" and of the density of the humors of the body.

The iatrochemists—philosophical heirs of Paracelsus—regarded the body as a laboratory where organic motion was the result of organic fermentation, a theory advanced by the Flemish mystic, Jan-Baptista van Helmont. He regarded water as the substratum of the body and the archaeus as the life-giving principle. His mild medicinal plant tinctures were a healthy reaction against the barbaric horse-medicine therapies of the period. His work was supplemented by Franz de la Boë or Sylvius, who showed that fermentation was but one of the many changes that occurred in the body, and by Thomas Willis, whose delicate, exquisite dissections, precise as enamel miniatures, laid bare the vascular ring at the base of the brain, now known as the "circle of Willis."

Among the systematists there stands out the figure of Thomas Sydenham, a soldier in Cromwell's Roundhead army, just as Harvey was a Royalist, a scholarly and kindly physician and a spiritual descendant of Hippocrates. Sydenham shut his books and opened his eyes to look at the patient; he recommended naturalistic clinical observation, the study of the *whole* patient, and of a "species" of diseases instead of "disease" in general, as had been the previous practice; he introduced the biographical element into clinical case histories. He divided diseases into two classes: acute, biological, or animal (epidemiological); and chronic, biographical, or human (psychosomatic). Once when asked by Sir Richard Blackmore to recommend a textbook of medicine, he replied, "Read *Don Quixote,* it is a very good book, I read it still."

There was little interest in therapeutics in the Baroque Age, though quinine and ipecacuanha had been brought from South America by the Spaniards. The forceps and blood transfusion were introduced. The enmity between physicians and surgeons persisted, until finally the latter were accepted by the medical class and were permitted to wear the "long robe." Always fighting barbers and charlatans, surgeons, with a few physicians, made this a period of "vampirism" in therapeutics. Their abuse of leeches and other forms of bleeding, it is said, drew more blood from the people than the French Revolution. Physicians prescribing such therapy became the target of Moliére's satirical darts.

Across the Atlantic, the *Mayflower* pilgrims—nearly half of whom died within three months after landing on American soil—in their struggle against a hostile nature, the Indians, and disease, particularly smallpox and typhus, initiated American medicine, the first seed of which had been planted by the conquistadors, who in the sixteenth century conferred, in Peru, the first degree in the New World of Doctor of Medicine, founded in Mexico the first chair of medicine, and printed also in Mexico the first medical book in the Americas.

Colonial physicians fought disease with the assistance of surgeons, like Lambert Wilson and Thomas Wooton, and of churchmen doubling as physicians, like Samuel Fuller and Cotton Mather, who practiced the first inoculations, and Thomas Thacher, who wrote the first American medical publication on smallpox. With this "angelic conjunction" of physician and pastor, America saw the beginning of what would eventually become the most advanced medicine in the world.

Everywhere on both sides of the Atlantic, man looked for new wonders. While the settlers struggled to conquer the rugged nature of America, in Europe a great physician and humanist, Sir Thomas Browne, wrote a beautiful and inspiring book, *Religio medici,* in which, in a prose as delicate and colorful as a Gobelin tapestry, he reconciled mystical faith and scientific skepticism. In the pages of this book he wrote his answer to man's eternal quest: "We carry within us all the wonders we seek without us."

F.M.I.

Following page: *Anton van Leeuwenhoek (1632-1723) is shown examining part of a microscope of his own construction. On his desk and table are detailed notes of his instruments and microscopic observations. The interior is in the manner of the Dutch painter Vermeer, whose friend Leeuwenhoek was. Painted by Hans Guggenheim.*

IX

BAROQUE MEDICINE

THE seventeenth century set a gigantic stage on which were played momentous events in western civilization, destroying most of the remaining dogmatic shackles of the Middle Ages and laying the political, social, and intellectual bases of the modern world.

In this era, which came to be known as the Baroque[1] Age, absolute monarchy was established, counterweighted by the rise of the English Parliament; the balance of power among nations was totally remolded by a series of wars and incessant intrigue; the decisive battle between Christendom and Islam was fought before the gates of Vienna; Protestants and Catholics spilled their blood for the last time in religious conflict; philosophy, science, and medicine soared in a revolutionary rebirth of reason.

This age also placed a powerful and inimitable imprint on all the arts, infusing them with new dimensions of motion and force, revealing the tremendous social and spiritual conflicts and aspirations at work.

THE STAGE. The baroque political scene was dominated by three main currents: the continued struggle between absolute monarchy and democratic parliaments which culminated in the Puritan Revolution in England; the implacable war between the Bourbons of France and the Hapsburgs of the Holy Roman Empire; the murderous clash between the Ottoman Empire of the Turks and the emergent Russian empire of Peter the Great over the weakened body of Poland.

Concurrent forces were the slow decline of the once all-powerful Spanish empire, the mighty development of France under the autocratic rule of Louis XIV, the growing strength of England, Holland, Sweden, and Russia. The greatest political tragedy of the period was the Thirty Years' War, which was fought mostly in Germany, causing unimaginable devastation by rapine, starvation, and disease.

Most of the political conflicts of this period were interwoven in the bitter feud between the Protestant sects born of the Reformation in the previous century and the powerful Counter Reformation movement led by the Jesuit order. Supporting the Reformation were England, Germany, and the Low Countries; champions of the Counter Reformation were Spain, the papacy, and Austria. One side effect of this conflict was the emigration of Protestants to the New World where colonies were founded throughout this century.

On the economic scene the once-dominant individualistic merchants of Germany and Italy were replaced by powerful English and Dutch mercantile companies. Whereas during the Renaissance banking was mostly controlled by such families as the Fuggers, seventeenth century trade became so far flung that it could only be financed by states, thus identifying politics with the mercantilist credo of expanding national wealth through protection of commerce.

THE SOCIETY. One of the leading philosophers of the Baroque Age, England's Thomas Hobbes, wrote: "So that in the first place, I put for a generall inclination of all mankind, a perpetuall and restlesse desire of Power, after Power, that ceaseth only in Death."

The foremost features that characterized this age were the rise of capitalism, theologic and military disputes, the creation of the modern concept of the state. In their search for power, autocratic princes waged seemingly senseless wars to aggrandize their dynastic power; statesmen and soldiers, prelates and courtiers waged constant combat for personal glory; baroque man reveled in the meteoric rise and fall of

185

conquering heroes and the cataclysmic clashes between powerful figures.

The age was one of spectacular display, as if the leading actors moved perpetually on a gigantic stage. During the first part of the century men wore long hair and beards, enormous plumed hats and oversized rapiers; later these were replaced by huge wigs and stately costumes profusely ornamented.

In spite of courtly manners and exaggerated etiquette, most of the wealthier classes were engrossed in excesses of eating, drinking, and sexual debauchery. A typical baroque contrast was the strict chasteness of Spanish and French cloisters (e.g., Port Royal), and the Puritanic asceticism in dress and mores.

A manifestation of baroque man's struggle for power in his own self was the incessant quarrelling and duelling that went on over matters of honor; in spite of sporadic and halfhearted attempts by the authorities to ban duels, thousands perished by pistol or sword.

Honor also played its part in the enormous importance attached to pomp, ceremony, and precedence. No nobleman was worthy of the name without his numerous kitchen staff, a chaplain, a choir, barber, confessor, secretary, master of ceremonies, and private physician.

Baroque man insisted with extreme punctiliousness on the precise degree of respect due to himself or to his office. Bickering over precedence could prevent princes and diplomats from negotiating, frequently increased political tension and generated incidents that led to war.

The greatest sufferers in this strife-torn age were the peasants of all lands. In addition to the feudal *corvées* that still had to be performed in some countries, the incessant wars and the entry of states into extensive mercantile enterprises steadily increased taxation. Princes also discovered that they could raise money by granting monopolies (such as that of salt); the monopolists in turn squeezed every penny they could from direct taxation of the peasants.

Additionally, the seventeenth century saw armies grow to enormous size, made up largely of brutal and licentious mercenary soldiery, who pillaged and raped with complete impunity. In between wars the countryside was ravaged by these same soldiers roaming in brigand bands.

Men and women of the leisured classes made great efforts to appear erudite, affecting hyperbole and an elaborate vocabulary embellished with classic allusions. Among women this led to the creation of circles of *précieuses* satirized by Molière in *Les Précieuses ridicules*.

Nonetheless the age that prided itself on its nascent science and scoffed at the Middle Ages was also the one engulfed in a stupendous mania for persecuting witches. A sincere belief in the reality of witchcraft was held by all classes in both Catholic and Protestant lands, even by such a scientist as Robert Boyle and a humanist like Sir Thomas Browne.

The mania led to the torture and execution of thousands of men and women suspected of practicing the black arts; it spread to the New England colonies where as late as 1692 a score of "witches" were executed at Salem, Massachusetts.

Equally bizarre was the great excitement caused throughout Europe by the publication in 1615 of *Confessio rosae crucis* by Johann Valentin Andreä, describing an esoteric society, variously called Rosy-Cross Knights, Rosy-Cross Philosophers, which claimed to be the repositor of the wisdom of the ages since ancient Egypt. Its secret members (Illuminati) studied occult symbols such as the rosy cross, swastika, pyramid to discover cabalistic messages. A virtuous rule was that members of the cult must give help to the sick poor.

THE ARCHITECTS. A passion for monumental building took hold of princes, noblemen, and wealthy bourgeois; the spirit of the age favored the expression of grandeur and power in stately manor houses and *châteaux*, richly ornamented with opulent curves, the sweep of magnificent staircases, vast gardens fashioned in formal designs.

Outstanding was the sculptor and architect Lorenzo Bernini whose first revolutionary creation was to place under Michelangelo's great dome in St. Peter's of Rome a bronze canopy 100 feet high with four gigantic twisted columns. A genius in spatial composition was Francesco Borromini, among whose masterpieces was the church of San Carlino of the Four Fountains.

In England Inigo Jones built town and country houses in the classic proportions of the Italian Renaissance architect Andrea Palladio. After the great London fire of 1666 Christopher Wren rebuilt St. Paul's and numerous other London churches along baroque lines.

Two monarchs in this century transformed Paris from a crowded medieval town with narrow, twisting streets into a city of broad avenues, spacious parks, and public gardens. Louis XIV expanded his father's hunting lodge at Versailles into the greatest and most ornamental palace in the world, costing the stupendous sum of 66 million livres.

PAINTING. Baroque painters generally led double lives. On one hand they were obliged to satisfy the demands of princes and prelates for grandiose works, many drawn from classic history or mythology, and for court portraits in sumptuous settings. By contrast they painted life as it was: peasants, vagabonds, street gamins, self-portraits or portraits of fellow artists, domestic scenes.

The French school of decorative art was led by Charles Le Brun (1619–1690) who painted according to the pomp and pretense dear to Louis XIV's heart. Striking landscapes and classic scenes were favored by Nicolas Poussin, whose "Rape of the Sabine Women"is one of the best-known paintings in the world.

One of the towering figures of baroque art was El Greco (1548–1614) who expressed the strain of mysticism that ran through that age, using as models for his saints the inmates of the mental asylum in Toledo. The ceremonial of court life and the heroic style of Spanish baroque were captured by the court painter Diego Velázquez, whose "Surrender of Breda" (1635) is a masterpiece of its kind.

The lustiness of the baroque period was amply recorded in the nudes by Peter Paul Rubens (1577–1640); his pupil Anthony van Dyck was the most accomplished painter of the nobility.

By contrast Dutch baroque art was rooted in the daily life of smiling burghers and healthy peasants, painted by Frans Hals (1584–1666) and his contemporary genius, Rembrandt van Rijn (1606–1666), magician of lights and shadows.

Baroque painters introduced the highly original notion of portraying deformed or pathologic specimens of humanity. Velázquez painted numerous achondroplastic and cretinoid dwarfs; Pieter Brueghel and Hieronymus Bosch delighted in cripples, blind men, grotesquely deformed creatures; Dutch painters represented chlorosis (called the *mal d'amour*), dropsy, fever, melancholy. This school also excelled in depicting scenes of medical interest: urine inspection, bedside consultation, surgery, and studies revealing the social rank and costume of physicians and the ritual of teaching dissection.[2]

MUSIC. As in architecture and painting, the underlying dynamic forces of the Baroque Age found their expression in a new style of musical composition, a welding of naturalism and formalism, emotion expressed through mathematically balanced tonal elements.

Revolutionary in this age were the development of the opera and oratorio, the flowering of church music, and the colorful extension of orchestral music into the overture and the concerto.

The opera was admirably suited to the baroque taste for grandiose spectacle; its offshoots, the ballet and the masque, became the favorite (and monstrously expensive) pastime of princes and the wealthy.

The greatest composer of choral music before Johann Sebastian Bach was Heinrich Schütz (1585–1672). The major technical improvements in his day were the growth of the organ and the refinement of the violin. Music in this age passed from amateur groups and guilds into the unfettered world of professional enterprise.

LITERATURE. All of the age's tremendous tensions, heroic pathos, gravity, pomp, and colorful move-

Baroque architecture concentrated on elaborate detail, created movement by twisting normally straight lines, carved niches and superimposed decorative effects to break up flat simple surfaces. Church of the Orphans, Córdoba.

Following pages: *Dr. Thomas Sydenham, reviver of Hippocratic medical ideals, riding a mule alongside a patient on horseback, near Pall Mall, 1660. He is holding a copy of Don Quixote, the book he recommended to physicians as the best guide for learning medicine. Painted by Hans Guggenheim.*

Thomas Sydenham
riding on a Mule with a Patient on
Horseback near his House in Pall Mall
looking south toward Westminster where
his Practice lay Taken from Pall Mall
showing the Palace and part of the Parish of
Westminster.   Landscape of
        16   60

ment were expressed by baroque poets, writers, and dramatists in richly ornate language.

In English literature the bridge between the renaissance and the baroque era was William Shakespeare in the later plays such as *King Lear* and *Othello*. In Spain the bridge was formed by Miguel de Cervantes whose immortal *Don Quixote* blended the romantically heroic and the realistically grotesque.

The most prolific Spanish literary form was the theatre, exemplified in the more than 2000 plays of Lope de Vega, the 500 productions of Pedro Calderón de la Barca, the equally prolific output of Tirso de Molina. The basis of most of the dramas was the passionate defense of honor, a fundamental baroque spiritual value.

From Spain, France's Pierre Corneille borrowed the theme of his famous *Le Cid* in which a character sums up the baroque creed:

Et l'on peut me réduire á vivre sans bonheur

Mais non pas me résoudre de vivre sans honneur.[3]

The baroque conflicts in the realm of passion were superbly presented by Jean Racine who raised love to the highest levels of tragedy; his characters were true baroque progeny, fiercely torn between individual preference and stern duty.

The mystic element that runs like a thread through the baroque era was strongest in England with the three Johns: Milton, Donne, and Bunyan. Their works revealed that even in the dynamic baroque world the somber echoes of the Middle Ages were not entirely mute.

Such mysticism underlay most of the published work of a gentle Yorkshire country physician, Sir Thomas Browne (1605–1682), whose *Religio medici* has been called the prose counterpart of John Donne's poetry. Wrote Dr. Browne:

> Whosoever enjoys not this life, I count him but an apparition, though he wear about him the sensible affections of flesh. In these moral acceptions, the way to be immortal is to die daily.

THE THINKERS. The three main problems that exercised the minds of seventeenth century philosophers were relations between the individual and the state, relations between man and God, the dichotomy of body and soul.

The most powerful advocate of the absolute power of the state was England's Thomas Hobbs (1588–1679), who in *Leviathan* expounded the doctrine that men in the state of nature live out "nasty, brutish and short" lives in perpetual strife and anarchy; in order to survive they must surrender their individual rights to a state; further, they must submit absolutely to a sovereign whose duty is to protect them from outside enemies.

The chief opponent of this view was physician-philosopher John Locke (1632–1704) who postulated that primitive men were equal, happy, and peaceful; the state was formed to protect them against those who were opposed to nature; the state must be guided by natural law and protect the rights of the individual.

The relations between man and God were viewed rationally by René Descartes (1596–1650), who believed that the idea of God in the thinker must have proceeded from a first cause, God Himself. Descartes propounded that the physical world and the mind were entirely separate, their only link being through God, thereby launching the doctrine of dualism that profoundly influenced western philosophy.

He thus postulated that man is both a *res cogitans* or thought, and a *res extensa* or physical body, the material world being independent of the mind and having "extension" as its main characteristic; for Descartes the human body was a machine influenced by thought, communication between thought and the animal spirits taking place in the pineal gland.

Descartes' scientific method was that of mathematic rationalism, endeavoring to reduce to geometric forms and algebraic formulas the complexities of nature. He rejected everything that man had hitherto been forced to take on trust, excepting only logic, geometry, and algebra. He established four basic rules of thought: never accept anything except clear and distinct ideas, divide each problem into as many parts as are needed to solve it, thoughts must follow an order from the simple to the complex, always check thoroughly to make sure that nothing has been overlooked.[4]

Blaise Pascal (1623–1662) opposed the Cartesian views, believed instead that there was a limit to scientific reasoning and that God could only be perceived intuitively or by some intense mystic experience.

The humble Dutch lens grinder Benedict Spinoza (1632–1677) held that all existence and all manifestations were but one infinite substance, God. This startling pantheism was regarded as highly blas-

Lope Félix de Vega Carpio (1562-1635). He wrote more than 2200 plays distinguished by wit, brilliant dramatic effects, fine character portrayal. His disregard of Aristotelian tragic unity had important effect on European drama.

CULVER

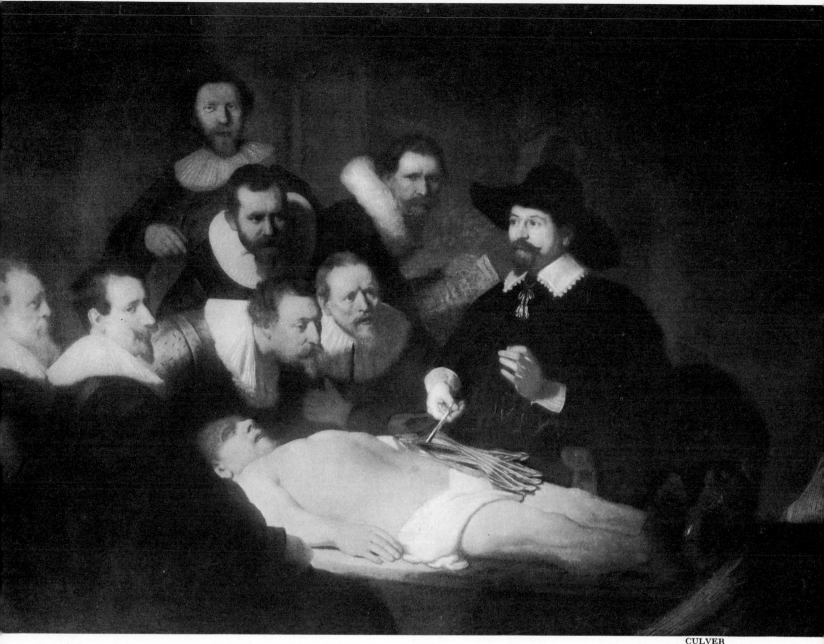

Prominence of Seventeenth century Dutch anatomists was celebrated in Rembrandt's The Lesson in Anatomy of Dr. Tulp.

phemous in his day and some of his works were banned.

Equally original was the theory proposed by scientist-philosopher Gottfried Leibniz (1646–1716) that reality was an arrangement of "monads," substances that mirrored the universe, each in a special way. The principal monad in the human body was the soul; all monads were ranged in an ascending hierarchy to reach the supreme monad, God.

THE SCIENTISTS. At the start of the century, England's Lord Chancellor, Francis Bacon, had postulated that the way to arrive at truth was not through established texts but through clear thinking; he urged men to discard inherited errors, traditions, prejudices (called "idols") and use empiric inductive reasoning in scientific research. In his Utopian

The New Atlantis (1627) he placed science at the very foundation of all knowledge.

The Baroque Age's great revolution was to sever the physical from the metaphysical, transforming natural science from a handmaid of theology into an independent intellectual entity. Baroque man developed a passion for observing and measuring the world around him.

Foremost measurer of the universe was Johannes Kepler (1571–1630) who, after years of studying the systems of Copernicus and Tycho Brahe, reduced planetary motion to three fundamental laws. He was followed by Galileo Galilei (1564–1642) who studied medicine but was not graduated), who developed the laws of motion based on his observation of pendulum movement and the acceleration of falling bodies. The Keplerian and Galilean laws were later combined in a dynamic synthesis by the genius of Isaac Newton to produce the epoch-making laws of universal gravitation, the foundation of the dynamics of the heavenly bodies.

In physics Galileo contributed the fundamental principles of dynamics, an astronomic clock, a hydrostatic balance, and the air thermometer. Holland's Christian Huygens (1629–1695) used Galileo's law to invent the pendulum clock, also suggested a wave theory of light.

In chemistry, the pioneer was Robert Boyle (1627–1691) whose revolutionary work, *Skeptical Chymist* published in 1661 discarded the sacrosanct Aristotelian theory of the four basic elements (earth, air,

Title page of Religio medici, *Sir Thomas Browne's major work. A confession of Christian faith, it is noted for a stylistic wealth of fancy and wide erudition.*

fire, water), proposed instead an experimental theory of the elements. He thus transformed the remnants of alchemy into scientific chemistry.

MEDICINE. Medical thought in the baroque period followed the same trends that characterized this age: while Galenism still guided most university teaching, many individuals were in revolt against sterile scho-

lasticism and were fired with a desire to penetrate the secrets of nature.

The two principal schools of medical thought were the iatrophysicists and iatrochemists, to which were added the individual approach of the systematists; these schools and individuals were generally at war with one another with all the violence of the age.

The iatrophysicists believed that all the phenomena of life and disease could be explained by the laws of physics; thus locomotion, respiration, digestion, were treated as purely mechanical actions. As the English iatrophysicists were influenced by William Harvey, so were the Italians by Galileo. An extremist of this school was Giorgio Baglivi (1668–1706), who considered the body to be made of "fibers" whose tensions or relaxations caused disease; it was a composite of many machines, teeth like scissors, chest like bellows, heart and vessels like a waterworks.

Leader of the iatrophysical school was the Paduan professor Santorio Santorio (Sanctorius, 1561–1636), father of metabolic physiology, who endlessly experimented on himself to measure what he called "insensible perspiration" during rest, work, digestion, emotion, sexual excitement. This was done on scales large enough to accommodate him, his bed, work table, and all the necessities of his daily living. Like Harvey, Santorio introduced mensuration in experimental physiology.

Another leading iatrophysicist was Alfonso Borelli (1608–1679), who sought to explain in numerical terms the movements of the heart and of respiration. He believed that digestion was a mechanical process, gastric secretion being induced by blood pressure; fevers, pains, convulsions, were caused by defective movements of the "nervous juices."

One of his pupils, Lorenzo Bellini (1643–1704), who taught medicine at Pisa when only 21, published important works on the physiology of the taste organs and the arterial pulse.

Foremost iatrophysicists in England were Archibald Pitcairn (1652–1713), who considered that fever was caused by an acceleration of the blood flow, and William Cole (1635–1716), who used bleeding to diminish the fever-induced tension of body "fibers."

The iatrochemical school, inspired by the nosology of Paracelsus, sought to explain physiologic and medical phenomena in terms of chemical processes. Its apostle was Belgium's Jan-Baptista van Helmont (1577–1644), who believed that each physiologic process was caused by a special ferment (Gas)[5] presided over by a particular archeus or spirit (Blas); all the Blas were controlled by the soul, located in the solar plexus. He advocated a mild therapy of diet, simples, and small doses of chemicals, a reaction against the enormous and often lethal doses of that period.

Many of Helmont's philosophic notions were

stripped off by Leyden professor Franz de la Boê (Sylvius, 1614–1672) who consolidated the iatro-chemical school as a systematic doctrine. He taught that digestion was a chemical fermentation, also propounded many original ideas on the ductless glands, acidosis, the tactile senses.

His most celebrated pupil was Thomas Willis (1621–1675), a Wiltshire farmer's son, whose *Cerebri anatome* (1664) was the most complete and accurate description of the nervous system yet produced.[6] He was also the first to notice the characteristic taste and odor of diabetic urine, gave the first description of

BETTMANN ARCHIVE

Sanctorius' measurements of changing body weight on a balance scale began the study of metabolism.

epidemic typhoid and puerperal fever.

Willis was one of a dozen learned men, several of them physicians, who met regularly to discuss science, medicine, and philosophy, an offshoot of the "Invisible College" as Robert Boyle called the group that met weekly in a tavern. Out of these meetings was born the Royal Society.

Another pupil of Sylvius was Holland's Regnier de Graaf (1641-1672), first to study pancreatic secretion by means of a fistula in a dog. He also published an original account of the testicle and the ovary.

ANATOMY AND PHYSIOLOGY. The brightest star in baroque medicine was undoubtedly William Harvey (1578–1657) whose work on the blood circulation was as great a milestone in medicine as Vesalius' *Fabrica* had been in the preceding century.

Harvey was the son of an alderman in the English fishing port of Folkestone. After taking a bachelor of arts degree at Caius College, Cambridge, he enrolled

BETTMANN ARCHIVE

Title page of Harvey's monumental work in 1628.

in the study of medicine at Padua, then one of the great centers of medical teaching to which flocked young men from all Europe, some threadbare and on foot, some bejeweled and attended by a retinue. They clustered on the steep tiers of the anatomic theatre to hear the lecture and watch the dissection done by Fabricius ab Aquapendente.

Fabricius' teaching on the function of the venous valves particularly interested Harvey; from another great teacher at Padua, Galileo, he acquired an interest in the motion of heavenly bodies and the principles underlying movement.

The circulation of the blood was at that time much discussed: Galen's theory of two vascular systems had been confirmed by dissection; Michael Servetus had described the pulmonary circulation; Realdo Colombo had discovered in animal experiments that

193

blood passed from the right to the left ventricles and changed color in the lungs; Andrea Cesalpino had postulated that the heart and not the liver was the central organ of a system which he was the first to call *circulatio*.[7]

Harvey climbed by a succession of honors to that of royal physician to the Stuart kings James I and Charles I.[8] He was generally indifferent to the great political and religious controversies, practiced very little, spent most of his time in research.

He experimented on some eighty animals, attempted, in the spirit of the time, to measure the rate of blood flow. He calculated that this was 8640 oz. per hour, obviously too much to be produced from food, replenished hour by hour, or contained in the tissues; he thus deduced that blood must flow continuously in a circle through the heart, to arteries, into the veins, and back to the heart; for the first time, mathematic calculation was used in biologic investigation.

His genius lay in not being satisfied to propound a physiologic theory based on mensuration alone; he supported it with scores of animal experiments, using ligation, cannulation, and perfusion. In his Lumleian lecture of 1616, delivered from notes in mixed English and Latin, he declared that the heart was a force pump that drove blood in a constant circulation through the vessels, a statement that then aroused hardly any interest.

The momentous seventy-five-page book, *Exercitatio anatomica de motu cordis et sanguinis in animalibus*, was not published until twelve years later in Frankfurt, a shoddy and hastily printed volume that rent the baroque medical world into two camps as hostile as Protestants and Catholics.

The first attack was launched by one Scottish fledging physician named James Primrose, but the most violent opposition came from the Paris Faculty of Medicine. One fanatically opposed physician was Jean Riolan who proclaimed that if dissection had proved Galen wrong it was because nature had meanwhile changed. Another was Guy Patin, dean of the Faculty, who called Harvey's theory "paradoxical, useless, false, impossible, absurd, and harmful."

To Harvey's defense came eminent physicians and anatomists from Denmark, France, Germany, Holland, and England, many of whom proved his experiments beyond a shadow of doubt; among them were Niels Stensen, Sylvius and Lowrer.

An eminent defender of Harvey's discovery was Descartes, whose treatise on physiology *Traité de l'homme et de la formation du foetus* (1664) stated unequivocally that blood in the body was in a state of perpetual circulation.

Harvey's epoch-making discovery obscured his other original work in embryology, in which he was

deeply interested. He performed innumerable experiments on chick embryos, shared his discoveries with his patient and patron Charles I. In his *Exercitationes de generatione animalium* (1651), he propounded the axiom that all living beings develop from an egg: *omne vivum ex ovo*. Harvey's work in embryology was a logical development of his thinking: he made of embryology *anatomia animata* in time, as he had earlier made of physiology *anatomia animata* in space.

Harvey sided with the Royalists during the Civil War, thereby lost many valuable scientific notes and materials when a mob sacked his London lodgings. When Charles I went to the scaffold in 1649, Harvey retired from the world to a brother's country house, where he died in 1657. His books and household furnishings were donated to the Royal College of Physicians to provide a fund to hire a librarian and establish an annual lecture.

The most important lacuna in Harvey's discovery

Anatomy theatre, Leyden, 1610. Between lectures, it was an informal, fashionable meeting place to chat and gossip.

spermatozoa, striped voluntary muscle, structure of the crystalline lens, besides making innumerable observations on a variety of microorganisms.

The earliest of the brilliant baroque microscopists was Athanasius Kircher (?1602–1680), a Jesuit who was also a mathematician, Orientalist, and musician. He was probably the first to use the microscope to investigate the cause of disease, also the first to propound the doctrine of *contagium animatum* in infection.

The doctrine of spontaneous generation was confuted by Francesco Redi (1626–1697) in a classic experiment demonstrating that maggots did not develop in meat preserved from outside contact. But this brilliant confutation remained valid only for visible creatures, was not applied to microorganisms.

A combination of microscopist and physiologist was Jan Swammerdam (1637–1680), first to describe red blood corpuscles, identify the lymphatic valves. He was ahead of his time in using plethysmographic methods to study the movements of heart, lungs, muscles.

His lifelong friend was Denmark's Niels Stensen (1638-1686), discoverer, while he still was a student, of the excretory duct of the parotid gland and the incisor foramen which bears his name. He investigated lacrimal glands, recognized the muscular nature of the heart, used mathematics to explain muscular contraction.

He and Borelli championed the basic concept of baroque anatomy and physiology, declared that the fundamental elements of the human body's solid elements were not the Galenic humors but fibers or tubular conglomerations of atoms.

So numerous were workers in anatomy and physiology during the Baroque Age that at least one half of the structures in the human body were named after seventeenth century discoverers, the heyday of eponyms: Aselli's pancreas, Graafian follicles, Haversian canals, Glaserian fissure, Pacchionian bodies, Bellini's tubes, antrum of Highmore, circle of Willis, Kerckring's folds, ossicles, valves, Schneiderian membrane, Casserio's fontanelle and ganglion, Peyer's glands and patches, Lower's rings and tubercle, Poupart's ligament, the Wormian bone, Ruysch's membrane, muscle and vein, Spigelian lobe, Ridley's sinus, Riolan's arch, bones, muscles, Tulp's valve, Rivinus' ducts, foramen, gland, membrane, Bartholin's duct and glands, Brunner's glands, Cowper's glands, the Meibomian glands.

Complementing the work of the anatomists and physiologists was that of many distinguished physicists and chemists. Harvey's great discovery was expanded by work on the physiology of respiration: Robert Boyle (1627–1691) showed that air was necessary for life; Robert Hooke in 1667 used bel-

was the terminal link between the arterial and venous circulations; this gap was closed by Marcello Malpighi (1628–1694) three years after Harvey's death.

Malpighi is generally regarded as the founder of histology, the one who established microscopic anatomy, as Vesalius had founded scientific macroscopic anatomy in the previous century. He was the author of many original works in embryology, histology, and physiology of glands, viscera, and pulmonary structures. He was a teacher at Bologna and physician to Pope Innocent XI, a gentle and fair-minded man, one of baroque medicine's most sympathetic figures. The work of Malpighi and other eminent baroque microscopists was made possible by a Delft draper named Anton van Leeuwenhoek (1632–1723), who in his leisure made more than 400 microscopes for which he ground the lenses; many of these were donated to scientific societies.[9]

Van Leeuwenhoek was the first to describe the

lows in a dog's trachea to show that the essential feature of respiration was blood alteration in the lungs; Richard Lower injected dark venous blood into the lungs, deduced that air turned it red;[10] his fellow Cornishman John Mayow completed the demonstration that venous blood turned red by absorbing what he called nitro-aerial spirit of air.

THE SYSTEMATISTS. So engrossed were many leading seventeenth century physicians with the experimental discovery of nature's secrets that medicine's main objective of healing was frequently neglected or left in the hands of mediocre men or outright quacks.

Greatest figure in clinical medicine of that age was Thomas Sydenham (1624–1689), member of a Puritan landed gentry family, who brought medicine back to the principles of Hippocrates.

He studied at Oxford and Montpellier, then fought as a trooper in the Parliamentarian forces during the Civil War. He afterwards received a doctorate in medicine from Cambridge, developed a large and wealthy practice in London.

In the ferment of that age, Sydenham remained completely aloof from raging controversies between iatrophysicists and iatrochemists; he was interested neither in Vesalius nor Harvey, disdained the squabbles between Galenists and anti-Galenists; his favorite books included Hippocrates and Bacon, and he once recommended to Sir Richard Blackmore that he could well learn medicine by reading Cervantes *Don Quixote.*

His simple and common sense theory of medicine

was that the cause of all disease resided in nature and that nature possessed an instinct to cure itself. Therapy consisted of diet, purgatives, discreet bleeding. He advocated fresh air in sickrooms, horseback riding for the tuberculous, cooling measures in smallpox, iron for chlorosis, and an opiate called Sydenham's Drops.

He was one of the first to recognize the therapeutic value of cinchona bark, recently brought from Peru.[11] The rest of his armamentarium consisted of vegetable simples, avoiding the nauseating ingredients of the current pharmacopeia.

Sydenham's acute observation at the bedside, unclouded by pompous verbosity, permitted him to leave lucid clinical descriptions of smallpox, malaria, pneumonia, scarlatina, St. Vitus' dance (Sydenham's chorea), and hysteria. He also left a remarkably vivid account of gout, from which he suffered.[12]

Fabricius ab Aquapendente, Harvey's professor at Padua, interested him in blood movements, fetal anatomy.

He classified diseases as acute (caused by God) and chronic (caused by man himself). His studies on the relationship between geography, weather, and disease made him one of the fathers of epidemiology. His great innovation was the recognition and classification of disease entities or "morbid species" with

Rene Descartes (1596-1650).

syndromes common to a specific disease apart from the individual patient, thus inaugurating specific diagnosis. One of his pupils was Walter Harris (1647–1732), physician to Charles II and William II, author of one of the first books on children's diseases.

The practice of observation in place of vituperative theorizing produced an entirely new school of legal medicine. Pioneer was Italy's Fortunato Fedele whose work published in 1602 dealt with the attestation of virginity, lethal wounds, the jurisprudence of poisoning, hereditary disease. Another landmark was Paolo Sacchia's *Quaestiones medicolegales* in 1621, a treasure of medicolegal case histories. The common problem of infanticide (especially among the poor) was greatly lightened by Swammerdam's discovery that lungs will float if a person was alive when drowned.

Another innovation of the period was the school of systematists concerned with occupational diseases. It was led by Bernardino Ramazzini (1633–1714) who noted the harmful effect of metals, especially mercury, described lead poisoning in painters, the diseases of those who handled antimony, stonemason's and miner's phthisis (silicosis), the ocular disorders of printers.

THE PRACTITIONERS. With few exceptions, seventeenth century universites were unwatered deserts of Galenic doctrine. Physicians emerged with a degree and a head full of antiquated theory, most of them never having seen a patient.

Confronted with disease, the typical seventeenth century practitioner relied on a pompous manner and garbled Latin to impress the patient, on massive purgation (especially by enema), and on radical venesection. The fashionable physician was often a coxcomb wearing the square professional bonnet on an oversize wig, red heels showing below his long robe.[13] Such men were the targets of Molière's bitter satire,[14] although he was himself on good terms with his sensible and kindly physician.

The average London physician's fee was half a guinea (worth some eight times as much today, about $12). A professor of medicine at Cambridge in 1626 received £40 yearly; a popular physician averaged £250. Most remunerative were court posts, where a physician was frequently paid enormous fees for curing a prince or a wealthy nobleman.

William Harvey left an estate worth £20,000 (about $500,000 today). In France, court posts were for sale: Mazarin accepted 30,000 *écus* from one physician; another bought a post for 50,000 livres, sold it to a colleague at more than double.

General practitioners during this period were occasionally admitted to deliveries, previously monopolized by midwives. An important innovation was the invention in 1647 by a member of the Chamberlen family of a curved and fenestrated obstetric forceps, a jealously preserved secret. Outstanding obstetrician of his time was François Mauriceau (1637–1709) whose treatise on the subject remained a classic for many years. Male midwifery in France was vastly advanced when one of Louis XIV's mistresses was delivered by a male physician.

During this century were laid the foundations of

Seventeenth century infants were wrapped in airtight swaddling. Frequent diaper change was thought dangerous.

medicine in America, first in Virginia, which attracted competent European physicians, later in New England. A fully fledged practitioner required a degree from Europe, usually Leyden, Oxford, or Paris, after which he imparted his knowledge to native apprentice physicians.

A distinguishing feature of American medicine was that the apprentice physician did not have his head stuffed full of theory, learned medicine by attending his master at the bedside. Moreover, in the rude conditions of Colonial life the bitter antagonism between physicians and surgeons could not flourish. Physicians' fees were for many years most frequently paid in corn, tobacco, or wampum.

SURGERY. Guy Patin considered surgeons as "a race of extravagant coxcombs who wear mustaches and flourish razors," succinctly expressing the contemptuous attitude of most contemporary physicians.

Surgery was generally at a low ebb during this era. Lithotomy was the most fashionable operation; illustrious practitioners included the French Colot family and Jacques de Beaulieu (1651–1714), a laborer turned Franciscan monk.

Blood transfusion was first described by the Padua professor Giovanni Colle. The French court physician Jean-Baptiste Denis in 1666 transfused blood from a lamb to a patient who had been weakened by phlebotomy; the man improved, then died. Transfusion was subsequently banned by the Paris Faculty of Medicine and by a Papal bull.

German engraving, 1667, of early intravenous transfusion, inserting a blood-filled syringe into a simple cut.

England produced one outstanding surgeon in Richard Wiseman (1622–1684); his *Severall Chirurgical Treatises* (1676) dealt with tumors, ulcers, anal disorders, scrofula, gunshot wounds, fractures, and luxations.

The prestige of surgeons received much needed support in 1686 when Louis XIV's anal fistula, resistant to all local treatment, was healed by surgery. The surgeon received a farm, 300,000 *livres*, was ennobled.

Among other outstanding surgeons of the period were Germany's Wilhelm Fabry, designer of the stick-twisted tourniquet, Italy's Guiseppe Zambeccari, who successfully excised spleen, kidney, gall bladder, and pancreas.

PHARMACOLOGY. The first edition of the London Pharmacopeia in 1618 contained about 1960 remedies, of which 1028 were simples. Remedies included worms, dried vipers, foxes' lungs, oil of ants and wolves.

A generation later the materia medica broadened to include cochineal, antimonial wine, mercurial preparations, the moss from the skull of a victim of violent death. The third edition of 1677 added cinchona bark, digitalis, benzoin, ipecacuanha, jalap, steel tonics, and the impressive *acqua vitae Hibernorium sive usquebaugh*, none other than plain Irish whiskey.[15]

This was the golden age of proprietary remedies and nostrums: Scot's Pills, a violent purgative; Dutch Drops, a mixture of ingredients in turpentine; Carmelite Water, an aromatic cordial. Charles II was reported to have offered thousands of pounds for the formula of Goddard's Drops, said to be made of raw silk. Antimony in various forms was tremendously popular, especially after it allegedly cured Louis XIV.

PUBLIC HEALTH. The health of a populace in this disturbed age was a parochial responsibility: street cleaning and garbage disposal were left to individual communities; water supplies were regularly contaminated by sewage and laundering.

The almost continuous movements of armies plunged this century into some of the most appalling epidemics in history: scurvy was common in northern Europe, the Scandinavian countries, and Germany; malaria killed 40,000 in Italy at the century's beginning, recurred in England in the 1650's. Typhus and typhoid (vaguely termed *peste*) reached a peak during the war in France, Germany, and the Low Countries, reappeared toward the end of the century with great virulence. Smallpox ravaged eastern Europe, killed 1500 in Engand alone in 1650; it traveled with the colonists to the New World. At about this time laryngeal diphtheria (*garrotillo*) spread from Spain to Europe.

Syphilis had ceased to be epidemic in this century, and leprosy had so far diminished that lazar houses in France could be converted into charity hospitals. Dysentery was epidemic in the countries martyred by the Thirty Years' War.

Most devastating was the return of bubonic plague in its severest outbreaks since the fourteenth century's Black Death: in 1628 it carried off half the population of Lyons, one million died in northern Italy in the next two years; the death of 500,000 Venetians in 1630 contributed to the decline of the city's greatness.

Plague spread through Germany and the Netherlands, struck eastern Europe in 1654, and reached a ghastly climax in London's great plague of 1665, when possibly 75,000 died.

Italian physicians pioneered in public health,

among them the Roman clinician and epidemiologist Giovanni Maria Lancisi (1654–1720), who pointed out the dangers of undrained swamps.

Thus closed a fabulous chapter in the history of western civilization; in the work of its philosophers, mathematicians, scientists, and physicians were sown the seeds of many advances that medicine was to make in the next two centuries.

The Baroque Age in art, architecture, and music actually spilled over into the eighteenth century, disregarding the calendar; similarly one of the great physicians of the Age of Enlightenment, Hermann Boerhaave, struck his roots in the seventeenth century. Medical science was to need many generations to assimilate the immensely rich heritage of the Baroque Age.

Fontana di Trevi, Rome, Italy.

BAROQUE SKETCHBOOK

Still cherished in Europe are the baroque churches, palaces, and gardens that testify to one of the

greatest periods in art. The vast spatial sense of luxurious architecture, intricate and exaggerated orna-

L'Opera, Paris, France.

mentation, and the pictorial effects characteristic of seventeenth century style are more strongly respected as the time gap increases and contemporary architecture concentrates on the streamlined effects of glass and steel.

New York artist Frank di Gioia has captured the rhythm, spirit, and mystery of the baroque with the excitement of a man who stands in wonder at the gate of a golden world, even though he may not enter.

Goya's Pantheon, San Antonio de la Florida, Madrid, Spain.

Literary soirée at the home of Denis Diderot. Painting by Meissonier (1879). Collection Baron de Rothschild.

X

Stars and Glowworms

O N one side of the heaving quicksilver strip of channel that separated her from England, eighteenth-century France was, first, a turbulent stage for the epic drama of the Revolution and, later, the horizon over which the historic career of Napoleon rose like a blazing meteor only to fall in the end like a burnt-out rocket. While the lamps of the Enlightenment illumined the royal courts and later the people's courts in France, Cossack swords were carving out the growing might of Russia. The eighteenth century was, like the ninth century (the time of Charlemagne), a century eminently *European* and not merely a period in which isolated nationalities prevailed. The French monarchy tumbled, with the walls of the Bastille, in a blood bath in which a number of physicians played a part, among them Marat, the rabid revolutionary—"physician of the incurable" and director of *L'Ami du Peuple,* the newspaper of the Revolution—and Dr. Guillotin, who bequeathed to posterity the huge bloody scalpel of "mercy"—the *louisette* or guillotine—that he invented with his colleague Dr. Louis.

The eighteenth century was bathed in the light shed by the new ideas of the Enlightenment—the triumph of reason; philosophical optimism; the quest for complete happiness; the scientific spirit; philanthropy; satiric writing—formulated by the ruling classes and the courtiers in power. This ideology, herald of the French Revolution and Liberalism, slowly emerged during the critical years of the century, from 1721, when Montesquieu published his *Lettres Persanes,* to 1780, when, after thirty years of labor, the *Encyclopédie* was completed. It is impossible to appreciate the spirit of medicine in the Enlightenment without at least a glance into the depths of this French encyclopedia, in which the image of the ideas that piloted its preparation is reflected.

Revolutionary in this encyclopedia was the alphabetic classification for the first time in a *printed* work of what eighteenth-century man knew. Until then all knowledge had been entrusted to memory, with the consequent chaos. A dictionary of scientific and technological subjects, between whose lines, however, flitted a political purpose, the *Encyclopédie* took its philosophical inspiration from Cartesianism, the empiricism of the physician-philosopher Locke, Newton's ideas on physics, Voltaire's rationalistic belief in knowledge, and Rousseau's enthusiasm for the sovereignty of the people. But its principal inspirational strength—which to a certain degree gives us the key to the philosophy of medical learning in this century—lay in Diderot's words: *"Hâtons-nous de rendre notre philosophie populaire"* ("Let us hasten to bring our philosophy to the people").

Because of this spirit, the true Encyclopedist was not a genuine investigator, since he thought he already knew practically everything, and his concern was rather to spread swiftly his knowledge among the people. The real creators of the science of the Enlightenment were not the active Encyclopedists but a minority of fertile minds who were concerned more with ferreting out the secrets of nature than with compiling dictionaries of their knowledge. But the *Encyclopédie* exerted a transcendental influence.

As the enlightened despotism of the courts was replaced by the historic rise of a cultured *bourgeoisie* and popular sovereignty, knowledge became democratized. Greater concern with public health caused a fall in mortality and a rise in population, and the cultural level also rose, thanks to two new foci for debate, polemics, and the exchange of ideas —namely, scientific meetings in the academies and popular gatherings in the cafés.

A typical example of the influence of the *Encyclopédie* on medicine was the advance of surgery, since the *Encyclopédie's* accent on the manual and mechanical arts enhanced the social status of the surgeon. Another example was the growth of scientific interest in botany, cultivated by many physicians, which paralleled Rousseau's call for man to return to nature, and the renaming, during the French Revolution, of the months of the year with natural names such as might have come out of one of Vergil's *Eclogues.*

Enlightenment art reached an early peak in that perfumed, garden-girt marble coffer that housed the court at Versailles, symbol of autocratic power. There, Madame de Pompadour, as expert on the royal couch as she was at the diplomatic table, sponsored an art that, through the brilliant brush of Boucher, glorified the feminine domination of the period. Ceramics, hangings, tapestries, and furniture already showed that the violence of baroque art was being tamed, leaving but a mere caged beast behind the golden bars of the rococo.

Like her predecessor, Madame du Barry stimulated the Arcadian and voluptuous art of Fragonard, who, with Watteau and his *fêtes champêtres,* left us a naïve, fairy-tale vision of the courtly world of the period, a sensual world beneath whose silks and satins throbbed the feline cruelty of professional seducers, exemplified in the novel by Pierre Choderlos de Laclos, *Les Liaisons dangereuses,* which enacted in literature the same erotic marathon that Casanova, in the same century, ran in real life. The whole of this art finally succumbed to the impact of Diderot's rhapsodies on feeling and Rousseau's return to nature, and was replaced by the naturalistic art of Chardin and the stoic and virtuous classic art of David, the art dictator of France, who restored the dignity of the man-in-the-street and social morality, becoming the artistic herald of the French Revolution.

This Europe, where fresh ideas were fermenting like new wine, exported its Encyclopedist tenets to North America, where the champion of the new ideology was the worthy and talented printer, Benjamin Franklin. The Encyclopedist school of thought was the great ideological trend behind the political forces that after the War of Independence gave birth to the United States.

Inspired by the concept of man as a rational animal endowed with the faculty to create and to attain, through intuition, reason, and experiment, a knowledge of the reality of nature, great systems of medical philosophy and speculative doctrines sprang up. Within this framework the physician developed his new concept of disease.

The faith of d'Alembert and Voltaire in reason, the faith of Rousseau and Diderot in feeling and sensation, and the faith of Buffon in the observation of nature, inspired fresh medical achievements. While in politics the two great characteristics of the age were enlightened despotism as a means of government for a nation and balance of power as a measure of international coexistence in Europe, in medicine, along with the philosophical "despotism" of a few great isolated physicians, there prevailed a conceptual balance between the various systems and doctrines of the age, which encouraged stabilization in medical thought. In this eighteenth century world, the sky glittered with both dazzling stars and mere glowworms.

The natural sciences—biology with Linnaeus, astronomy with Laplace—advanced under the impulsion of the new ideas. Physics adopted the rational mechanics of Euler and Watt. A new wondrous physical force called electricity, which had one day convulsed the frogs' legs that Galvani was preparing for his wife Lucia, revolutionized the world as well as the literature and poetry of the age. Poets and writers spoke of "electrifying" ideas, of the "spark" and "current" of love. A group of talented chemists, including Priestley and Scheele, the discoverers of oxygen, and Lavoisier (Lavoisier, who discovered the similarity between combustion and hematosis yet whose head rolled at the foot of the guillotine because, as they said, "The Revolution has no need for savants!") initiated modern chemistry.

One of the most famous medical systems then current was *animism,* created by two friends who later become irreconcilable enemies: the brilliant, magnetic Friedrich Hoffmann, who revived the Methodism of Themison, distinguished himself in medical chemistry, and held that the force of the vital principle, or ether, was transmitted through the nerves to the organic "fibers," any disturbance in which caused "atony" or "hypertonia"; and the surly, taciturn George Stahl, an adherent of expectant therapy, whose animism, a Christian version of the Hippocratic system, made him the herald of vitalism.

The second system, *vitalism,* which maintained that life was a property of living matter, reached its peak with Théophile de Bordeu, pioneer in endocrinology, Barthez, and Philippe Pinel (who perhaps should be acclaimed more as a classifier of diseases than as a psychiatrist), and was resurrected later by Bichat and Laënnec. Its exponent in Scotland was William Cullen, whose "neuropathology" claimed that the nervous "tone" of the solid parts was the supreme property of life, disease being caused by

"Masked Ball" by Pietro Longhi whose career was devoted to picturing the amusements of eighteenth century Venetian life.

changes of this into "spasm" or "atony." He formulated the concept of lesion of sensitivity and movement without inflammation of the organs (equivalent to our current concept of neurosis). This system was opposed by the Scotsman, John Brown, a roistering cleric, who held that life depended upon excitability, which mobilized organic energy, and disease was caused by excessive or deficient—stenhias and asthenias—excitability and should be treated by the drastic *contraria contrariis.* It has been said that the Brunonian system destroyed more lives than the French Revolution itself. The National Convention of the Revolution approved this Brunonian system, which was to be modified in Germany by Reid and by Goethe's physician, Hufeland.

Above all these speculative systems towered the great figure of Herman Boerhaave, the "Batavian Hippocrates," who in a twelve-bed hospital taught medicine to half the physicians of Europe. Boerhaave originated bedside instruction and the comparative study of clinical case histories, diagnosis, and autopsy. He was so beloved by his fellow countrymen that on one occasion, when he recovered from a severe attack of gout, bells were rung and the whole city of Leiden was lit up with torches.

The utilitarian "mechanical" spirit of the age spurred progress in comparative, topographical, and surgical anatomy, which advanced from Fallopius' "texture" to Bichat's "tissue." Outstanding was the *anatomia animata* of Morgagni, who, in his five volume magnum opus, published in his eighties and containing seventy letters to a young friend (medical knowledge in those days was diffused by letters in default of periodicals), left a veritable gallery of the dead, a collection of autopsies of princesses, prostitutes, bishops, and bandits. Morgagni showed that every disease had its seat in *a particular organ*, and his dynamic pathology contrasted sharply with the still prevalent static anatomy. Other leading lights in this field were the Monros, Gimbernat, Scarpa, and Winslow.

Physiology advanced with the Swiss titan Albrecht von Haller, poet and polyglot, who left 2000 articles, 14,000 letters (despite his Catholicism, he corresponded with atheists like Voltaire and libertines like Casanova), and a mountain of papers on medicine, religion, philosophy, and botany. He held that irritability was a property of the muscles; sensibility, a quality of the nerves; and life, a specific property of living matter.

Other shining lights in physiology were the Abbé Lazzaro Spallanzani, who, with cloth bags and perforated wooden tubes filled with food that he himself swallowed, proved that digestion was not simply putrefaction; and the Reverend Stephen Hales, who studied arterial pressure by introducing glass tubes into the arteries of horses. Embryology—physiology in time—advanced when its modern founder, Caspar Friedrich Wolff, demonstrated that the organs are not preformed but *progressively* differentiated, which earned him scientific ostracism and led him to voluntary exile in Russia under the generous protection of Catherine the Great.

The heritage of Leiden passed to the Old Vienna school, founded by Gerhard van Swieten and continued by Anton de Haen, to the Edinburgh and English schools. In music-loving Vienna, Leopold Auenbrugger, musician and physician, copying his father, a vintner whom he saw tap his wine casks to gauge their contents, tapped his patients' chest to listen to their sounds. This discovery, unrecognized in Auenbrugger's lifetime, was reintroduced and championed in France by Napoleon's physician, Corvisart, who—despite his rejection by the Necker Hospital for refusing to wear the wig *de rigueur*—eventually became director of La Charité. Auenbrugger's discovery, a "musicalization" of the sounds of human diseases, reflected the sensualism of some of the Encyclopedists and the musical atmosphere of Vienna.

Specialties made progress, particularly in pediatrics, spurred by the interest in children aroused by the writings of Rousseau and Pestalozzi. Public health advanced with Johann Peter Frank, advisor to emperors, whose idea of a "health police" to protect the people's health (even supervising the closing time of dance halls) made him the father of modern social hygiene. In psychiatry, Pinel freed mental patients at the Bicêtre from their fetters, championed the rights of the mentally ill at the National Assembly, and made diagnosis an "exact" science based on a Linnaean type of classification of diseases.

The leading lights in England were Mead, Huxham, Pitcairn, and various other nosographers, while Scotland shone with the Monros, Bell, the Hunter brothers (world leaders in surgery), and Cullen. Heberden during this period wrote his classic account of angina pectoris, and Withering rifled an old wives' rustic folklore for the secret of the foxglove (digitalis) in treating dropsy.

Therapy was traditional, with a fashion for clysters administered beneath the skirt to the beautiful court favorites in the royal boxes during plays and concerts. Phlebotomy degenerated into blood-sucking vampirism, while surgery progressed with the separation of surgeons from barbers.

While the heavens of the Enlightenment Age glittered with the dazzling stars of medicine, on earth glowworms too gleamed. The Viennese Franz Anton Mesmer, inventor of mesmerism, clad in a purple robe and surrounded by foppish assistants (soon to be beheaded in the Revolution), mobilized the "magnetic fluid of the universe" onto his hysterical female clients with a magic wand and to the accompaniment of sweet music. The German Samuel Hahnemann held that diseases were of "natural classes" and treated them with drugs, in infinitesimally small doses, that caused mild forms of similar diseases, thus inventing homeopathy. Quacks and charlatans flourished, such as the fabulous Venetian Giovanni Jacopo Casanova, Cagliostro, the Comte de St. Germain, and the Scotsman James Graham, whose Temple of Health featured an electrified "celestial bed" for the connubial use of love-bitten couples.

The atrocious epidemics that scourged Europe—smallpox alone killed sixty million people—compelled fashionable ladies to insert in their powdered wigs sponges soaked in honey and vinegar to attract and confine lice. And then, on a memorable day for medicine, a country doctor, Edward Jenner, whose blue topcoat and silver spurs were well known to the local villagers, inoculated pus from a dairymaid with cowpox into a small boy, who later successfully withstood a smallpox inoculation. Thus Jenner's merciful vaccination replaced variolization.

The discovery of vaccination led to a glorious page in the history of medicine, when the Spaniard Francisco Javier de Balmis journeyed around the world with twenty-two children, in whose arms he kept the vaccine alive by passing it from one to the other, and vaccinated hundreds of thousands of people around the globe. Balmis was assisted in South America by his heroic colleague and martyr to medicine, Francisco Salvany, who lost a hand and an eye and finally died of tuberculosis in Bolivia, a victim to this epic campaign. Facing terrible dangers, the antagonism of his fellow men, and a hostile nature, Balmis took the children carrying the vaccine to the Caribbean, Mexico, the Philippines, Canton, and Macao, thus making the first and only tour around the world accomplished by a physician on a heroic errand of mercy.

In the United States, life in the colonies was settling down. Physicians traveled to England and Holland to study. Great medical figures (Cadwalader, Shippen, Morgan, Benjamin Rush) shone brilliantly at the same time that Benjamin Franklin promoted the ideas of the French Encyclopedists, which, a quarter of a century after Rousseau had expounded them in his *Social Contract*, were finally incorporated into the United States Constitution. Then began the memorable westward trek across the vast, green prairies, where the Sioux and the buffalo reigned, opening up new horizons to American medicine, then still struggling with the problems imposed by its historical youth.

But even before the eighteenth century came to a close, the bells of history were already tolling the knell of Enlightenment encyclopedism in Europe. The romantic seed scattered by Rousseau was germinating, while in another direction naturalism was flowering with renewed impetus. By the end of that century, Germany was already on the road to romanticism, whose philosophical idealism was to guide the first half of the nineteenth century, just as the second half was to be dominated by the positivism and naturalism of France and England. But in the first hour of the new dawn, there still lingered the light shed by the ideas of the sun-men of the Age of Enlightenment, a strong brilliant light that made the light of the glowworms fade.

F.M.I.

CULVER

Sir William Herschel's 40-foot telescope built in 1789; he studied planet rotation, catalogued over 800 double stars; in 1781 he discovered the planet Uranus.

X
MEDICINE
IN THE ENLIGHTENMENT

Europe in the eighteenth century formed the cradle of a vast intellectual revolution that blew away the remnants of feudal anarchy and medieval dogmatism.

In this Age of Enlightenment, also sometimes called the Age of Reason, men came to believe that, by applying the unvarying laws of nature to politics, philosophy, ethics, religion, and economics, they could build the perfect society.

The leaders of this age were supremely optimistic, sturdily confident in human progress, and imbued with a broad humanitarianism in place of the cruel passions of the preceding century. The universe was looked upon as a gigantic machine; all that was required was to discover the immutable laws that governed its operation.

This was the era that deified science, seeking to reduce all intellectual and moral processes to precise Newtonian principles of matter, motion, space, time, force. In doing, many gifted men discovered basic data in chemistry and physics that indirectly helped the progress of medicine.

THE SETTING. The first three quarters of the century were lived under the political system of absolutism, based on the divine right of kings, which invested a monarch with sovereignty, supported by the aristocracy and the Church.

The principal preoccupation of many thinkers of that period was to evolve a philosophy of politics that would be universal and could be deduced by reason from a few simple general principles. Several monarchs who were called "enlightened" embraced some of these principles, but many others tried to suppress them and to enforce rigid absolutism. These

were the basic political stresses that led to the American and French Revolutions, and eventually toppled most of the *ancien régime* monarchies from their thrones.

The most significant change in European politics was the rise of Russia, which until the rule of Peter the Great had little part in the great political clashes between England, France, Austria, and Spain. Having built a "window into Europe" at St. Petersburg and developed a powerful army and navy, Peter I and his successors (notably Catherine II) henceforth played a powerful role in the fate of Europe. Conversely, the eighteenth century saw the steady disintegration of the Ottoman Empire which later became known as the Sick Man of Europe.

The principal conflicts in Europe revolved around dynastic and colonial rivalries; monarchs forged alliances to further their immediate aspirations, cynically ready to break pacts when conditions changed. International diplomacy was based on untiring court intrigue and a vast system of espionage and bribery. The large professional armies and navies were used as chessmen in a game of balance of power politics; a decisive factor was the development of a new type of army by the rising state of Prussia.

THE LIFE. In eighteenth century Europe life was still predominantly rural, although by 1750 England began to develop the urban centers of the industrial revolution. Ways of life were divided into separate patterns: the court aristocracy, landed gentry, bourgeoisie, peasants, artisans, unskilled laborers. Each section of society had its own way of dressing and living, often its own dialects.

The fundamental difference between the English

Facing page: *Albrecht von Haller, called the Great, painting plants and flowers from nature. Besides a prodigious career as botanist, lexicographer, physiologist, physician, teacher and philosopher, Haller was a poet who combined Christian revelation with love of nature. Painted by Federico Castellon.*

and continental society was that the English aristocracy was predominantly landed, and the increasingly prosperous merchants bought estates; both classes tended to invest money in agriculture and improve their land by modern methods of farming; this kept them in close contact with yeomen and farm workers.[1] On the continent the aristocracy was expected to spend lavishly at court or serve in luxurious regiments, thereby draining estate revenues and creating a deep rift between landowners and their peasants.

England further differed from its neighbors by launching vast changes in industry, notably in textiles. The export of cotton goods increased tenfold between 1765 and 1780; the new process of puddling greatly stimulated the production of iron; the introduction of steam engines into mining around 1770 enormously extended England's production of coal.

Rural England steadily emerged from medieval squalor, building farmhouses in stone and brick, planting orchards, draining swamps. Until the end of the century, when the Napoleonic wars caused hardship, England's rural population lived more comfortably and abundantly than its opposite numbers across the Channel.

Among the aristocracy and the landed gentry the passion of both sexes was gambling: immense sums (and often estates) exchanged hands over cards and dice. Before tea and coffee came into general use, great quantities of ale and wine were drunk in town and country. In England between 1720 and 1750 the working class in the towns was able to procure extremely cheap gin, leading to the degrading misery portrayed by Hogarth.

All gentlemen wore swords and dueling went on incessantly throughout most of the century. Fox hunting in England and stag hunting on the continent were two favorite sports of the gentry; the sport of the peasantry continued to be what it had been since time immemorial, poaching for game.

THE CULTURE. Architects were mostly inspired by classic models, produced such structures as the royal palace in Madrid and the Panthéon in Paris. English builders developed the elegant simplicity of the Georgian style, which was transplanted to the American colonies.

This was the golden age of landscaping, vast sums being spent on formal gardens, classic-style grottoes, fountains, statues, yew hedges clipped into fantastic shapes; in England this fashion gradually gave way to the untamed garden of rolling lawns and luxurious trees.

Studied elegance in dress and home furnishings was the hallmark of polite society; a profusion of crystal chandeliers and mirrors multiplied the light of wax candles. Elegant furniture was made in the new more graceful rococo style; porcelain factories produced the wares of Wedgwood, Sèvres, Dresden. This period also saw a great extension in the craftsmanship of jewelry and in clock and watchmaking.

Literature, art, and music in this century fell into two quite separate patterns: in the first half they were largely inspired by the age's passion for classicism; in the closing decades were sown the seeds of romanticism.

The extension of education among the middle classes produced a new reading public that demanded a standardized vernacular prose style; the

Hôtel de Ville, Bordeaux

vigorous prose of John Dryden, and later the polished style of Joseph Addison, were regarded as the models by most writers in England. The aristocracy and wealthy bourgeoisie on both sides of the Channel became addicted to writing, producing volumes of correspondence and a plethora of memoirs.[2]

The romantic trend in literature began around the middle of the century, inspired by Jean-Jacques Rousseau's idealized portrayal of the "noble savage" (mostly the American Indian). A landmark in romanticism was the publication in 1774 of Johann Wolfgang von Goethe's *The Sorrows of Young Werther*, an autobiographic novel based on his unhappy love for Charlotte Buff; the work touched off a worldwide wave of morbid sensitivity and several suicides of lovelorn swains.

The last quarter of the century also saw the birth of the *Sturm und Drang* (Storm and Stress) movement, a passionate revolt against the cold classicism of preceding decades, expressed in a rage for lurid deeds performed in medieval settings.[3]

Painters were torn between depicting the gaiety

THE PHILOSOPHERS. The Age of Enlightenment was *par excellence* the age of philosophers, those who attempted to reason out man's relations to the state, and man's relations with other men, following in the footsteps of Descartes, Spinoza, Leibniz, and philosopher-physician Locke in the previous century.

The basic principles of most of the thinkers in the enlightenment was a high regard for the natural rights of man, a hatred of injustice and all irrational attacks on the individual; against these principles they examined all traditions and institutions.

The crucible of French philosophic speculation

The rococo style that flourished in France combined grace and elegance with ornaments.

and frivolity of polite society, as did Antoine Watteau in France, and the mordant satires on contemporary life of William Hogarth and Spain's Francisco Goya.

In harmony with the spirit of the age, music was intellectual, written by composers who were preoccupied with the mathematic elegance of polyphony and counterpoint. Symphonic music was dominated by Germans or Austrians;[4] opera was the prerogative of Italians.

was the monumental *Encyclopédie* (28 volumes) around which were grouped the brilliant intellects that expressed the skepticism and rationalism of the century: Baron de Montesquieu, whose work *l'Esprit des Lois* (1748) profoundly influenced the philosophy of the French Revolution; Jean le Rond d'Alembert, author of the encyclopedia's preamble in which he expressed the group's views on tolerance and the laws of nature; François-Marie Arouet (Voltaire) whose thousands of pamphlets and letters sowed the new ideas throughout Europe;[5] Jean-Jacques Rousseau, ardent advocate of the natural laws governing mankind; Denis Diderot, the indefatigable editor of the immense work and a prolific propagator of the enlightened philosophy.

The epitome of the age's skepticism was Scotland's philosopher David Hume (1711–1776) who had the temerity to assert that the human mind was incapable of knowing anything, material or spiritual, except through sense impressions; he unleashed bitter disputes with his contention that no universal principles of reason were valid.

He was answered by Germany's Immanuel Kant with his transcendental philosophy which contended that what is called nature is not the ultimately real world but only a world of human consciousness; thus the principles of human reason are universally valid because what cannot conform to these principles cannot enter human experience.

Paralleling the growth of new political and social concepts was the rise of a new rationalistic theology, a natural religion (deism) that claimed that God was merely the First Cause that started the universal machine, helpless thereafter to interfere with its workings; the deists also strongly rejected revelation and miracles as irrational.

Deism was encouraged by the growth of Freemasonry, an organization that united a number of secret societies composed largely of enlightened persons. By the end of the eighteenth century there were thousands of lodges in the English-speaking world and the movement had spread throughout Europe. Deist doctrines also led quite naturally to the rise of atheism, which became most popular among the enlightened aristocracy.

Among humbler folk the reaction to the established church forms came in the form of Pietism in Germany, the Moravian Brethren who preached pious living and divine love, the Society of Friends (Quakers), and especially in John Wesley's Methodism (founded 1744), which exerted an enormous influence in England and the American colonies.

THE SCIENTISTS. Science in the Age of Reason was still relatively simple, and it was possible for many gifted amateurs with makeshift laboratories to make basic discoveries in chemistry and physics. They were enabled to exchange data through the numerous scientific societies and clubs founded in the eighteenth century.

A leading astronomer of the age was Sir William Herschel (1738–1822), who, with the aid of his sister Caroline, discovered the planet Uranus, catalogued 800 double stars and 2500 nebulae, conceived the theory of solar systems moving through space.

Other leading contributors to astronomy were Edmund Halley, who astounded his contemporaries by actually calculating the orbital movement of the comet that now bears his name; Jean Laplace, who advanced the nebular hypothesis which made the solar system the product of whirling fiery gases; James Bradley, who discovered that the motion of light is deflected by the movements of the universe.

In botany and zoology the Swedish physician Karl von Linné (1707–1778), known as Linnaeus, completed an epochal taxonomy, or classification of biologic data by the now universal binomial method. In his *System of Nature* he placed man with apes, lemurs, and bats in the order of primates, subdivided human races according to color and characteristics.

The age's passionate interest in natural history cul-

"The Lunatic Asylum" by Goya. His satiric art reflects a sensitive reaction to a world given over to corruption.

minated in an encyclopedic compilation of all known animal life by French zoologist Comte de Buffon (1707-1788). His fifteen volume *Natural History* dated creation at about 60,000 years earlier, calculated the age of the earth at 2,993,280 years. His work gave new meaning to the biologic doctrine of evolution.

The physicists of this era were mostly interested in applying mathematic laws to natural phenomena and dynamics. Three types of thermometers were invented between 1714 and 1742,[6] achromatic lenses greatly improved telescopes, sound vibrations were calculated, Leonhard Euler made many notable contributions to hydrodynamics and optics and James Watt perfected the steam engine.

The phenomenon that excited the century most of all was electricity. Static electricity was known to the ancients, and the method of generating it by friction was developed in the Baroque Age. The outstanding

Lavoisier as hydrogen); Joseph Priestley correctly showed that oxygen was required in respiration.

The outstanding chemist of the period was France's Antoine-Laurent de Lavoisier (1743–1794) who demonstrated the process of combustion and established that combustion and respiration were identical forms of oxidation, thereby showing that living processes had a chemical basis.[7]

THE INVESTIGATORS. Following the trail blazed by William Harvey in the preceding century, the eighteenth century produced several brilliant anatomists and physiologists.

The father of pathologic anatomy was Giovanni Battista Morgagni (1682–1771), whose *De sedibus et causis morborum per anatomen indagatis* published in 1761 was a masterpiece of observation of diseased organs compared with normal ones.

Morgagni was for nearly sixty years professor at the University of Padua; his memorable work of 750

Portrait of William Poyntz by Thomas Gainsborough.

Portrait of Giovanni Morgagni engraved by J. Renard.

discovery of 1746 made at Leiden University was that electricity could be "stored in a jar," thus making it available for experiments. In America, Benjamin Franklin's discovery that lightning was an electric spark led to the invention of the lightning rod.

Chemistry was for many decades retarded by the theory that combustion was only possible in the presence of a substance called phlogiston. Charles Cavendish demonstrated that water was composed of oxygen and "inflammable air" (later identified by

pages contains some 500 case histories of necropsy findings. His concept that diseases can occur in one or several organs displaced the ancient humoral notion of a morbid cause. He was the first to describe hepatic cirrhosis, renal insufficiency, and the Adams-Stokes syndrome. His major contribution to the progress of medicine was to correlate clinical symptoms and anatomic lesions, and integrate them into the *species morbosa.*[8]

Wider fields of descriptive anatomy were opened by France's Marie-François Xavier Bichat (1771–

1802) who devoted his life to dissection, vivisection, and necropsy; in one winter he autopsied more than 600 cadavers, living and sleeping in the autopsy hall.

Bichat considered life to be a group of functions that resist death; he described 21 tissues endowed with various properties, considered a tissue to be the basic unit of the living organism and the site of all pathology; his systematic study of tissues earned him the title of one of the fathers of histology and a pioneer in embryology.

The father of modern embryology is generally considered to be Caspar Friedrich Wolff (1733–1794) who revived William Harvey's doctrine of epigenesis, i.e., the gradual building up of parts. In his *Theoria generationis* (1759), he enounced the basic principle of vitalism, that living beings grow impelled by an essential force (*vis essentialis*) and are only restrained by the capacity of organic matter to become solidified.

The first systematic text on pathologic anatomy was published by Matthew Bailie in 1793, correlating postmortem findings with case histories.

The master physiologist of the century, a truly universal man, was Swiss-born Albrecht von Haller (1708–1777), who as a *Wunderkind* produced a Chaldean grammar, a Greek and a Hebrew dictionary, poems, biographies.

At the University of Göttingen he taught all branches of medicine, established botanic gardens aud churches, wrote thousands of scientific papers. He became eminent as a botanist, anatomist, novelist, poet, public health official, founder of an orphan asylum, head of his native canton of Bern. He carried on a gigantic correspondence (some 14,000 letters) with many eminent figures of the enlightenment, ranging from Voltaire to the arch-lover Giovanni Casanova.

Haller's finest work was done on the physiology of the blood vessels and of the nervous system; he established that irritability is a property of muscles, while sensibility is characteristic of nerves; these observations correctly supported the myogenic theory of the heartbeat. He also established the role of bile in the digestion of fat and was a pioneer in the study of angiology and microscopic anatomy.

Haller can be considered a man of the preceding Baroque Age for his cult of God and nature; his rational empiricism and belief in scientific experiment place him in the eighteenth century. His concept of physiology was that of *anatomia animata*, the science of biologic movement.

Another experimenter in the physiology of digestion was René-Antoine de Réaumur (remembered for his thermometer), who used a pet kite to collect gastric juice and demonstrate its solvent effect on food.

This work was extended by an investigator of sin-

Illustration of pellagra (mal de la rosa) *lesions of the shoulder, chest, hands, and feet, from the* Historio natural y médica de el Priscipado de Asturias *of Dr Gaspar Casál.*

gular talent, Lazzaro Spallanzani (1729–1799), whom Empress Maria Theresa installed in the chair of natural history at the University of Pavia. In self-experimentation he swallowed cloth bags containing nutrients, obtained gastric juice by vomiting, demonstrated the dissolution of food by gastric juice in a test tube.

One of Spallanzani's most memorable demonstrations was the experimental refutation of the Needham doctrine of spontaneous generation of microorganisms in putrefying meat. He was also a pioneer in experimental morphology, succeeded in producing regeneration of the heads, tails, and limbs of tadpoles and earthworms.

The first experimental measurement of blood circulation was done by English clergyman Stephen Hales; using a glass tube inserted into a horse's artery, he was able to produce quantitative estimates of blood pressure, cardiac capacity, velocity of the circulation.

On a summer's day in 1786 Italian physician Luigi Galvani noticed muscular spasms in frogs' legs suspended by copper hooks from an iron bar, thereby

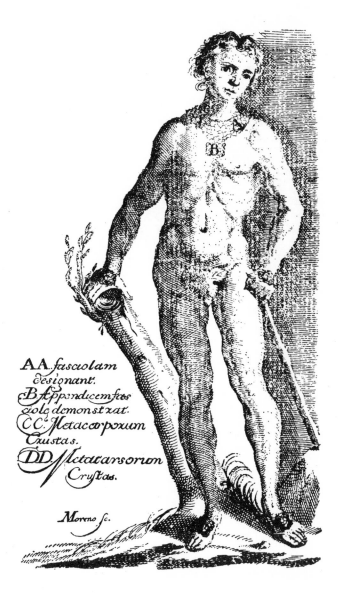

AA *fasciolam designant.*
B *Appendicem fasciole demonstrat.*
CC. *Metacarporum Crustas.*
DD *Metatarsorum Crustas.*

Moreno sc.

launching a whole new field of electrophysiology, extended before the end of the century by Count Alessandro Volta.[9]

THE TEACHER. In Leiden University and its hospital, many of the distinguished eigtheenth century European and American physicians learned their medicine from gentle, kindly Hermann Boerhaave (1668–1738), teacher and clinician, whose Hippocratic influence was spread by his pupils from Edinburgh to Vienna.

He was born near Leiden and studied at its university; in 1701 he obtained the chair of theoretical medicine, which included teaching chemistry, botany, and physics. His principal influence on medicine was in reviving the Hippocratic method of approaching clinical problems, following in the wake of Thomas Sydenham in the previous century.

In an era of theoretic discussions about medical systems, Boerhaave taught the simple truth that the principal aim of medicine is to cure the patient. His observations were made not from textbooks but at the bedside. Although he embraced the many erroneous theories of that time about diseases of the solid parts and those of the supposed humors, his practical approach to each patient made him a giant in clinical medicine.

Boerhaave's practice became legendary: his consulting room was thronged from early morning; ministers of state waited for him at the lecture theatre door (even Tsar Peter the Great). Severe attacks of gout obliged him at sixty-one to give up his professorships of chemistry and botany but he continued in practice and teaching, corresponded actively with former pupils throughout Europe until his death at seventy of cardiac insufficiency.[10]

Boerhaave was neither discoverer nor innovator; but he was a great teacher who integrated the medical knowledge of the Baroque Age with that of the Age of Enlightenment. His principal contributions to medical literature were *Institutiones medicae in usus annuae exercitationis domesticos digestae* (1708), a simple concise physiology text, and *Aphorismi de cognoscendis et curandis morbis in usum doctrinae medicae* (1709), which embodies his clinical observations; these two slender works were distributed throughout Europe in numerous editions and translated into many languages, including Arabic.

THE SCHOOLS. In 1745 Maria Theresa summoned Gerhard van Swieten[11] (1700–1772) from Leiden to serve as her personal physician, to reorganize medical teaching at the university, and to revitalize Austrian medicine. As Boerhaave's disciple, van Swieten remodeled the university on the lines of Leiden, placed it under state control.

He made Vienna a major center of clinical instruction, imported Dutch clinicians, established a small hospital similar to Boerhaave's, an herb garden and a laboratory, encouraged anatomic dissection; he in fact created what came to be called the Old Vienna School.

He was aided by compatriot Anton de Haen (1704–1776), another pupil of Boerhaave, who expanded the function of the hospital from hospice-chapel to a center of medical research and instruction; he discovered that continual observation of a patient in hospital isolation could expedite the study of a disease; he also introduced the study of thermometry in his clinical case histories.

An immortal member of the Old Vienna School was Joseph Leopold Auenbrugger (1722–1809) of the Spanish Hospital in Vienna, who discovered experimentally that the thorax gives off different sounds on percussion according to the condition inside. In his *Inventum novum* (1761) he described this revolutionary method of auscultation, but it was generally rejected until one year before his death when Baron Corvisart demonstrated its value.

The Edinburgh school of medicine, which throughout the century trained many of the leading American physicians, became internationally famous in the eighteenth century through the teaching of anatomy by the three Alexander Monros, a remarkable dynasty that held the chair of anatomy for 126 years.[12]

British schools of clinical medicine produced John Huxham, an advocate of cinchona tincture and the use of a vegetable diet in scurvy; James Lind whose work *Treatise of the Scurvy* (1753) persuaded the Royal Navy to distribute lemons and limes in its ships;[13] and William Heberden who published the first scientific description of angina pectoris and gave it its name.

William Withering (1741–1799) discovered that some Shropshire farmers were remarkably successful in treating dropsy with foxglove (*Digitalis purpurea*); he introduced digitalis into the materia medica, also demonstrated that dropsy could be due to cardiac weakness; his classic work was *Account of the Fox-glove*, published in 1785.

THE SYSTEMS. In this Age of Reason physicians were tempted to erect medico-philosophic systems to classify diseases and their cure along rational lines.

Propounded by the Bavarian chemist and physician Georg Ernst Stahl (1660–1734) under the name of "animism" was the theory that life is the activity of the soul (*anima*), disease the consequence of the soul's misdirection. A pathologic condition was either tonus or plethora, for which he prescribed copious bleeding and balsamic pills to stimulate the curative movement of the anima; he also believed in secret remedies as having a beneficial effect by suggestion.

A rival animist, Prussia's Friedrich Hoffmann (1660–1742), described the vital principle as ether-

---

Following pages: *Dr. Hermann Boerhaave, most renowned clinician and teacher of his time, lecturing from a patient's bedside while his students follow his observations made from direct examination of the patient. Neither discoverer nor innovator, but a master teacher, Boerhaave left noteworthy descriptions of a fatty tumor of the mediastinum, ruptured esophagus, heat stroke. Painted by Federico Castellon.*

Georg Ernst Stahl (1660-1734), physician-chemist, wrote Theoria medica vera, *advanced the system of animism, considered life as activity of the soul, disease as misdirection of the soul.*

like, communicated to the fibers via the nerves; disease was the result of an alteration in its nature; acute diseases were spasmodic, chronic ones were atonic; they could be treated with either sedative or stimulant medicine.

A leading proponent of vitalism in France was Théophile de Bordeu (1722–1776) who theorized that each organ contributes a mysterious substance to the blood and that on these secretions depends the body's integration, a theory that brought him singularly close to endocrinology.

Brilliant vitalist of the Edinburgh school was William Cullen (1710–1790) who described the property of life as due to a nerve fluid which established the tone of the body's solid parts; changes in this tone caused either spasm or atony, and thus disease.

Most sensational of the systems was the invention of John Brown (1735–1788), a Scottish parson turned physician, who held that the property of life was its excitability, and that diseases were either sthenic or asthenic according to the degree of excitement. Treatment was then either stimulative with alcohol,

or sedative with laudanum. His system became the rage in Italy, led to brawls in German universities, was taken up by Benjamin Rush in Philadelphia; the therapy was said to have caused more deaths than the French Revolution and the Napoleonic Wars.[14]

THE PHYSICIAN. Quaint theories notwithstanding, the eighteenth century physician was a force in society, a respected scholar, a man of substance. He was elegantly dressed and wigged, usually carried a gold-headed cane.

Physicians lived like gentlemen, engaged in the arts of playing a musical instrument and writing poetry; in the country they enjoyed the life of a squire. Many had fine libraries and were serious scholars in fields other than medicine.

As in the preceding century, physicians engaged in furious pamphleteering, sometimes coming to blows or duels; famous was an aborted duel between Richard Mead and a colleague over the treatment of smallpox; another argument with swords and pistols concerned bilious fever and ended fatally for two physicians.

A successful London practitioner's office fee was generally a guinea, two guineas for a house call, a half guinea for a prescription he might write in the coffeehouse without seeing the patient. An average income was £5000 a year.[15] Prescriptions formed a substantial part of the physician's income; so great was the century's faith in drugs that a large medicine spoon was a normal item in a bride's trousseau.

A physician of repute could hardly fail to become wealthy no matter how humble his origin; if he successfully served royalty he might also gain titles and estates. Many were distinguished by their generosity to the poor, also to younger colleagues, rising statesmen, and literary men.[16] The library and anatomic museum collected by William Hunter in his lifetime, which he bequeathed to Glasgow University, was valued at £100,000. Sir Hans Sloane, first physician to be made a baronet, was a president of the Royal Society; his museum and library later became the nucleus of the present British Museum.[17]

THE SPECIALITIES. Born in this century was the trend toward specialization: cardiology had its germ in the work of Antonio Guiseppe Testa (1764–1814); in Germany, Haller's friend and fellow poet Paul Gottlieb Werlhof (1699–1767) laid the groundwork for hematology with his original description of purpura hemorrhagica.

Cardiac disease won the special attention of two French clinicians: Jean de Senac recognized asthma, orthopnea, edema of the legs, and hemoptysis as symptoms of cardiac ills; Jean Nicholas Corvisart (des Marets) originated the term carditis and was the first to call himself a heart specialist.

A pioneer practitioner and teacher in obstetrics was William Smellie, who, in spite of the vile attacks

Caricature of Scotland's "excitable" Dr. John Brown.

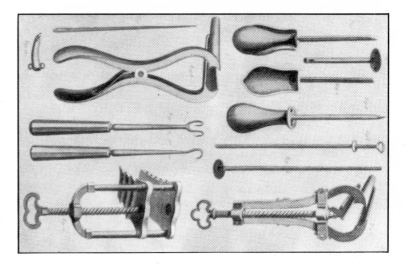

Surgical tools, from Diderot's Encyclopédie, *1763.*

of jealous midwives, demonstrated his art with a leather and bone mannikin. To his house came twenty-three-year-old William Hunter, the elder of the famous brothers, who later produced one of the classic obstetric works, the superbly illustrated *Anatomy of the Human Gravid Uterus.*

Shocking infant mortality rates and the teachings of philosopher Rousseau and pedagogue Pestalozzi sharpened the era's awareness of the medical needs of children; an early work on pediatrics was William Cadogan's *Essay upon Nursing and the Management of Children.* Children's hospitals and foundling homes were opened in London during the century. Eccentric merchant philanthropist Jonas Hanway (the early advocate of the umbrella) urged London parents to send their infants to the country for wet nursing.

Advances in the anatomy and physiology of the eye, stimulated by Leonardo da Vinci's "visual attitude" to anatomy, and in the science of optics were made by many of the century's physicians; combined with the physicists' studies on light and color they made ophthalmology into a scientific specialty;

Jacques Daviel taught the first surgical procedure for cataract extraction. In Vienna, Maria Theresa in 1773 established the first school of ophthalmology on the continent, installed Joseph Barth as its first lecturer.

THE SURGEONS. Surgery during this century was finally able to strike off the shackles that had bound it to barbers and bonesetters; by midcentury the leading universities of England, France, and Germany were offering chairs in surgery; in the next decades surgeons attained a position equal to physicians.

The first to forbid barbers to practice surgery was France, which in 1731 founded the Royal Academy of Surgery; its first president, Jean-Louis Petit (1674–1760), invented the screw tourniquet and developed a procedure for mastoidectomy. His pupil Antoine Louis (1723–1792) wrote an important memoir on the differential signs of murder and suicide; he collaborated with Dr. Joseph-Ignace Guillotin in perfecting the Revolution's effective engine of execution.[18]

An outstanding surgeon in England was William Cheselden (1688-1752), also a skilled architect who drew the plans for Surgeon's Hall in London; one of the era's most rapid operators, he once performed a perineal lithotomy in 54 seconds.

His most gifted pupil was John Hunter (1728–1793), one of the century's giants who raised surgery from a technique to a science, firmly based on physiology and pathology.

Hunter was the youngest of a poor Scottish family; when he came to London he dissolutely frequented taverns and theatres. He was taken in hand by his brother William and taught dissection; he soon grew into a skillful surgeon and an ardent investigator.

He was a restless experimenter in pathologic anatomy, comparative physiology, and morphology. He described shock, phlebitis, pyemia, made valuable studies of inflammation, gunshot wounds, defects of the blood vessels. He inoculated himself with lues and differentiated between the hard (Hunterian) chancre and the chancroid ulcer, but he confused gonorrhea with syphilis, a common error of the time. His great innovation in surgery was the principle that aneurysms could be treated by a single proximal ligature instead of amputation, a technique that was said to have saved the limbs of thousands.

Hunter was a quick-tempered man who also suffered from angina pectoris. He once predicted: "My life is in the hands of any rascal who chooses to annoy and tease me." In a public debate with colleagues he was contradicted, became angry, and died within a few hours.

His contemporary, Sir Percival Pott (1714–1788), who had the largest surgical practice in London, wrote masterful treatises on hernia, head injuries, hydrocele, anal fistula, and the classic account of chimney sweep's scrotal cancer; confined to his bed after a street fall, he wrote his description of a common fracture of one or both bones above the ankle, which bears his name.

Another important work on hernia was that of Spain's Antonio de Gimbernat (1793), founder of the Royal College of Surgery in Madrid. His contemporary, also an outstanding surgeon and anatomist, was Pedro Virgili, founder of the Royal College of Surgery in Cadiz.

CULVER

Dr. John Hunter by Sir Joshua Reynolds. His anatomic collection was the nucleus of the Hunterian Museum.

THERAPY. The eighteenth century introduced no revolutionary methods of therapy: continued in vogue were bleeding, cupping, purging, dieting; venereal diseases rampant in a libertine era were still treated with massive doses of mercury, phlebotomy, and baths.

The rage for electricity launched a primitive electrotherapy: Christian Gottlieb Kratzenstein in Copenhagen used electricity to treat paralysis; before the century's end, many hospitals owned electrostatic machines.

Hydrotherapy became extremely popular; the cold pack in fevers was revived by Sigmund Hahn; cold baths were recommended in a widely circulated work by Sir John Floyer; James Currie poured cold sea water over typhoid patients. The fashionable spas such as Bath provided facilities for bathing in spring pools or in the sea.

Despite botanic and chemical progress, pharmacology lagged; many items in the materia medica were leftovers from the Middle Ages. Introduced in this century were Fowler's arsenic solution, Hoffmann's anodyne, Gregory's powder, potassium chlorate, phosphoric acid, quassia, angostura bark, Canada balsam, logwood, and the buccaneer-physician Thomas Dover's famous powder; some of these new remedies came from American Indian medicine.

The last years of the century saw a dramatic change in the attitude of medicine toward mental disease, the victims of which were until then treated in filthy lazarets with the utmost cruelty. France's Philippe Pinel (1745–1826), physician at the Bicêtre Hospital in Paris, obtained permission in 1796 to strike the chains from some fifty insane patients.[19] He affirmed that mental disease was caused by pathologic changes in the brain.

Pinel was the son of a country physician; he first studied divinity, then turned to natural science and medicine. At Montpellier he embraced the popular vitalism theories, achieved his first fame with a classification of diseases following a naturalistic botanic method.

A pioneer in psychiatry was Italy's Vincenzo Chiarugi who in 1793 presented one of the first works diagnosing and classifying mental diseases; he advocated stimulative or sedative treatment according to the condition.

Another pioneer was the German vitalist Johann

Friedrich Hoffmann held that vital force, ether, was transmitted through nerves to organic "fibers."

Christian Reil who saw the life force as a chemical interaction between body substances; he described the island of Reil in the brain (insula), established the brain's functional independence.

On the fringe of neurophysiology stood Franz Joseph Gall who maintained that most intellectual and emotional functions are localized in areas of the brain and can be recognized by bumps in the skull; he was the father of phrenology, a pseudo-science that was to become extremely popular in the next century.

THE GREAT ILLUSIONISTS. The worship of natural sciences in the eighteenth century had an obverse effect of making many people easy prey to any charlatan who combined some kind of contraption with his abracadabra.

King of the century's illusionists was Franz Anton Mesmer (1734–1815), a pupil of van Swieten and de Haen and a friend of Mozart, who at one time had most of Paris society at his feet. In his doctoral dissertation he espoused the astrologers' notion that the planets influence human beings, to which he added the principle of "magnetic therapy" through the imposition of hands.

In Paris he founded a Magnetic Institute with the help of King Louis XVI and Marie Antoinette, counted many of the most eminent persons of the day among his clients (including General Lafayette).

Prominent in his treatment were the magnetic *baquets* (tubs) which contained a mixture of innocuous chemicals; patients stood around these tubs, holding hands and in contact with an iron ring; the basis of the healing principle was "animal magnetism." Other therapeutic measures consisted of frankly hypnotic techniques, touching patients with a wand in various parts (including the erogenous zones in women), bringing the subject into a hypnoidal state during which a cure was suggested.

Mesmer acquired enormous renown, despite the furious opposition of medical faculties and the unfavorable report of a commission, which included Benjamin Franklin. The Revolution drove him from France (some of his assistants were guillotined) but he continued to practice in Switzerland where he attracted numerous pupils and followers.

The most picturesque of the great quacks was an Edinburgh saddler's son, James Graham, who studied medicine under Monro *primus*; without a degree he went to Philadelphia where he heard of Franklin's discoveries in electricity. Back in London under the patronage of the Duchess of Devonshire, he built his Temple of Health (1780), which contained bacchantic statues, lascivious paintings, glass globes, flame-breathing dragons, incense burners. The main attraction was the Celestial Bed erected on 40 glass pillars and bristling with electric devices, where the impotent could seek rejuvenation and the childless would manage conception. Officiating at sensuous ceremonies was a dancer named Emma Lyon, later to become Lady Hamilton and Lord Nelson's mistress.

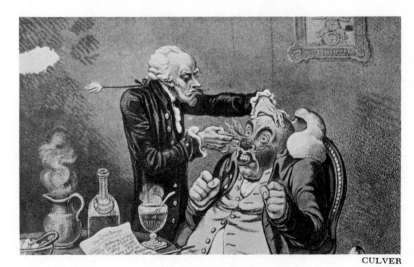

Doctor Elisha Perkins using quack "metallic tractor."

PUBLIC HEALTH. Although the open type of city of the eighteenth century was a great improvement on the cramped medieval towns, sanitation continued to be primitive and a rich source of disease. Offal and excrement were thrown into the street, sewers were inadequate, streets were filthy and unpaved.

Epidemics were frequent, although less virulent than in previous centuries: bubonic plague killed more than 300,000 in Prussia in 1709; 30,000 French died of exanthematous typhus in 1741; malaria, diphtheria, and pertussis took heavy tolls; in 1723 yellow fever appeared for the first time in Europe.

The greatest single scourge of the century was smallpox, from which neither high nor low was immune. Familiar to physicians was the Oriental custom of variolation; in Turkey this was common practice with Circassian slave girls to protect their famed beauty.

A report on variolation reached the Royal Society in London in 1713 from the Greek physician Emanuel Timoni of Constantinople; the idea won little attention until Lady Mary Wortley Montagu (wife of the British Ambassador) wrote from Turkey in 1718 that she had had her young son inoculated; three years later during an epidemic in London she did the same for her five year old daughter, urged that the royal children be similarly protected; after the method had been tested on several criminals and orphan children, the young princes were inoculated in 1722.

The most spectacular advance in public health was the introduction of widespread inoculation against smallpox, the achievement of Edward Jenner (1749–1823), a pupil of John Hunter. Jenner had learned of the phenomenon that milkmaids who contracted cowpox did not take smallpox. He conceived the idea of a large-scale inoculation program, wrote of it to his former master; replied Hunter bluntly: "Don't think, try, be patient, be accurate."

Following eighteen years of collecting data, in 1796 he performed his historic experiment on the eight year old James Phipps, inoculating the boy first with matter from a dairymaid's cowpox pustule, then several weeks later with smallpox virus; the boy remained immune even after a second smallpox inoculation.

After treating twenty-three cases he published in 1798 the seventy-five page *An Inquiry into the Causes and Effects of the Variolae Vaccinae;* this was coolly received in England at first but enthusiastically taken up on the continent and in the newly emerged United States of America; in less than a year over 6000 people had been vaccinated with success.[20]

During Jenner's lifetime a Spanish physician, Francisco Javier de Balmis, took twenty-two children who had been inoculated on a vaccination

Mental patients at Bicêtre being unchained through humane intervention of pioneer psychiatrist, Dr. Pinel.

journey around the world, inoculating hundreds of thousands of persons in Mexico, the Philippines, Macao, and Canton.

A man dedicated to the notion that rulers and governments are responsible for the living conditions and health of the people was Johann Peter Frank (1745–1821). His passionate single aim was to persuade authorities to safeguard public health by a system of state medical police with legal authority over every aspect of life from womb to tomb, regulating food, clothing, recreation, prenatal and child care, accident prevention, ventilation of schools, even conjugal relations.

Similarly obsessed was the Englishman John Howard (1726–1790) who, after suffering imprisonment in France, devoted his life and fortune to the cause of prison reform. He traveled 50,000 miles visiting the foul jails of Europe, published in 1789 his influential *Account of the Principal Lazarettos in Europe.*

The decline of monastery hospitals, and the swelling population of the cities, made the care of the indigent sick an urgent problem; by 1760 London's great general hospitals and lying-in and foundling institutions had been built; attention was turned to hospitals for special diseases, e.g., smallpox, venereal disease, or for special social groups such as seamen. On the continent a similar growth was mainly under government auspices; in the New World colonies the Pennsylvania Hospital of Philadelphia led the way in 1751, the New York Hospital followed in 1791.

AMERICAN MEDICINE. Although there were many practitioners in the American colonies, there was no distinct American medicine until after independence had been won.

The War of Independence brought into prominence two figures: John Morgan (1735–1789), trained by both William Hunter and Monro *primus* at Edinburgh, who was made by Congress, Director General and Surgeon General of the American Army; William Shippen, Jr. (1736–1808), second Surgeon General and first public teacher of obstetrics, whose private lying-in hospital was the first in the country.

Physiology and pathology were neglected; anatomy was first taught by Philadelphian Thomas Cadwalader (1708–1779); because of prejudice against dissection, cadavers had to be snatched from graves.

The most controversial figure of the period was Philadelphia's Benjamin Rush (1745–1813), one of the signers of the Declaration and a founder of numerous societies, sometimes hailed as the American Sydenham.

Rush was not an original thinker and adhered to many of the erroneous ideas of the time. But he was a penetrating observer, a fine clinician, and an outstanding teacher.

The Age of Enlightenment closed quite unlike the way it had begun. Some absolute monarchs were toppled from their thrones, the power of the aristocracy passed into the hands of the middle classes, the worship of reason gave way to passionate romanticism, skepticism was replaced by irrational dogmas. But in science and medicine the reverse was true: at the century's end the Age of Reason had laid sound foundations for the coming Age of Science.

LIGHT OF THE ENLIGHTENMENT

Enduring monument of the Enlightenment is the *Encyclopédie, ou Dictionnaire Raisonné des Sciences, des Arts et des Métiers* ("Encyclopedia, or Reasoned Dictionary of the Sciences, Arts, and Trades") edited by Denis Diderot (1713–1784), who advanced the cause of progress and liberalism and preached the dignity of labor by organizing and making public the technical, philosophic, and political ideas conceived in this age.

Contributors included D'Alembert, Rousseau,

In a copperplating shop the plates are inked (fig. a), the surface wiped clean (fig. b), leaving ink in the grooves. The press (fig. 1) forces the paper down into the grooves. The press is cylindrical and passes the paper and the plate between rollers.

Montesquieu, D'Holbach, Saint-Lambert, Condorcet, Jaucourt, Voltaire. In a France still partly medieval in its social and economic structure, liberal thought had to be clothed in innuendo and irony; Diderot's genius as editor was to use technology to clothe ideology: thus the article on salt goes beyond the properties of sodium chloride to comment on the injustice of taxing one of life's necessities; the article on political authority opens with "No man has received from nature the right to rule others."

Suppressed by censors, condemned by the Church and the state, the *Encyclopédie,* the first volume of which was published in 1751, was finally completed in 1772. The 17 volumes of text and 11 volumes of plates (five additional volumes appeared under different editorship) stand as a monumental tribute to liberty and human dignity, also present the most complete picture of the working life of eighteenth century France.

A coining press, fitted with two matrices: one prints the head of Louis XV on one side, the escutcheon on the other. Blanks from basket P are stamped and tossed into basket Q.

In a jeweler's shop are seen, left to right, *the engravers, goldsmith, bellows boy. Jeweler is engaged with a client in background.*

Vertical treadmill converts manpower by way of block and tackle to provide pressure in paper press.

After Napoleon's defeat, Congress of Vienna restored territorial, dynastic status of Europe before French Revolution.

XI

Tapestry with Figures

THE beginning of the nineteenth century centered on the military exploits of Napoleon, until his dreams of world conquest were shattered on the snow-whipped steppes of Russia and on the sun-baked plains of Spain by those valiant Spanish *guerrilleros* whose heroism was immortalized by Goya. In his ill-fated Russian campaign, typhus and typhoid decimated Napoleon's forces, and there, probably, the curative power of artificial hibernation was for the first time envisaged, when it was observed that many of the soldiers half frozen by the glacial cold of the steppes survived their wounds.

After the defeat of the Napoleonic eagle, whose wings for a decade had arrogantly battered the skies of Europe, the Old World, exhausted by so much warfare, lapsed into a period of political apathy. With the gradual rebirth of imperialism, Napoleon III made of Paris a city of enchantment and wonder, of broad vistas embellished with leaf-shaded avenues and a tapestry of green parks and white sculptures under blue sky.

To the east, Nicholas I and his Russians gazed enviously toward Constantinople, that gorgeous gem of gold-domed mosques that for centuries had been coveted by many invaders.

When the long-cherished French dream of setting up a universal empire was finally shattered, the nations of Europe strove to consolidate a system of equal and opposite forces in equilibrium, the so-called balance of power developed by Metternich and other diplomats at the Congress of Vienna. This "dancing congress" was attended by a great array of monarchs and princes from all Europe. Since then no other single assembly has commanded so many heads of states, except perhaps the great 1960 session of the United Nations in New York, at which there was no dancing but there were far more verbal fireworks.

As one of the diplomats of the time remarked, the monarchs who congregated in Vienna, no longer troubled by Napoleon, watched one another grow fatter and fatter. This balance of power lasted, with some modifications, until the outbreak of the first world war.

During the course of the nineteenth century, Great Britain and France aided Turkey against Russia, Italy was consolidated into a single kingdom, the Franco-Prussian war ended in the defeat of France, and Germany became a unified empire. The last quarter of the century was a period of relative calm and stability in Europe. On the American continent, the victorious march of the Latin American countries toward independence paralleled the technological progress of the United States after the horrors of the Civil War, and the march to its destiny as a mighty democratic nation.

Political influence in Napoleonic France stimulated a sober realism that crystalized into positivism and encyclopedism. In contrast, Germany sought refuge in idealism and gave birth to the antiencyclopedist idealist Natural Philosophy, the daughter of romanticism, whose standard-bearer, after Fichte and Hegel, was Schelling, a philosopher and honorary physician whose Brunonian therapy killed his own ailing daughter. Nature and mind were essentially identical in this philosophy, nature being reason in a dormant state, one degree before intelligence. Natural Philosophy and Kant's enormous influence aroused interest in pathology and anthropology. Natural Philosophy postulated three basic energies in nature: electric, magnetic, and chemical; and three parallel energies in the body: irritability, sensibility, and reproducibility.

While in Germany the gala celebrated on January 1, 1800, at the court of Weimar (where the incomparable Goethe played the part of Olympian Jupiter in the presence of many courtiers, including Schiller) symbolized the rebirth of a classico-romantic art and the birth of the nineteenth century, a mounting wave of technological progress was sweeping the world. Watt's steam engine, Fulton's steamboat, Stephenson's locomotive, Karl Benz' internal combustion automobile engine, Bell's telephone, and Marconi's wireless—these were some of the inventions that determined the climate in which modern medicine was to flourish.

This was the century when history, by paradoxical contrast, became national in the various countries and universal in its expansion throughout the world. This universalization was fostered by the opening of the Panama and Suez canals, the westernization of Japanese medicine, the first appearance of the modern nurse in the person of Florence Nightingale, the "Lady of the Lamp," and the creation of the International Red Cross by Jean Henri Dunant. At that time there began simultaneously the struggles of peoples for the sovereignty of their rights and for constitutional regimes, labor movements, and democratic ideas. Constitutional monarchies and the balance of power replaced the old absolutisms, and a renewed religionism took its stand against the positive philosophy of Auguste Comte in France, although he demanded merely the scientific analysis of data obtained through the senses. In turn, John Stuart Mill's logic, Herbert Spencer's social evolution, and Darwinism, in England, opened new paths of historic adventure.

Nineteenth-century art began under the dictatorial tutelage of David, the paramount painter during the French Revolution, to whose brush we owe the cruel portrait of Marie Antoinette on her way to the guillotine, and the picture of Marat, the physician, drained of blood by the knife of Charlotte Corday as he sat in the medicinal bath he took for his eczema. It was David who guided the neoclassicism of the Napoleonic empire, embodied in the Greek purity of the Madeleine, in the Roman arrogance of the Arc de Triomphe, and in the classic charm of his own portrait of Madame Recamier.

Cold neoclassicism, however, could hardly satisfy the spiritual needs of a Europe convalescing from bloody crises. This dissatisfaction inspired the artistic romanticism of Gros, Girodet, Géricault, Delacroix, and the prose of Chateaubriand. Meanwhile Ingres' classicism was battling the romanticism of Delacroix and his "drunken brush," while the great English painters—Constable with his landscapes, Reynolds with his portraits, Blake with his visions, Turner with his nature studies—and the Pre-Raphaelites were making art history on the other side of the Channel.

The second half of the nineteenth century witnessed the advent of the painters of light, color, and gaiety, all of whom, with the exception of Holland's van Gogh, were French. The break with the academic tradition came in 1863 when the painters who had been rejected by the official Salon exhibited their work in the *Salon Des Rejetes*. The public came to laugh at Manet's "Le dejeuner sur l'herbe" (today a priceless masterpiece) and were horrified by his nude "Olympia." Alongside Courbet's realism flourished the cruel antimedical satires of Daumier, the golden poetry of Renoir, the sheer magic—air, light, and water—of Monet, the pure impressionism of Pissarro, the pointillism of Seurat, the geometry of Cézanne, the decorative displays of Gauguin, the violet world of van Gogh, the enchanted ballets of Degas, and the strange sorcery, almost Japanese in its expressive economy of line and color, of Toulouse-Lautrec. In this period medicine took a definitive step forward.

People were at that time experiencing the *maladie du siécle*, a nostalgic yearning for the Middle Ages. The Napoleonic period in the history of romanticism was followed by the reactionary and the progressive-liberal periods. People doted on "romantic" diseases, such as chlorosis, tuberculosis, fever, and "mortal pallor," but veneral diseases were considered a stigma. The towns were like pigsties and the mortality from infection was enormous. Medical practice was empirical, rational, or mystico-suggestive. But in the end, the romantic speculations of Natural Philosophy were replaced by the mensurative and practical examination of nature.

Modern histology and topographical anatomy were founded in Paris by Xavier Bichat, who in a single winter dissected 600 cadavers. Bichat localized disease in a *specific* organ and, in accordance with his concept "*La vie est l'ensemble des fonctions*

Napoleon and Dominique Larrey, chief Army surgeon, who created "flying ambulances," light vehicles which were used to collect battlefield wounded.

qui resistent a la mort," regarded life as a complex of functions resisting death. Bichat's "membranes," or tissues, became the basic unit of the living creature.

Progress with the microscope led to the development of the cell theory, thanks to Schleiden and Schwann, whose work was completed by Henle and Remak. At the same time, physiology made progress with the support of Bichat's vitalism and the work of Magendie and Johannes Müller. Müller, the great encyclopedist of sensory physiology, inspired by Goethe (who gave medicine his theory of light and colors), studied the nervous system, the physiology of secretions, and embryology, using the microscope for that purpose, as Bichat had used his eyes to create macroscopic anatomy.

In Vienna, the new school of medicine dug roots into the foundations provided by the founder of modern physical diagnosis, by von Hebra, and by Schönlein, a man prodigal in action but sparse with words, who used hardly twenty lines to report his discovery of the fungal agent in tinea favosa. Another member of the Vienna School was the great Billroth, as expert at resecting an intestine as he was at playing the violin.

Pediatrics flourished, warmed by the love for children, kindled through Dickens' sentimental novels; so did psychiatry. Surgery advanced with the work done by the surgeons of the Napoleonic armies, Percy and Larrey (the latter created the "flying ambulances" and took part in the holocaust of Waterloo), and in the United States with the work of Philip Syng Physick, James Marion Sims, architect of the vagina, and Ephraim McDowell. Surgery became more an intellectual than a manual task, but the pleuroperitoneal cavities remained sanctuaries uninvaded by the scalpel.

A notable achievement in the United States was the discovery of anesthesia, in whose romantic history the names of Crawford Williamson Long and the dentist Horace Wells, who used ether and nitrous oxide, still figure controversially. Surgical anesthesia began in Boston when the dentist William Thomas Morton, trained by Horace Wells and Charles Thomas Jackson, anesthetized a patient who was operated on by John Collins Warren, Jr.; chloroform fumes were used in surgery in Edinburgh by James Young Simpson.

Clinical medicine made headway with the discovery of the stethoscope by a French physician, the monarchist Catholic pupil of Corvisart, René Théophile Hyacinthe Laënnec. At the Necker hospital in Paris, finding it difficult to auscultate with the naked ear a plump young woman, and remembering some children on the street making noises at one end of a hollow tree while their playmates listened at the other end, Laënnec rolled a sheet of paper into a tube and applied it to his patient's chest. Thus the stethoscope was born, and pathology, which hitherto had been visual only, became auditory. The physician could now listen to the noises of disease, the language of pathology that nobody had heard before.

France in that period produced an abundance of clinicians, outstanding among whom were Broussais, who inspired an era of "vampirism" in therapy, increasing France's annual consumption of leeches to more than forty-one million; Louis, a master of medical statistics; and Corvisart, the wizard of cardiology. In England there flourished Graves, Stokes, Corrigan, Bright, Addison, and Hodgkin. Germany also had its share of outstanding men. Specialization forged ahead, but therapy, based on vegetable substances, electrotherapy, and hydrotherapy, was either empirical or nihilistic.

In the latter half of the century, medicine ceased to be European and became national, positivist, and vernacular, perhaps because the nineteenth century was not a European century like the eighteenth, but particularist and nationalist as the seventeenth had been. Progress in diagnosis reflected man's curiosity about himself and the universe, and medical progress began to be made in the hospital instead of in the library.

In his turn, the physician, who had been an artisan in ancient Greece, a priest in the Middle Ages, and a doctor since the Renaissance, now became a hospital physician and public health servant, with the increasing development of health welfare services.

Anesthetics made more delicate surgery possible. Other developments were the cell concept of disease; the study of metabolism, of the role of the nervous system as an organic regulator, and of the unity between psyche and soma; the concept of the microbial origin of infections; immunization; and new instruments. The human body was studied in space (morphology and anthropology) and in time (genetics and embryology).

Hippocrates' humoral pathology was placed on the intimate level of the cell by the German Rudolf Virchow, who, with his cell concept of disease, displaced the concept that disease was seated in an organ, as asserted by Morgagni, or in a tissue, as Bichat maintained. Virchow also replaced the ancient "absolutist empire" of the organic humors with his "cellular democracy" or "republic of the cells," in which the cells were social classes, the organs and systems were their territory, and disease was a civil war between germs and the police of the cell state, the leukocytes. Then was born a new science with the work of the romantic revolutionary Jacob Henle, the Vesalius of histology and father of modern embryology.

Claude Bernard, born in the sun-radiant vineyards of the valley of the Rhône, was more than a physiologist—he was physiology itself. A failure as a playwright, in his married life, in his candidature for professorship, and in his early experiments, he succeeded as an experimenter and eventually became a teacher at the Collège de France and at the Sorbonne. He taught the medical world to "think physiologically," discovered the glycogenic function of the liver, and established the concepts of the *milieu intérieur*, functional correlation, and the principles of physiological experimentation: observation, hypothesis, experiment. Claude Bernard consolidated the philosophical positivism of his time, inspired Emile Zola's literary realism with his concepts, and affirmed his credo with the words "*L'Art c'est moi, la Science c'est nous.*"

Other landmarks of progress in this period were the discovery of enzymes, clinical thermometry, thermodynamics, physiological recording apparatus, and the growth of public health, dramatized by Max von Pettenkofer's gesture in quaffing a culture of cholera bacillus. The laws of heredity were evolved by the Augustinian friar Gregor Mendel while counting his rosary of peas, and Wilhelm Roentgen discovered x-rays.

Britain ousted France from clinical leadership. But bacteriology originated with the remarkable work of a fine and noble French chemist: Louis Pasteur, investigator of wine diseases and ferments, microbe-hunter and maker of vaccines, who identified microbes with the ancient (and still mysterious) *contagium animatum*, and, seventy years before Fleming, studied the effect of *Penicillium* on ferments. Linked with him are the names of Koch, who established the microbial specificity of infections and isolated the tuberculosis germ; von Behring, master of toxins and antitoxins; Klebs and Löffler, fishers of bacilli; Jaime Ferrán and his vaccines. The wave of discoveries that started the new biological therapy, with its serums, vaccines, antibodies, and phagocytes, the forerunner of the bacteriostatic and bactericidal drugs, was symbolized in the fight against tropical diseases and in the achievement of the Cuban Carlos Finlay, whose discovery of the transmissibility of yellow fever by mosquitoes made possible, with the support of Walter Reed, its elimination in Cuba and the opening of the Panama Canal.

The arsenal of therapeutics was enriched by new drugs, particularly by chemotherapeutic agents, introduced in his Frankfurt institute by Paul Ehrlich, who proceeded from his chromotherapy, or therapy through colors, to his anti-treponema arsenical "magic bullets," the forerunners of which were Paracelsus' non-Galenic heavy metals, just as Galenic phytotherapy was the forerunner of antibiotics.

Medicine became more physiopathological and physiochemical in its substrate, and clinical case histories became more dynamic and historico-biographical.

Outstanding in neurology—which was started as a specialty by Duchenne in Paris —were Charcot, the neurosurgeon, Paul Broca, and Pierre Marie, and in England John Hughlings Jackson, who explored the levels of the nervous system. Psychiatry took a step forward when Philippe Pinel liberated the mental patient from his chains and codified 2700 diseases in an endeavor to make medicine a natural science. Noteworthy was the psychiatric nosology of Emil Kraepelin, who reduced the chaos of mental syndromes to a cosmos of classifications.

Mental diseases remained dramatically *visual* until Charcot, but were made auditory by the Viennese psychiatrist Sigmund Freud, who "listened to" neuroses instead of looking at them. Freud, a poet in medicine, created a new medical anthropology with his therapeutic evaluation of the human instincts and his original concepts of the unconscious, and by integrating the patient's disease into his life history and using dialogue with the patient as a curative instrument.

The greatest advance in surgery of this century was antisepsis—*physical* disinfection of instruments and wounds with carbolic acid—initiated by the Scotsman Joseph Lister, the Lincoln of surgery, who liberated humanity from the chains of infection. Antisepsis later became asepsis—*chemical* and *preventive* disinfection of the air and wounds—which made surgery more physiological and less heroic.

Maternal mortality from puerperal infection was drastically reduced by Ignaz Philipp Semmelweis in Austria, who intuitively instructed his colleagues and students to disinfect their hands with a calcium chloride solution, and by the impassioned campaign of the Bostonian Oliver Wendell Holmes, who independently discovered the infectious origin of puerperal fever. Antisepsis and anesthesia overcame the two age-old enemies of surgery—infection and pain.

In America there proceeded the westward expansion across the prairies, traversed successively by pioneers and trappers, traders, preachers, and physicians, with a transition from the empirical apprenticeship of physicians to schools of medicine, the regulation of instruction, and the founding of the great medical associations and medical magazines.

There arose the memorable figures of the statesman and pioneer psychiatrist Benjamin Rush, one of the signers of the Declaration of Independence; Ephraim McDowell, who performed the first resection of an ovarian cyst; the country surgeon Daniel Drake, who compiled a masterly medical geography; William Beaumont, who studied gastric function in vivo in a halfbreed's stomach laid open by gunshot; Guthrie and his chloroform or "sweet whisky"; Sims who performed the first vesicovaginal fistula operation; Oliver Wendell Holmes, physician and poet; Silas Weir Mitchell, neurologist and novelist; John Shaw Billings, the superb medical bibliographer and cofounder of the Surgeon General's Library; and Canada's Sir William Osler, professor at the universities of McGill in Montreal, Pennsylvania, Johns Hopkins, and Oxford, the modern ideal of the humanist-physician, good, kind, and courageous, whose wise and gentle voice still inspires today's physicians.

F.M.I.

Following page: *Claude Bernard, an errant pharmacy student, at a performance of his vaudeville* Rose du Rhòne *at the Théâtre de Célestins outside Lyons in 1833. After completing a five-act historical drama* Artur de Bretaigne, *Bernard was advised by critic Saint-Marc Girardin to abandon the theatre and pursue medicine. by Hans Guggenheim.*

XI
NINETEENTH CENTURY MEDICINE

THE nineteenth century wove more radical changes into the fabric of human society than had been seen in the thousand preceding years. It was a century of revolution in thought, economics, mores, politics, and technology, spanning the enormous gap between the world of sailing ships and mounted couriers and that of transatlantic steel liners and radio, between imperialism and socialism, between dueling and the rule of law.

Unlike previous centuries, the nineteenth lacked homogeneity: the world of Beau Brummell in the 1820's was totally unlike that of the Gay Nineties; the reckless romanticism of the Napoleonic era was utterly foreign to the sober respectability of the late Victorian age. In medicine there was an equally wide gulf between the massive bloodletting of the early decades and the era of anesthesia and asepsis in the second half of the century.

The political atmosphere in Europe was dominated by two main forces: the struggle of liberal and republican movements against monarchy and the remnants of feudalism; the growth of nationalist feeling in peoples long under alien domination.

One result of Napoleon's domination was to arouse intense nationalist feeling, exemplified by the desperately heroic fight of the Spanish people against Napoleonic troops in the Peninsular War. Between 1815 and 1850 the Greeks revolted against their Turkish masters, Hungarians sought to throw off the Austrian yoke, the Poles attempted to regain their liberty from Russia, the Prussians sowed the seeds of a unified Germany, the Italians fought in secret societies and daredevil legions to gain independence from Austria and to unify their country. By the century's end,

Italy, Germany, Serbia, Belgium, and Greece had become independent nations; so had most of the former Spanish and Portuguese colonies in South America.

This was also the golden age of new empires: the rapid expansion of British possessions in Africa, Asia, Canada, and the Antipodes, the development of French territories in Africa and Southeast Asia, the growth of Russia in the east and central Asia. In the second half of the century Japan and China were opened to trade with the Western nations, creating colossal markets and sources of supplies.

In the economic field, the nineteenth century transformed the way of life through a vast extension of the industrial revolution that had begun in the previous century. In four brief generations, candles gave way to gas, which in turn was superseded by electric lighting, railroads supplanted stagecoaches, steamships crossed the Atlantic, followed soon after by a telegraph cable, steel manufacture was revolutionized by the Bessemer process, agriculture was transformed by machinery and chemistry, balloons and airships invaded the clouds, people communicated by telephone and radio, and the more adventurous raced at thirty miles an hour in horseless carriages.

Until this era, man had obtained power only from his or animal muscles, wind, and water; with the steam engine (and later oil and electric motors) man unleashed a tremendous source of energy that transformed the world and gave to the nineteenth century the name of the Industrial Age.

The impact of this age on human affairs was so drastic that the two halves of the century appear almost as separate civilizations.

Gottlieb Daimler, left, and his automobile, ca. 1890.

The widespread reaction to the industrial revolution took many forms, from the Luddites in England, who smashed the newfangled machinery, to the emergence of modern socialism; in the process, the whole fabric of economic and social thought of the century was rewoven in a pattern that would have astounded Voltaire and Rousseau.

After their initial violent reaction against machinery was spent, the working classes formed numerous associations to promote better working conditions and higher wages; their leaders were at first persecuted (some were sent to the galleys or transported to Australia), but the movements grew steadily throughout the century, culminating in the formation of powerful trade unions. Two side streams of this tide were the rapid growth of cooperative societies and the mushrooming of workmen's institutes to educate the working classes.

As the blight of industrial towns spread over the land, a romantic reaction took the form of utopian communities generally based on a form of primitive communism.

The most significant reaction to the new age was the emergence of humanitarianism. In England and America reformers sprang up in every field of life; slavery was abolished in the British Empire in 1833, and in that same year a Factory Act set a legal limit of ten hours on the working hours of children and young persons. Charles Dickens and Charles Kingsley aroused widespread sympathy for the plight of the young poor, leading eventually to societies for the prevention of cruelty to children.[1] Innumerable charitable organizations were formed and it became the fashion to make gifts of food and necessities to the poor; safety in mines and factories became the care of the state; workhouses were reformed, as was the distribution of alms to the needy.

Women played a leading role in this tide of humanitarianism: Mary Wollstonecraft sounded the tocsin for the rights of women, Elizabeth Fry worked untiringly for prison reform, Mary Carpenter founded the first "slum school" in 1846, Florence Nightingale reformed the nursing profession; women everywhere organized kindergarten schools (initiated by Friedrich Froebel in 1840), crèches, foundling homes.

The tide flowed over the entire world through hundreds of missionary societies established to improve the lives and morals of pagans in the Orient and Africa, based on the then novel principle that all men are brothers; throughout this century the missionary and the empire builder took over the task of expanding man's knowledge of the earth.

THE SETTING. The nineteenth century produced two cultures that reflected the enormous changes wrought in Western countries by the economic and industrial revolutions.

In the first four decades before the expansion of railroads, Europe was largely rural, a blend of small towns and many villages. The aristocracy still owned vast estates and lived extravagantly; men wore colorful clothes, dueled at the slightest provocation (by pistol instead of the earlier sword), gambled immensely, affected an extravagance in speech and sentiment; women wore daringly décolleté dresses, flirted outrageously, entertained lavishly. This was the glittering world of Stendhal's *Le Rouge et le Noir*, of Beau Brummell and the dissolute society of the Regency, of the brilliant *salons* of Lady Blessington and Madame Récamier.

By the middle of the century, European society was largely dominated by the new middle class that arose from the mercantile, industrial, and financial worlds, the new bourgeoise of money that flowered under Queen Victoria in England and Napoleon III in France.

Men now dressed in somber hues, mostly in stiff black clothes; women wrapped themselves in yards of heavy cloth or girded on voluminous petticoats or crinolines. The correct behavior in this era was decorum, respectability, stiff formality, strict social restrictions. Well-to-do young women were expected to live inactive lives, look interestingly pale, sew or embroider interminably, faint at the drop of a handkerchief.

This middle class in England was strongly religious, with a rigid Puritanism that despised idleness, poverty, frivolity, extravagance, and most forms of amusement. This was the world in the novels of Anthony Trollope and Honoré Balzac, a widely different world from that of Samuel Pickwick and his jolly companions in the 1830's.

THE CULTURE. As in the mores, the cultural environment of the century fell into two clearly contrasted forms: romanticism in the first half, realism in the second.

In literature, romanticism produced the imaginative poetry of Byron, Shelley, Chateaubriand, Heine, the medieval romances of Sir Walter Scott and Alexandre Dumas. Romantic architects erected neo-Gothic buildings; painters portrayed historical or fanciful scenes vibrant with emotion; musicians composed tempestuous or sentimental music.

Honoré Balzac

Sir Walter Scott and friends. The group includes poets William Wordsworth, Crabbe, and Moore.

In the second part of the century flourished the novelists who described everyday life, artists who painted what they saw, musicians unafraid to develop new forms, architects who were more functional than fanciful.

The profoundest revolution in culture during this period was the rapid extension of literacy among the middle and poorer classes, producing an enormous demand for reading matter and vastly expanding the dissemination of news and opinions through newspapers, news agencies, pamphlets, and books.[2]

Culture in America also followed two different currents: the wealthier classes in the large cities adopted the European patterns in literature and music, while frontiersmen developed their own simple culture of Bible, ballad and rough humor.

THE PHILOSOPHERS. The schools of thought in the nineteenth century covered an extremely broad spectrum of philosophies, ranging from pessimistic mysticism to practical positivism.

Charles Dickens

Walt Whitman

235

The popular apostle of the cult of individualism that flourished in the first decades of the century was Johann Gottlieb Fichte (1762–1814), who propounded the doctrine that the indivisible ego is the source of all experience. His friend Friedrich Wilhelm von Schelling (1775–1854) saw history as a series of stages progressing toward a general harmony.

The historical process was regarded by Georg Wilhelm Hegel (1770–1831) as the result of an interplay of forces, a thesis producing its opposite (antithesis), the two in turn creating a synthesis. This doctrine was developed by Karl Marx and Friedrich Engels to illustrate their concept of how human societies evolved.

The leading schools of social and political thought throughout the century were divided between those who believed in the power and purpose of the state and those who viewed any form of government as the work of the devil.

Hegel and his followers believed that an organized state was the expression of the highest human idealism and the finest good of mankind; Pierre Joseph Prudhon and his disciples thought all forms of government and property ownership were evil and should be abolished, an anarchist philosophy that was preached in Russia by Michael Bakunin and Prince Peter Kropotkin.

The most prominent protagonist of the doctrine of inevitable progress was France's Auguste Comte (1798–1857), who, with England's Herbert Spencer (1820–1903), was a leading light in the school of positivism. At the other end of the spectrum Arthur Schopenhauer (1788–1860) preached that the will of the universe is blind and purposeless and that social progress was pure illusion; to this despairing nihilism Friedrich Nietzsche (1844–1900) added the doctrine of the superman above good and evil.

The most revolutionary thinker of the century, against his will, was Charles Robert Darwin (1809–1882) whose theory of the origin of species propounded just over a century ago rent the Victorian world asunder, unleashing decades of bitter debate between scientists and between naturalists and Churchmen.

The second half of the century was dominated by this controversy between revealed religion and science, between fundamentalists who accepted the Creation as described in the Bible and those who propounded what a contemporary called the "monkey damnification of mankind."

The essential current of thought in the second half of the nineteenth century was optimism and a solid belief that mankind was steadily climbing toward greater economic security, more enlightened political and social forms, expanding science and tech-

Thomas Addison, pathologist at Guy's Hospital, London. Among his contributions were descriptions of adrenal gland disorders. He is eponym of the disease.

nology, and toward a society of civilized respectability, all summed up in the concept of Progress.

BASIC SCIENCE. In this century men embarked on scientific voyages, explored jungle and desert, searched for lost cities. The century began with the rebirth of the atomic theory and ended with the discovery of radiation; midway, the theory of evolution severed man from ancient self-centered philosophies, unfolded a new perspective on his relationship with other species.

Astronomers in 1800 disposed of catalogues listing only about 3000 stars; by the century's end some 450,000 astral bodies had been mapped.

In 1803 the Englishman John Dalton revived the ancient Greek theory that elements are composed of ultimate particles or atoms; by 1869 the Russian chemist Dmitri Mendeleyev had published his periodic classification of the elements.

Early in the century, chemists synthesized ethyl alcohol and urea, proving that substances hitherto found only in living matter could be made in the laboratory. Numerous hypotheses were offered to explain the complex structures of organic compounds, until in 1865 the German chemist Friedrich Kekulé von Stradunitz dreamed of snakelike chains of molecules, awoke to work out the theory of the benzene ring, of fundamental importance in modern chemistry.

The greatest advance in physics was the formulation of the law of the conservation of energy, which opened the door to the rich field of thermodynamics and the many practical applications of energy derived from heat. England's Michael Faraday discovered the principle of electromagnetic induction in 1831, thereby launched the electric generator and later the electric motor; the first workable electric incandescent lamp was built by America's Thomas Alva Edison in 1879.

The study of optics and the nature of light in this century led to one of the fundamental discoveries of physics and chemistry, spectrum analysis, a technique that enabled man to penetrate both into the intimate nature of molecules and the nature of stars millions of miles away. In 1895 Wilhelm Roentgen's short-wave ray enabled man to see through matter.

By the end of the century, some 70,000 chemical compounds had been discovered and analyzed; in 1898 the Curies discovered the element radium, which was to revolutionize the treatment of cancer.

The Darwinian theory of evolution published in 1859 brought dynamism to biology, which in this century became a science independent of medicine. Daughter sciences were born: paleontology grew out of the work of comparative anatomists led by Georges Cuvier (1769–1832); genetics began in Gregor Johann Mendel's cloistered garden; after him

Gregor Mendel hybridizing garden peas. His article setting forth his system of heredity, translated as Experiments in Plant Hybridization, *was published in 1868.*

the Dutch botanist Hugo de Vries evolved the mutation theory of evolution; Ernst Haeckel propounded the theory of recapitulation in embryonic growth.

The discoveries of human fossils, beginning with the Neanderthal skull in 1856, launched the new science of anthropology.

ANATOMY AND HISTOLOGY. The most fruitful legacy to the budding nineteenth century was the work of France's Marie-François Xavier Bichat (1771–1802), who developed the idea that the living body was not merely an association of organs that could be studied apart, but an intricate network of "membranes," or tissues. For this Napoleon of Medicine (as the inscription on his monument reads), the tissue was the physiologic and morphologic unit of the living creature, irrespective of the organ from which it was derived. This teaching, based on the dissection of more than 600 cadavers in one winter, was to lead directly to the cellular theory of Virchow some decades later. Bichat's ambition, thwarted by premature death, was to transform medicine into an exact science based on anatomy and pathology.

Improvements such as the achromatic lens made the microscope an increasingly accurate tool; discoveries in microscopic structures came in rapid succession, many of them made by pupils of Johannes Müller in the great century of German medicine.

The 2000 year old humoral theory was challenged by Rudolf Virchow, a giant of nineteenth century medicine, born in Pomerania in 1821. In his historic work, *Cellular Pathology* (1858), he described the body as a community of cells, a "cellular democracy" opposed to the "absolutist empire" of the humors. He defined disease as "life modified by cellular reaction against abnormal stimuli."

Bridging the century's end was the great Spanish histologist Santiago Ramón y Cajal (1852–1934), artist and philosopher, who in 1906 shared the Nobel Prize with the distinguished Italian Camillo Golgi (1843–1926) for histologic study of the nervous sys-

Rudolf Virchow established the principles of cellular pathology which were described as marking the greatest advance scientific medicine made since its beginnings.

tem. Ramón y Cajal made giant strides in neurophysiology, developed his famous neuron theory about 1890. The summation of his work (*Textura del sistema nervioso*) was published at the turn of the century.

THE PHYSIOLOGISTS. In the first half of the century, physiology finally freed itself from metaphysic speculation and became a natural science based on experimental research.

The giant of this fecund era was undoubtedly Claude Bernard (1813–1878) whose research and concepts laid the foundations of modern physiology. Born the son of a winegrower in the Rhône valley, he first tried his hand at pharmacy and playwriting, was persuaded to study medicine, which he did at the Collège de France under Magendie.

His early research work was done in a damp cellar laboratory, with equipment put together by himself; his experiments on live dogs were viewed with the deepest suspicion by the police, and with horror by his family. He discovered the glycogenic function of the liver, for which he coined the term "internal secretion"; he also showed that a puncture of the fourth ventricle of the brain caused temporary diabetes. He demonstrated the various functions of pancreatic juice, made important studies on smooth muscle, the vasomotor mechanism, carbohydrate metabolism, and the action of curare and other poisons.

His greatest contribution to physiology was the concept of the constancy of vital phenomena independently of external factors, what he called the *milieu intérieur*, a concept that was to establish the basic biologic principle of homeostasis. He was also the founder of experimental medicine and the enemy of unsupported theories. Wrote he in 1865 in the epoch-making *Introduction à l'étude de la médecine expérimentale:* "One must break the bonds of philosophic and scientific systems as one would break the chains of scientific slavery. Systems tend to enslave the human spirit."

Bernard taught his students to leave off their imagination as they would an overcoat on entering the laboratory, but to put it on again when leaving. His famous dictum: *L'art c'est moi, la science c'est nous;* fathered the concept of teamwork in scientific research.

His teacher had been the pioneering physiologist François Magendie (1783–1855) who had no respect for vitalistic or other theories and regarded medicine as a science in the making (*une science à faire*). Wedded to experiment, he sought to explain physiologic processes in terms of physics and chemistry, performed innumerable experiments on animals, produced important findings on the physiologic role of the spinal cord.

Bernard's counterpart in Germany was Johannes

Francois Magendie, founder of experimental physiology, distinguished motor and sensory portions of peripheral nerves; he studied vein function.

Müller (1801–1858), a brilliantly versatile man equally eminent in biology, morphology, and pathology, and a magnetic and inspiring teacher. He contributed greatly to the understanding of nerve structure and energy, a field that was widely developed in the second half of the century; he discovered the Müllerian duct, described the finer anatomy of glandular and cartilagenous tissue, explained color sensation in the retina, and formulated the principle of eccentric projection of sensation from peripheral sense organs. His famous Law of Specific Nerve Energy was a seminal idea that was extended by modern neurophysiologists. In addition to his research and teaching he was founder and editor of *Archiv für Anatomie und Physiologie* (popularly *Müller's Archiv*), long the leading journal in scientific medicine.

Important contributions to the physiology of digestion were made in this period by two Americans: John Richardson Young (1782–1804), who demonstrated that digestion in the stomach was the result not of trituration but of the solvent action of gastric juice; William Beaumont, surgeon in the United States Army, who observed digestion through an accidental gastric fistula in the Canadian Alexis St. Martin, published invaluable data on the nature of gastric juice, the process of digestion, and the physiology of gastritis.

This field was further enriched in the second half of the century by Ivan Petrovitch Pavlov (1849–1936) with the technique of establishing gastric pouches and pancreatic fistulas in dogs. His work not only contributed new data on gastric and pancreatic digestion, but also led to the highly important concept of the conditioned reflex.

This period also saw the foundation of physiologic chemistry, a pioneer of which was Justus von Liebig (1803–1873). He established the relation between organic chemistry and physiology through a careful study of all matter ingested and excreted; he discovered the excretion of the all-important urea and hippuric acid, investigated numerous organic compounds including fats, blood, and bile; he was first to introduce the concept of metabolism (*Stoffwechsel*).

In the physiology of vision, England's Thomas Young (1773–1829) first described astigmatism and proposed a theory of color vision. This work was advanced by Bohemia's Johannes Evangelista Purkinje (1787–1869), who discovered how to observe the fundus of the eye, an epoch-making step in diagnosis. Purkinje also discovered the ganglionic cells in the cerebellum that bear his name, the Purkinje fibers of cardiac muscle and of the uterus. He was a pioneer in the description of most of the subjective visual figures that appear under various stimuli, was the first to study the vertigo and nystagmus produced whenever the body is repeatedly rotated.

Another giant of physiology in this era was Hermann Ludwig von Helmholtz (1821–1894), a pupil of Müller. He established that the muscles are the main source of animal heat, measured the velocity of nervous impulses, studied the mechanism of hearing. His lasting contribution to medicine was the invention of the ophthalmoscope; he also extended the Young theory of color vision into a wider realm of optical physiology.

Helmholtz's inventive mind ranged in many fields, including acoustics, dynamics, electromotive force, but he never forgot that he was a physician. Wrote he: "Medicine was once the intellectual home in which I grew up; and even the emigrant best understands and is best understood by his native land."

The second half of the century abounded with hundreds of investigators in physiology, broadening the work of the great masters of the first half, applying new laws of electromagnetism and mechanics to physiologic research. Discoveries followed fast one on another, contributed by scientists of many nationalities. Physiologists during this period profited enormously from the newly acquired ability of surgeons to penetrate into body cavities. The nineteenth century could truly be called the cradle of modern physiology.

THE PATHOLOGISTS. Jean Cruveilhier (1791–1874), first to hold the newly established chair of pathology at Paris University, believed that phlebitis was the dominant factor in all disease; François Broussais (1772–1838), noted clinician and professor of general pathology in Paris, held that all disease was a chemical reaction to excessive stimuli, the inflammation being transmitted along the gastrointestinal mucosa. His therapy was starvation and leeching; under his sanguinary tutelage imports of leeches in France

Boating *by Edouard Manet.*

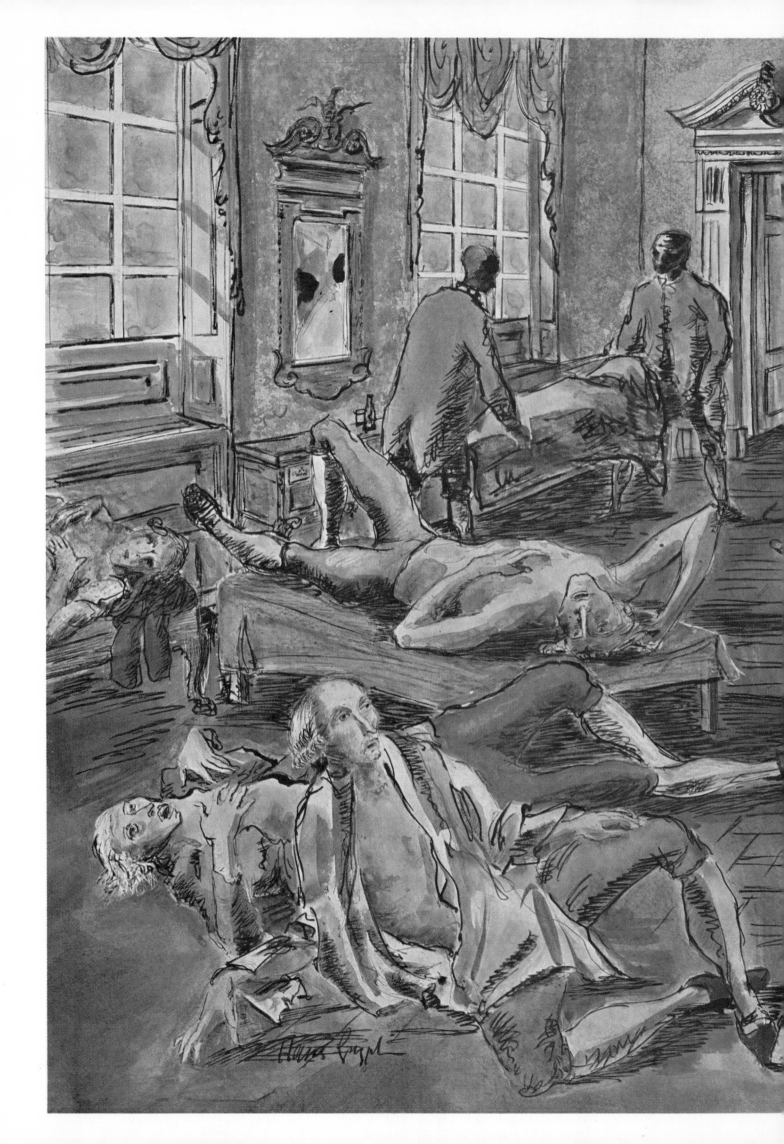

The Barricades, *July 28, 1830, by Delacroix.*

rose from two or three million to 41.5 millions per year.

Among the keenest observers was the Breton, René Laennec (1781–1826), pupil of both Bichat and Corvisart. From watching children at play with a hollow log, Laennec improvised his first stethoscope out of a rolled tube of paper, then changed to a hollow wooden tube. With this device and his sensitive musician's ear (he played the flute) he investigated the diseases of the chest, described audible pulmonary and cardiac lesions, which he later confirmed visually at numerous autopsies performed by himself.

Toward midcentury, Vienna rose to leadership in pathologic anatomy with the new school inspired by Baron Karl von Rokitansky (1804–1878); he performed more than 30,000 autopsies in his lifetime, taught his pupils the nature of diseases retrospectively from postmortem findings.

London and Dublin led in the description of disease entities and left many eponyms to immortalize their nosographic brilliance, beginning with the classic description in 1817 of paralysis agitans by John Hunter's pupil James Parkinson (1755–1824). There

followed the three great men of Guy's Hospital: Richard Bright (1789–1858), Queen Victoria's physician, who made urinalysis a significant diagnostic technique; Thomas Addison (1793–1860) and his classic description of the adrenal deficiency syndrome; Thomas Hodgkin (1798–1866), who gave his name to the disease of the lymphatic system.

The Irish school added some original findings in thoracic lesions: John Cheyne (1777–1836) and William Stokes (1804–1878) who combined their findings in a description of the now classic Cheyne-Stokes respiration; Stokes also collaborated with Robert Adams (1791–1875) in a description of the Stokes-Adams syndrome. Robert Graves (1796–1853), who gave his name to exophthalmic goiter, reversed tradition by feeding fevers instead of starving them; he innovated the counting of a pulse by the aid of a watch. Two other members of the Irish school left their mark on medical history: Sir Dominic John Corrigan (1802–1880) who described the "water-hammer pulse" in aortic regurgitation (Corrigan's pulse); Abraham Colles (1773–1843), father of the law and the fracture that bear his name.

The outstanding American pathologist was Wil-

Preceding pages: *Dr. Benjamin Rush, right, at Bush Hill Hospital, Philadelphia, a converted residence, during the yellow fever epidemic of 1793. Because of understaffing, prostitutes were pressed into service as nurses; Negroes were believed immune from the disease. Although Dr. Rush's treatment by bleeding and purgatives was thought fantastic, he gave the best description of the epidemic and noted the prominence of mosquitoes during the outbreaks of yellow fever. Painted by Hans Guggenheim.*

liam Henry Welch (1850–1934), a pupil of Julius Cohnheim; Welch also distinguished himself as a pioneer bacteriologist.

CLINICIANS AND SPECIALISTS. The greatest advance made in clinical medicine during the nineteenth century was in the art of diagnosis. One of the best known physicians of his time was Josef Skoda (1805–1881), who taught that observable physical phenomena are of the highest importance in diagnosis. This era produced a large number of physical signs (Skoda's, Babinski's, Magendie's) associated with a disease or a dysfunction, enriching the eponymic literature by several hundred names.

The weakness of this phase of clinical medicine was that a number of physicians considered it sufficient to make a correct diagnosis and let treatment look after itself; this came to be called "therapeutic nihilism."

Among the specialties, obstetrics and gynecology made many advances; the historic landmark was the fight against the high mortality from puerperal fever. Oliver Wendell Holmes had in 1842 recommended that women in childbed should not be attended by physicians who had conducted autopsies unless they washed their hands in calcium chloride and changed their clothes. Five years later, Vienna's Ignaz Philipp Semmelweis (1818–1865) demonstrated that puerperal sepsis mortality could be reduced by about 80 per cent by the use of calcium chloride washes; he met violent opposition and ridicule, which caused his sensitive nature to sink into insanity and an early death.

The cause of anesthesia in childbirth was won almost singlehanded by James Young Simpson, the Edinburgh baker's son whose skill and personal charm made him the era's most famous obstetrician; opposition faded when Queen Victoria accepted chloroform anesthesia in delivery.

Ovariotomy was first performed in rugged surroundings by Virginia-born Kentucky surgeon Ephraim McDowell (1771–1830); the many innovations of South Carolina's James Marion Sims (1813–1883) raised America to leadership in gynecology. Sims, with the cooperation of long-suffering Negro patients, finally succeeded in mending vesicovaginal fistulas, one of women's most grievous conditions until that time. The Woman's Hospital he established in New York in 1853 became an international center; in 1861 Sims made a triumphal European journey to demonstrate his technique.

The century witnessed a concerted attack on childhood diseases; sensible infant nutrition prevented diseases that had carried off thousands of children. German obstetrician Carl Siegmund Credé (1819–1892) in 1884 inaugurated silver nitrate instillation against gonococcal conjunctivitis of the newborn; in laryngology Cleveland physician Joseph P. O'Dwyer perfected the technique of intubation in membranous croup; in the next decade Emil von Behring (1854–1917) began large-scale production of his newly developed diphtheria antitoxin.

The specialty of urology was born in the latter half of the century with advances in prostate surgery and renal catheterization, endoscopy and cystoscopy; it

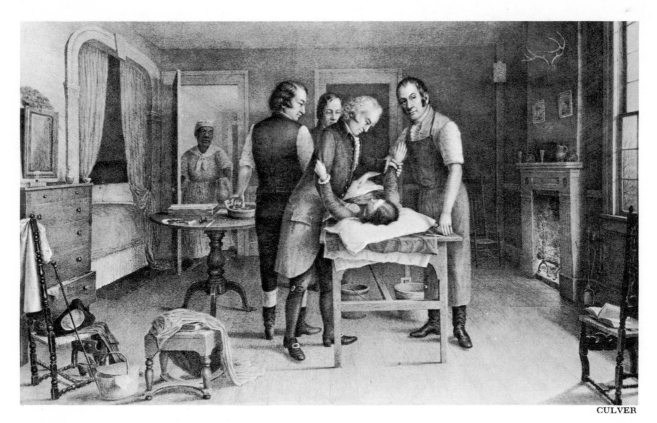

CULVER

Ovariotomy performed by Dr. Ephraim McDowell, 1771-1830, practicing in Danville, Kentucky. In 1809, under most primitive conditions, without anesthesia or antisepsis, Dr. McDowell successfully removed an ovarian tumor from a Mrs. Crawford who sang hymns during surgery. His feat marks the beginnings of abdominal surgery.

owed much of its progress to French clinicians, many of them trained in the famed urologic service of the Necker Hospital.

Dermatology began a rapid development with the histologic approach of Ferdinand von Hebra (1816–1880) and his son Hans of the New Vienna School. With the new techniques of microscopy and histology, numerous skin lesions were identified for the first time; in venereology, Baltimore-born Paris-trained Philippe Ricord (1799–1889) finally established the distinction between syphilis and gonorrhea.

In neurology France provided leadership: for the first time this branch acquired a scientific base in

Charcot (1825–1893), to whose neurologic lectures at the Salpêtrière came physicians from all lands. German and Italian psychiatry contributed descriptive studies of mental illness, culminating in Emil Kraepelin's (1856–1927) great work on systematic classification.

ANESTHESIA AND ASEPSIS. The century began with the discovery of nitrous oxide in 1800 by Cornishman Humphrey Davy, but this remained a mere fad (laughing gas soirées) until 1845 when a Connecticut dentist named Horace Wells administered it for an extraction.

The first use of ether in anesthesia is credited to Dr. Crawford Williamson Long (1815–1878) of

Johann Nepomuk Czermak, Bohemian physiologist, made significant studies in larynx diseases. Photograph shows assistant examining him with a laryngoscope.

Albrecht von Graefe, German ophthalmologist, introduced iridectomy in the treatment of glaucoma and iritis. He is eponym of eye sign in exophthalmic goiter.

anatomic and physiologic research, such as Magendie's and Bell's studies in the motor and sensory nerves, also the electrophysiologic researches of the eccentric Guillaume Duchenne (1806–1875); an atlas of the brain was begun by Paul Broca (1824–1881); Joseph Babinski (1857–1936), Polish protégé of Charcot, developed the knowledge of the reflexes as diagnostic signs.

In England John Hughlings Jackson (1834–1911) shared the field with such brilliant countrymen as Sir William Richard Gower (1845–1915) and Sir Charles Sherrington.

Psychiatry also took its first steps in France: the pioneer work of Pinel in mental illness early in the century bore fruit in the teachings of Jean Martin

Georgia, but he published no reports; in July, 1844, William Thomas Green Morton (Wells' partner) successfully used ether in filling a tooth; two years later he persuaded Dr. John Collins Warren in the Massachusetts General Hospital to use the anesthetic in surgery. The discovery was announced to the world on November 18, 1846 and was taken up by some of the great surgeons of the time; chloroform was introduced in the following year. The terms "anesthesia" and "anesthetic" were proposed by Dr. Oliver Wendell Holmes.

Local anesthesia became possible with Karl Koller's discovery in 1884 of the anesthetic properties of cocaine; the French surgeon Paul Reclus introduced the infiltration method; the German surgeon August

Bier used intraspinal anesthesia with cocaine in 1899. There followed the endoneural method of Crile and Cushing, and sacral, venous, and arterial anesthesia pioneered by José Goyanes Capdevila, which launched the twentieth century's methods of banishing pain.

Although anesthesia made it possible for surgeons to work at greater leisure and to explore body cavities, a large number of patients still died of infected wounds and septicemia. Louis Pasteur established the germ theory of disease in the early 1860's; in 1865 Quaker physician Joseph Lister (1827–1912) experimented with carbolic acid as an antiseptic, published his startling results two years later.

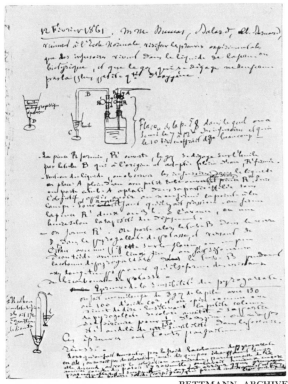

Laboratory notes in Pasteur's handwriting of experiments with bacteria, preserved in the Pasteur Institute.

The son of an Essex wine merchant who was by avocation a skilled microscopist, Lister completed his surgical training under the distinguished Edinburgh surgeon James Syme, whose daughter he eventually married. He had been professor of surgery at Glasgow for five years when his concern at losing 45 per cent of his amputation cases to infection raised doubts in his mind on the validity of the prevailing doctrine of laudable pus.

His report in *The Lancet* in 1867 on the use of phenol sprays during surgery aroused bitter controversy, especially in England, but on the Continent distinguished surgeons such as Theodor Billroth espoused Listerism; the Franco-Prussian War in 1870

afforded ample proof of the effectiveness of antisepsis.

THE MICROBIOLOGISTS. The germ theory of disease, the century's greatest single gift to medicine, came from a scientist who was not a physician, a tanner's son named Louis Pasteur (1822-1895). Physicians before him had reached toward the truth: Gerolamo Fracastoro wrote of "seeds" of contagion in 1546; Father Athanasius Kircher spoke of "animate contagion" in 1658, a few decades before Leeuwenhoek saw animalculae in his microscope.

The Italian pathologists Francisco Acerbi in 1822 and Agostino Bassi in 1846 spoke with certainty of living organisms as the substance of contagion. It

Carlos Juan Finlay. His suggestion that the Aëdes *mosquito was vector of yellow fever brought United States Yellow Fever Board under Walter Reed to Cuba.*

remained for a French chemist, concerned with France's wines, dairy products, and silks, to provide the proof in his studies of fermentation.

In his ill-lit laboratory, with a ceiling too low for him to stand upright, Pasteur made his historic contribution to immunology with attenuated virus vaccines against chicken cholera, anthrax in swine, and rabies. He watched the effects of *Penicillium glaucum* in ferments and demonstrated that bacteria could be used against each other. The world showered honors on him; when he was sixty-seven years old France established the Pasteur Institute.

On the other side of the Rhine, a German district physician, using a microscope bought by his wife out of her housekeeping money, tracked the elusive anthrax bacillus through its spore stage; among other discoveries of Robert Koch (1843–1910) were the tubercle bacillus and the fact that the bubonic plague was almost always transmitted by rat fleas.

One of his students at the Berlin Institute for Infectious Diseases, Emil von Behring (1854–1917), was another of the era's great bacteriologists; among his contributions was the discovery of bacterial toxins against which the body forms antitoxins. His diphtheria antitoxin swiftly proved its efficacy by a marked decline in mortality from this hitherto prevalent childhood disease; he later developed similar immunization against tetanus. Spain's Jaime Ferrán (1849–1929) followed with the pioneer experiments in active immunization, first against cholera (1881) and later against typhus.

Another leader in the new microbe empire was Edwin Klebs, discoverer of the diphtheria bacillus[3] and innovator of the laboratory technique of microbe culture. The Cuban physician Carlos Juan Finlay (1833–1915) paved the way to the conquest of yellow fever with his hypothesis of 1882 that a mosquito was the vector.

Climax of the century's united attack on microbes was Paul Ehrlich's (1854–1915) discovery of salvarsan, which gave rise to the concept of a chemotherapeutic "magic bullet" against specific infectious organisms.

THE SURGEONS. In the first half of the century surgical techniques were not far different from those of Ambroise Paré in the sixteenth century; the principal difference was that surgeons were more thoroughly versed in anatomy and pathology than their Renaissance colleagues. The qualifications for being a brilliant surgeon in these first decades were speed and daring.

Leading surgeons in this period were France's Baron Guillaume Dupuytren (1777–1835) who acquired an enormous fortune, England's John Bell (1763–1823), and Sir Astley Paston Cooper (1768–1848), one of the first to amputate at the hip joint, America's Philip Syng Physick (1768–1805), generally called the father of American surgery, famous for removing several hundred stones from the bladder of Chief Justice Marshall.

With the advent of anesthesia and antisepsis (followed soon after by asepsis) surgery in the second half of the century entered into a brilliant period of exploration and innovation.

In 1873 the eminent Sir John Erichsen could declare: "The abdomen, the chest, and the brain would be forever shut from the intrusion of the wise and humane surgeon." Before the century was ended all these regions had been explored by the sensitive scalpel.

Pioneer in visceral surgery was Germany's Theo-

dor Billroth (1829–1894) who performed a large number of intestinal resections and enterorrhaphies. A man of high intelligence and culture, Billroth was also an accomplished musician and an intimate friend of Johannes Brahms.

His pupil Johann von Mikulicz-Radecki (1850–1905) invaded the thorax in 1886 with a plastic reconstruction of the esophagus; the genitourinary tract became the specialty of America's Henry Jacob

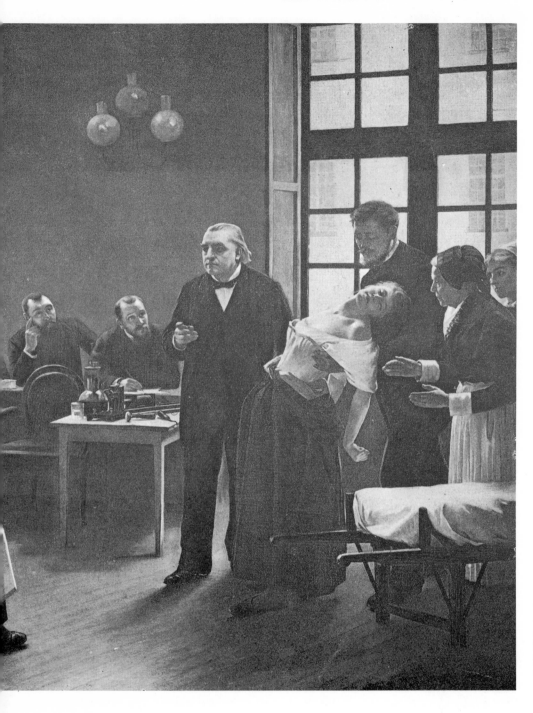

*Dr. Charcot's Clinic at the Salpê-
trière. Charcot was one of the first
neurologists to understand the
broad aspects of psychoneurotic
behavior. His insights into the nature of hysteria contributed to the
psychoanalytic formulations on the
subject by his pupil, Sigmund
Freud.*

Bigelow (1818–1890); the brain cavity was invaded
in 1884 by the removal of a cerebral tumor; plastic
surgery, which had been practiced in ancient times,
was revived by several surgeons in the 1870's. The
most notable contribution from America came from
William Stewart Halsted (1852–1922), who introduced the use of rubber gloves, pioneered silk liga-
tures and infiltration anesthesia.

AMERICAN MEDICINE. Along the frontier that moved
restlessly westward, medicine retained its pioneer
quality, while Philadelphia, Boston, and New York
throve as centers of American medicine, fertilized
constantly by contact with European schools and by
the advances made abroad in the basic sciences.
Among the greatest contributions made by Americans were the discovery of anesthesia and advances
in gynecologic surgery and gastric physiology.

Westward expansion spawned numerous medical

Robert Koch's first laboratory. In 1873, at age 30, he had already begun his great study of anthrax bacillus.

Dr. Daniel Drake wrote Diseases of the Interior Valley of North America, Practical Essays on Medical Education and the Medical Profession in the U.S.

Paul Ehrlich, whose concept of specific chemical combining sites on antigens and antibodies, based on stereo-chemical structures, is basis of immunochemistry.

schools whose inadequate teaching standards fostered quackery, encouraged medical sects. But with the founding of the American Medical Association in 1847, medical ethics began to improve.

A milestone in medical education and research was the founding in 1876 of Johns Hopkins University; with a brilliant faculty that included Sir William Osler and William Henry Welch; endowed with a research laboratory and a hospital, it became a model for the teaching of scientific medicine.

One of the many picturesque physicians of the West was peripatetic, self-taught Daniel Drake (1785–1852), born in a log cabin in the Kentucky wilderness, whose superlative writing style and eloquent lectures on the need for good medical education made him famous. Unique in medical literature was his great work, *Diseases of the Interior Valley of North America,* a brilliantly observed study of the topography, hydrography, climate, meteorology, flora and fauna, diet, habitat, and occupation of the inhabitants of the Mississippi Valley.

A man of letters and a distinguished neurologist was Philadelphia's Silas Weir Mitchell (1829–1914), the first to describe causalgia, erythromelalgia, and

Portrait by John Singer Sargent of Johns Hopkins' "Big Four," left to right, William Henry Welch, William Stewart Halsted, William Osler, Howard Atwood Kelly. In tribute to them, Sargent indicated El Greco's "Saint Martin and the Beggar" behind them, the saint's cloak being the symbol of profound chastity.

Johns Hopkins in 1889 shortly after Dr. William Osle

postparalytic chorea; he pioneered studies on the effect of meteorologic changes on traumatic neuralgia.

Often called the greatest medical teacher of his time, Canadian-born Sir William Osler (1849–1919) taught at McGill, Pennsylvania, Johns Hopkins, and Oxford universities, inspired a generation of medical students with his boundless enthusiasm and radiant personality; his *Principles and Practice of Medicine* (1892) combined fresh sources of information with provocative literary allusions. His contributions to medicine included studies on the blood platelets, monographs on abdominal tumors, malignant endocarditis, the cerebral palsies of children, chorea and choreiform affections, then popular dysfunctions.

THE PHYSICIAN. As medicine grew to depend heavily on science, and the laboratory assumed a dominant role in problems of disease and death, the image of the nineteenth century physician changed: no longer a man with semi-miraculous powers, he partook of the era's positivist tendency, recognizing only those conclusions that were based on objective facts. He shed his theatrical robe and wig, his gold-headed cane and Latin phrases, reverted to simple bedside behavior.

Towards the end of the century dawned the trend which was to lead medicine into the paths of clinical-laboratory diagnosis and specialization. The family physician began to lose ground to the hospital diagnostician, and the frock-coated practitioner began to borrow the white coat of the scientist, two trends that were to lead physicians away from a holistic view of medicine in the next age.

At the nineteenth century's dawn, practitioners of "physic and surgery" in New York State received $1 per visit, twelve cents each for pills and powders, $5 for consultation or night call, $2 for bloodletting, $4 for cupping, $125 for a hernia, stone, or cataract operation.

Until 1870, British physicians charged a guinea (just over $5) for a consultation, a guinea a mile for travel; country physicians charged the poor sixpence to ten shillings; in midcentury they received £20 ($100) a year for tending the sick of an entire parish.

Half the Berlin physicians in 1892 earned less than three thousand marks annually. A prominent German professor had these various sources of income: $300 as city hospital physician, $2000 from the state for teaching, $5000 in student fees, and the earnings from his afternoon consultant practice.

In 1846 a census held in Scotland showed that out

250

oined Drs. Welch, Kelly, Halsted on the hospital staff.

of 253 doctors, 208 had not only treated patients free but, on occasions, had given them food, wine, and clothing. One physician had received three shillings for 12 years' attendance on 70 constant and 13 occasional paupers; another attended 400 paupers for eight years and was never paid a farthing, even for drugs; another visited 350 paupers, some of them living at 30 miles distance, at an estimated cost to himself of £75 a year.

The physician's professional horizon expanded with widening social and political vistas; great wars and epidemics demanded medical men with talents in surgery, medicine, and hygiene; the extension of commerce encouraged investigation of naval hygiene and tropical diseases. Expanding industry and urban crowding spurred the study of occupational disease and public health problems.

Governments increasingly invoked the aid of physicians, stimulated them to think in new terms of so-cial and political medicine; some physicians attained high intellectual and artistic stature.

The artistic and literary output of physicians was imposing: the Bells, Bright, Hodgkin, Lister illustrated their own works; Pasteur, Charcot, and Richter were talented in drawing; surgeon Sir Seymour Haden was an outstanding etcher and Alfred Boucher a brilliant sculptor.

At the close of a momentous century, the physician found himself at last free from the quicksands of dogmatism and metaphysics, armed with solid scientific principles, endowed with a large armamentarium of instruments and drugs. By his side strode chemists, physicists, and engineers, ready to offer their help to the healing art.

Four thousand years of striving and searching had thus brought the physician to the threshold of the age of aviation, electronics, atomic power, and space medicine. In the nineteenth century he had hurtled toward his modern destiny at breathtaking speed.

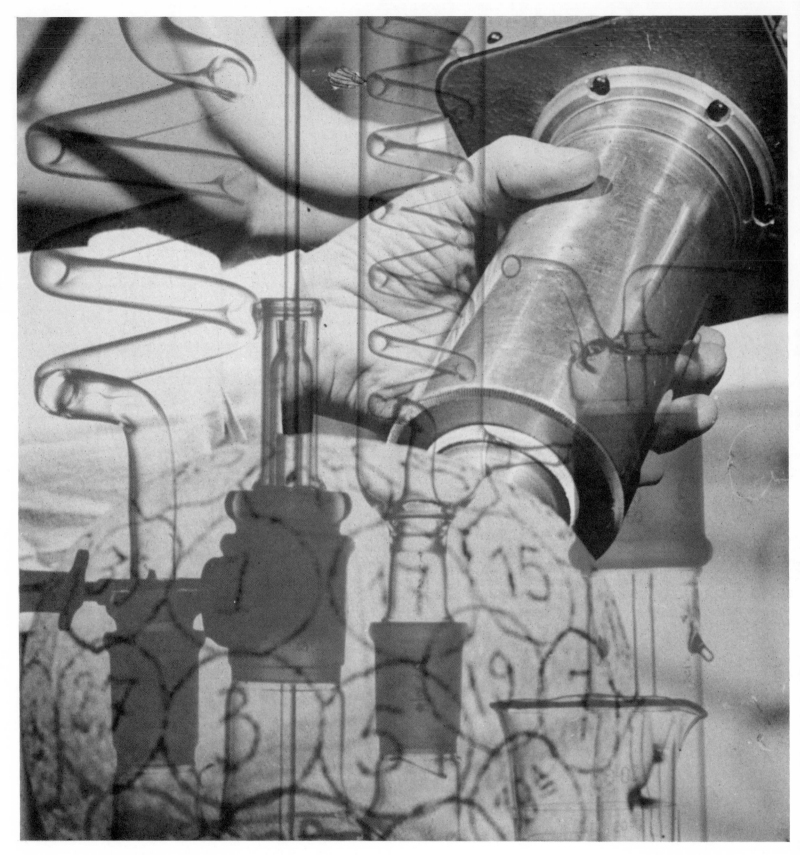

A montage of two superimposed photographs projects five specific areas of great medical progress in the twentieth century: surgery, biochemistry, atomic medicine, space medicine. Shown are radioactive tracer apparatus used to locate brain tumors, patient wearing a numbered, circled cap to locate brain areas, a distillation column attached to other laboratory glassware.

XII

The Vast Threshold

THE twentieth century dawned on such trivialities as the still heated debate among Parisians as to whether the Eiffel Tower enhanced or impaired the beauty of Paris. Parisian wits retorted that the best view of Paris was from the Eiffel Tower, since that was the only place in the city from which one could *not* see the Eiffel Tower! But behind this mask of frivolity, the new century already loomed as a vast threshold to the most important era in the history of mankind.

It is impossible for twentieth-century man to write the history of this century, since he is actually living it. The history of contemporary medicine is not to be found in books; it is being made now, in magazine and newspaper articles, in the daily bustle of hospitals, in current clinical case histories, in medical schools and public health centers, in the world-wide endeavors of the great international medical organizations; it is being made, above all, by general practitioners, that glorious infantry of medicine, and by investigators, clinicians, teachers, and administrators, who with their dedicated and often anonymous toil are writing today the history of the medicine of tomorrow.

In this world of teamwork, trends and ideas appear more important than men, even though without the latter the former could not exist. The medical panorama of today is a faceless one. Only now and then a face, a name, leaps out from the crowd of dedicated men. Here therefore only ideas and discoveries will be mentioned. The few names evoked by them are very well known, and the reader may enjoy filling them in himself.

What I am going to show here will be like a richly embroidered Chinese robe turned inside out. The resplendent dragons on the outside appear then as a golden labyrinth of threads glittering against the black silk, threads that are the key to the sumptuous design on the other side.

At the beginning of the century, balance of power seemed to be the answer to all international problems. In art, Pablo Picasso's "Les Demoiselles d'Avignon" initiated cubism, which together with the rest of modern art—neoimpressionism, dadaism, futurism, surrealism, abstract art—was to disintegrate the human body, just as physics was to disintegrate the atomic universe.

Soon afterward the world plunged into the scarlet nightmare of the First World War. Then came the Russian Revolution, followed, after the failure of the League of Nations, by that great crusade for freedom, the Spanish Civil War, and then the Second World War and the Korean and other local conflicts. Our time includes also the atomic age, which began in 1945, and the aerocosmic age, which began in 1957 with the Sputniks, man's first attempt to conquer outer space.

The twentieth century has witnessed such spectacular inventions and discoveries as the airplane, radio, the splitting of the atom, radar, television, and space satellites. The natural sciences advanced with Planck's quantum theory, which revolutionized concepts of matter and energy, just as Einstein's theory of relativity revolutionized concepts of space and time, both theories combining to form a finite, curved, four-dimensional universe and a space-time continuum.

Physics, with its electron microscope and its new techniques for visualizing and measuring substances hitherto invisible and immeasurable, has technicalized medical research. New medical instruments and methods include electrophoresis and. microspectrophotometry, pyelography, intracardiac catheterization, ventriculography, and tomography. Chemistry has become integrated with physics. Biology has been investigating the link, represented by viruses and genes, between the inorganic and the living. Anatomy, guided by the concept that form is function, has developed new methods of vascular injection, anatomical cinematography, and sectioning frozen human tissues. Physiology has become biochemical, studying hormonal and neurovegetative correlations, enzymes, and the adrenal-pituitary-hypothalamic axis. Anthropology has progressed with the study of anthropoid fossils and of blood groups and the Rh factor in the different human races. Psychology has advanced with the systems of Freud, Adler, and Jung and the new schools of physiodynamic psychiatry, psychobiology, psychosomatic medicine, medical anthropology, and psychoanalysis.

Medicine, which today is made in laboratories, just as in the nineteenth century it was made in hospitals and in the Middle Ages in libraries, has become more and more a technology.

Clinical practice also has changed. The family doctor is being replaced by the physician-counselor and the physician-statesman. The physician now is not only the man who heals; he is also the man who plans, organizes, and promotes health in public health centers. This means that medicine is increasingly becoming a *social* science that uses the methods of a natural science.

In scientific research, the lucky accident of olden times is being supplanted by meticulous planning and design. The lone investigator of yesterday, like Jenner, is now being replaced by organized research teams, often in huge centers like the Rockefeller Institute, the Mayo Clinic, Johns Hopkins University, the Pasteur Institute, and the Oswaldo Cruz Institute.

Medical education, which became more *auditory* and *verbal* when dialogue with the patient (the method used by the Assyrian priests and Hippocrates) as a tool for diagnosis and cure was revived, has also become more *visual*, with the use of the cinema and television and of new techniques that have laid bare the hitherto inaccessible recesses of the human body.

Contemporary medicine is more technical in instruments and methods but more human in its approach, more social and preventive, more specialized in its practice, more encyclopedic in its horizon. The principal task of medicine today is to fight diseases arising not, as of yore, from without (traumas, toxicoses, infections), but from

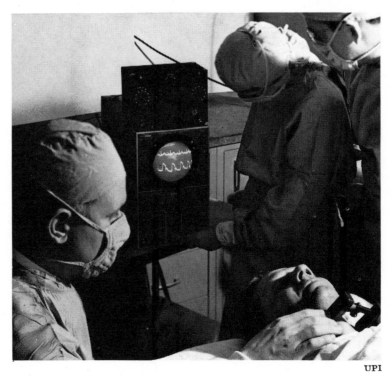

UPI

Electronic switch on a single-beam oscilloscope allows simultaneous monitoring of separate functions. On screen, top curve shows electrocardiograph; bottom, arterial pulse.

within (psychoses, degenerative diseases, cancer, hypertension). In this respect, Karl Jaspers, the philosopher-psychiatrist, established a philosophical distinction between the three main groups of diseases by labeling them somatoses (organic), bioses (functional), and neuroses (psychogenic). Nonetheless, of the more than two thousand known human diseases we know the etiology of only about half, the *biological* diseases common to man and mammal, while we know almost nothing of the etiology of the *biographical* diseases strictly inherent in human life.

Spectacular changes have occurred in the great branches of medicine. Remarkable advances have taken place in biochemistry and genetics, possibly the key to the still unrevealed secret of cancer, though the probability of recovery from some of its forms is now one in three, due to the multiple techniques used in its treatment.

Surgery, inspired by the new principle that form *is* function, is being integrated with medicine as it becomes more physiological and conservative. Asepsis and antibiotics have freed surgery from the shackles of infection, making it less heroic. Instead of a mad race between the clock on the wall of the operating theatre and the surgeon, bending with his scalpel over his patient like an archangel with his shining sword, surgery is now an adaptation to the patient's "biological clock." Today the surgeon works as much with his brain as with his fingers. Moreover, pain has been eliminated by the new anesthetics and analgesics, a more stable metabolism can now be maintained, early ambulation is practiced, and blood and organ banks are in use.

Artificial hibernation, a revolutionary method (foreshadowed when those soldiers who were half-frozen in Napoleon's Grande Armée in Russia survived their wounds) was introduced in 1905 and later revived by an inspired French investigator to control the often excessive organic reactions to disease, sends—as he himself said—the adrenal-pituitary "couple" off on a "chemical vacation" by means of a "lyric cocktail" that puts the body in a state of suspended animation, thus preventing the organic defenses from becoming excited to an extent that might be mortal in its violence.

Besides the steel scalpel, the invisible ultrasound scalpel and the chemical scalpel of the enzymes are now used in surgery. The surgeon's ideal is to readapt his patient to society as quickly as possible. With this in mind, the physician and the surgeon, divorced from each other during the Middle Ages, have come together once more.

Freud's consulting room, 19 Berggasse, Vienna. Objets d'art *show his historic interests, especially in ancient Egypt.*

Enriched with biologicals, vaccines, and sera at the end of the nineteenth century, therapeutics in the present age (in which, perhaps because of atomic threats, the urge to find speedy and effective cures for all its ills is greater than ever before) relies on the magic alphabet of the "vital amines," or vitamins, and on new nutrition principles.

The flourishing field of immunobiology also relies on vaccines, such as the new antipoliomyelitis vaccine, to conquer many dreaded infections. The treatment of infections down the ages has changed from the archaic concept of exorcising demons to fighting miasmas by physical means to attacking germs, at first with the magic bullets of chemotherapy, later with "bacterial hypnotics" that produce microbial lethargy, like the sulfonamides, and finally with antibiotics. First came the golden magic of penicillin, accidentally discovered by a kindly Scottish investigator when a spore fell from the

Dr. Alexander Fleming discovered penicillin in 1928. It was developed by Howard Florey and Ernest Chain.

gray, smoky skies of London into a *Staphylococcus* culture in his laboratory; then streptomycin, discovered by a keen-minded Russian-American scientist in a lump of earth lodged in the throat of a chicken; and later the broad-spectrum antibiotics. The antimicrobial spectrum is now widening ceaselessly as new antibiotics are isolated or synthesized. A new approach in the battle against pathogenic germs is based on throwing metabolic "monkey wrenches" into the biological machinery of bacteria to disintegrate their biochemical structures. But perhaps the future lies in peaceful coexistence between man and bacteria.

The new therapies contrast sharply with the rather nihilistic therapies of the past century. This is illustrated in the humorous remarks of Oliver Wendell Holmes and William Osler, two of the greatest physicians to witness the transition from the nineteenth to the twentieth century. Wendell Holmes said, "If the whole *materia medica,* as now used, could be sunk to the bottom of the sea it would be all the better for mankind—and all the worse for the fishes." And Osler said, "The young physician starts off in life with twenty drugs for each disease, and the old physician ends up by having a single drug for twenty diseases!"

In endocrinology new hormones have been isolated from the pituitary gland and numerous derivatives have been produced from adrenal cortisone. Revolutionary concepts—stress, for instance, an outstanding contribution by a Viennese-Canadian—have changed whole fields of medicine. Full of promise is the exploration of the role of the

hypothalamus, the terra incognita of psychiatry, and of the adrenal-pituitary hypothalamus neuroendocrine axis, whose pathophysiology is a treasure chest full of fascin-
ating surprises.

The symbolical search for mental peace in our age of anxiety—not unlike the search
for the philosophers' stone in the forever simmering crucibles of the alchemists during
the Middle Ages—has led to the development of the ataraxics (some of which can be
traced back to the ancient folk medicine of India), which give the mind a chemical
holiday, opening the door to mental peace. Hallucinogenic agents have also been introduced, creators of "pocket psychosis," which may some day prove that a simple organic mistake in the production of a hormone may be the determining factor of artistic
genius in one man and of schizophrenia in another, depending on the quantitative
magnitude of the error. It may yet be shown that many mental diseases are neither
diseases nor mental, but alterations in the neuronal biochemistry sometimes unleashed
and sometimes followed by an emotional and psychic change.

Other valuable conceptual contributions to modern psychiatry are the studies on
the neuron and the "neuron jungle" by a Spaniard and on conditioned reflexes by a
Russian; psychobiology by a Swiss-American; the integration of the nervous system by
an Englishman; the neuroendocrine and physiodynamic mechanisms of psychosis by a
team of young New York psychiatrists; shock- or seismo-therapies, introduced by a
Viennese (insulin), a Hungarian (Metrazol), and an Italian (electroshock); psycho-
surgery, introduced by a Portuguese (leukotomy); and the biographical approach in
psychoanalysis, conceived by a genius from Vienna and rounded off by two eminent
followers, a German (inferiority complexes) and a Swiss (analytic deep psychology of
the unconscious).

Important advances have also been made in classic specialties—for instance, the
discovery by a Spanish oculist of the value of chymotrypsin in facilitating cataract removal—and new specialties are being born all the time. Of great and growing importance in present-day society, where heads turned silver by the years are more abundant
than ever, are gerontology and geriatrics. The classic specialties have spread all over
the world with the World Health Organization and the World Medical Association,
creations of the modern political Aesculapius. Social welfare and industrial, forensic,

*Ivan Petrovich Pavlov and his staff demonstrating conditioned reflex phenomena in a
laboratory dog. For his work in the physiology of digestion published in 1897 as* Die
Arbeit der Verdauungsdrüsen *he was awarded the Nobel Prize.*

geographical, and military medicine are flourishing on national and international scales.

Of quite recent date are atomic medicine, which employs radioactivity to destroy necrosed tissues; travel medicine, which studies the ecological changes of man in motion; and aerocosmic or space medicine, which studies means of protecting man in interplanetary flights and is providing the key not only to the conquest of outer space but also to the physiological conquest of man's inner space.

Medical communication has kept pace with all this progress in medicine. Thousands of medical magazines, records, radio, films, television, and other means of communication are spreading medical knowledge on a vast scale.

Another outcome of present trends in medicine is the growth of a new humanism in medicine, characterized by the public's interest in medical problems and the physician's desire to know man better in all aspects. This desire is exemplified in the rising interest of physicians individually and of universities in the history of medicine, in the epic and romance of the physician of the past, as a means of fitting their present knowledge into the frame of history and acquiring a better perspective of the future.

We stand on the vast threshold of the medicine of the future, a medicine that will be dedicated—to quote the World Health Organization—to promoting health, preventing disease, healing and rehabilitating the patient, and lengthening life, just as of old it concentrated solely on healing disease. The present medical panorama is so vast that a historian, looking from the skyscraper height of his subject, can recognize but a few faces in the large crowd of men who, with their toil, ideas, and ideals, are shaping the medicine of today, cradle of the medicine of tomorrow.

If medieval medicine—"Gothic medicine" I would call it—soared vertically, even as the spires in Gothic cathedrals did, in search of God and the soul, and if Renaissance medicine spread horizontally to explore the nature of man, even as the navigators of the time explored the seas of the earth, contemporary "neo-Gothic" medicine combines the horizontal and spatial exploration of man's body with the vertical and historical exploration of his biological biography and his mind.

But medicine's greatest conquest in the future will not be that of cosmic outer space, nor even that of man's physical and mental inner space, but the reconquest of service and love for man as enjoined, more than 2000 years ago, by a venerable Greek physician in his oath of ethics and morals, an oath that still guides the physician of our space age, who is becoming ever more the best ambassador of good will among men and of health and peace on earth.

Thus, the Epic of Medicine will forever continue its search for new horizons to conquer, as the most noble expression of man's quasi-divine urge to be of service to man.

F.M.I.

Exhibited at the Soviet Industrial Exhibition, London, 1961, was a new electronic microscope with magnification up to 200,000.

Following page: Flight of Mercury-Redstone III carrying Major Alan B. Shepard, first United States manned rocket, travelling at a speed of 4500 mph, photographed by a sequence camera operated by remote control from the block-house.

XII
TWENTIETH CENTURY MEDICINE

THE first six decades of the twentieth century produced more revolutionary changes in man's way of living than were produced by the preceding six centuries, profoundly altering his social and economic life, shrinking distances on the earth, and immensely expanding man's horizon in the universe.

Similarly, medicine made more progress in those decades than it had done since Hippocrates, unraveling the mysteries of somatic and psychic disease, exploring the mechanism of metabolism, boldly probing into every body cavity, constructing chemical compounds to combat specific ills.

In this age medicine became allied with other sciences, drawing on physics for electronic equipment, on biochemistry for diagnostic aid, on sociology and anthropology for an understanding of endemic diseases. In this process of amalgamation the old frontiers between anatomy and physiology, between the organic and the inorganic, became too blurred to have any further meaning.

THE SETTING. The political scene of this century was totally disrupted and altered by the collapse of the nineteenth century system of balance of power, the emergence of fascism and communism, and the collapse of the great colonial empires that had evolved in the previous centuries, to be replaced by a score of new nations.

While the traditional great powers such as Britain and France waned, the world became clearly divided into two spheres of influence dominated either by the Union of Soviet Socialist Republics or by the United States of America; rising as a new and potentially powerful force was the communist state of China. Also emerging as a separate force in the twentieth century version of balance of power were the newly created Middle Eastern, African, and Asian nations.

In the social and economic fields, two world wars and several civil wars and revolutions between 1914 and the present utterly transformed Western society. The immensely wealthy industrial, mercantile, and financial dynasts of the preceding century were succeeded by gigantic corporations; concurrently the trade unions that were struggling for existence at the turn of the century themselves grew into enormously wealthy and powerful structures; women were emancipated from their Victorian subservience to men; social and economic restrictions against non-white peoples steadily crumbled; strict caste or class distinctions gradually eroded, destroying numerous symbols of inequality among men and making available to millions the comforts that were previously reserved for the chosen few.

Technologically the present century vastly accelerated and advanced man's control of his environment, transforming into reality many notions that were until then held to be fantastic: he fulfilled Leonardo da Vinci's dream of flying, realized Jules Verne's concept of a radio-television machine, accomplished the dream of nineteenth century Utopians to make machines liberate man from toil.

Chemistry freed man from a dependence on animal or natural resources, replacing wool and cotton by synthetic fabrics, steel and wood by plastics; atomic physics unlocked a source of power that made man independent of combustible fuel supplies; the new technique of electronics provided man with "brains" far superior in calculating power than any natural organ.

In the arts, music divorced itself from its romantic traditions to evolve twelve-tone systems and dissonances; musicians created sounds with electronic oscillators, composed works by pruning and splicing magnetic tape.

Painting and sculpture reflected the changes in

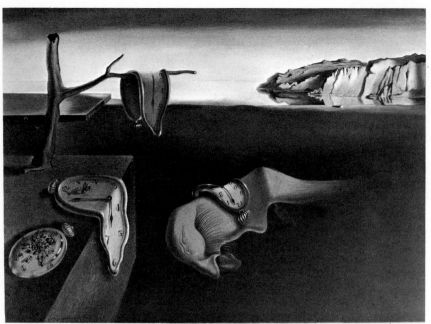

The Persistence of Memory, *1931, by Salvador Dali.*

man's image of himself and his universe in a series of schools of abstract art, beginning with cubism in the early decades of the century. The impact of Sigmund Freud's school of psychoanalysis was seen in the surrealist art that visualized the amorphous and ghostly world of the unconscious.

Architecture responded to the technologic era with a new awareness of man's need for light, air, and space, developed the open construction of dwellings with large windows, balconies, and terraces; urban skyscrapers replaced stone sheathing with glass; some attempts were made to plan communities as integrated elements of parks, "green belts," recreation zones.

The speculative philosophy of past centuries receded before the dynamism of science; the realism of George Santayana and the idealism of Benedetto Croce and Henri Bergson yielded to mathematic logic as developed by Alfred North Whitehead and Bertrand Russell, the structures of symbols and language elaborated by Ludwig Wittgenstein. Humanism found an eloquent voice in José Ortega y Gasset with his concept of the self,[1] a mystic one in Miguel de Unamuno, whose concept of a "tragic sense of life" is based on the awareness of inevitable death.

The loss of traditional faiths and the shaken concept of man's place in the cosmos led to a search for new beliefs in such Oriental philosophies as yoga and Zen Buddhism, also a revival of the Danish mystic Soren Kierkegaard's Christian existentialism; among twentieth century exponents were theologians Paul Tillich and Reinhold Niebuhr. German existen-

tialists Karl Jaspers and Edmund Husserl took a psychologic approach; their "phenomenologic" system preached an individual introspective guidance to behavior on the basis of experience. The atheistic existentialist doctrine of "absurd" man living in a meaningless (i.e., Godless and irrational) world as though it had meaning was propounded by Martin Heidegger, was later widely publicized by his pupil Jean-Paul Sartre after the second world war.

While Marxian materialist determinism dominated thinking in the communist sections of the world, historians of the West such as Oswald Spengler predicted the end of Western culture; historian Arnold Toynbee saw hope only in a resurgence of religious faith.

THE NATURAL SCIENCES. The most dramatic revision of man's concept of his universe appeared in physics when Germany's Max Planck in 1900 advanced the hypothesis that the transfer of energy in radiation was not a continuous flow as was believed, but a series of discontinuous unit amounts (quanta); Albert Einstein in 1905 postulated light quanta (photons) comparable to energy quanta; Niels Bohr in 1908 extended the theory to the structure of the atom. In 1919 the British physicist Ernest Rutherford proved that the supposedly irreducible atom was composed of space and a nucleus of hydrogen and helium atoms: he bombarded the atoms of various elements with helium particles, forced them to yield hydrogen. The process of atomic fission was supplemented by the process of fusion, providing man with a source of power potentially as great as the sun.

Man's concept of a universe in which time and space were absolute entities was revolutionized by Einstein's theory of relativity in which time and space are relative to moving systems; the maximum velocity attainable in this universe is that of light; mass appears to increase with velocity, while mass and energy are interchangeable and equivalent properties, spectacularly demonstrated by atomic fission.

The astrophysicists further described the universe as expanding, measured it in light years, calculated the date of its birth; they debated whether it was born in a single explosion of a "universal atom" or was constantly renewed by a process of continuous creation; they speculated that life must logically exist on perhaps ten million planets with an atmosphere, temperature, and water similar to earth. In the second half of the century was born the technique of sending vehicles into orbit around the earth, also that of shooting rockets containing humans into outer space and returning them unharmed.

During this time chemists and biophysicists explored the living cell, traced some of its metabolic cycles, discovered the genes, and sought to solve the puzzle of how genetic information is transferred; they reproduced in a test tube the gaseous atmos-

LILLIE P. BLISS BEQUEST   MUSEUM OF MODERN ART, N. Y.

Les Demoiselles d'Avignon, *1907, by Pablo Picasso.*

phere in which life probably first began, succeeded in synthesizing an organic molecule. Virologists took apart and reassembled a virus, debated whether it was a living creature, a cell fragment, a microbial chemical "seed."

Physiologists studied enzymes, metabolites, and electrolytes, traced hormonal interrelations through their functional complexities; of special interest were researches in the neurovegetative and the hypothalamic-pituitary-adrenal systems.

The electron microscope brought a change from bacteriologic and microchemical analysis to molecular and atomic investigation of bacteria and viruses, also of biochemical lesions, collagen diseases, the hyaluronidase system.

Of immediate and practical value were the diagnostic tools derived from advances in physics: radioactive isotopes, electrophoresis, microspectrophotometry, the electrocardiogram, electroencephalogram, and electromyogram; the techniques of pyelography, ventriculography, intracardiac catheterization, stratigraphic radiography greatly extended the clinician's understanding of body function.

THEORIES OF DISEASE. A fresh concern with the interrelation of psyche and soma stemmed in part from the theories of Freud, Carl Jung, and Adolf Meyer; one early outgrowth was the psychosomatic approach to disease. Other new concepts introduced into medical thinking during the last decades were those of allergy and anaphylaxis.

A novel concept of disease was that of Dr. Hans Selye who theorized that nonspecific stress produced a series of reactions in the body in an attempt to restore homeostasis; this was termed the adaptation syndrome, characterized by changes in the body's endocrine balance and hyperplasia of certain organs. In his unified theory of medicine, based on numerous animal experiments, Selye postulated that nonspecific stress may be at the root of many chronic and as yet unexplained ills such as the collagen diseases. Also demonstrated by Selye was that animals treated with corticoids and sodium salts rapidly developed fatal cardiac necroses followed by myocarditis, suggesting that stress-induced hormonal imbalance in humans may be a cause of the currently prevalent heart diseases.

THE PSYCHOLOGISTS. The young discipline of psychology, born in the previous century, achieved stature along two lines: experimental investigation in the laboratory and subjective psychobiography innovated by Sigmund Freud. Psychologic testing, intro-

EUROPEAN

Among the leading influences on Twentieth century thought were, left to right, Alfred North Whitehead and Bertrand Russell whose Principia Mathematica *had a decisive influence on symbolic logic, Karl Jaspers who taught that truth required a reexamination of individual experience.*

José Ortega y Gasset in whom humanism found a vigorous voice.

Albert Einstein, left, century's greatest scientific personality, with Charles Steinmetz who discovered the law of hysteresis and calculated alternating current phenomena.

One of the century's chief contributors to nuclear physics was Max Planck, whose 1900 quantum theory revolutionized concepts of energy distribution.

Sigmund Freud pioneered in psychoanalysis.

Dr. Hans Selye, who postulated that body's reaction to nonspecific stress is the basis of various diseases.

Carl Jung postulated a collective unconscious.

duced with the intelligence tests of France's psychologists Alfred Binet and Théodore Simon in the first decade, developed into tests for measuring aptitudes and personality, were used in education, vocational guidance, personnel selection, psychiatric diagnosis.

The animal experiments of Russia's Ivan Pavlov (1849–1936) in conditioned reflexes drew the attention of educators and sociologists to the factor of conditioning in studies of social and cultural effects on individual personality.

In opposition to this physiologic approach was the Gestalt psychology developed by Germany's Kurt Koffka with Max Wertheimer and Wolfgang Kohler: this school held that learning is accomplished through perceived configurations or patterns (*Gestalt*), that with experience and insight the learner fills in gaps in a pattern by extrasensory mental processes. A physiologic interpretation of consciousness was proposed by American philosopher William James and Danish physiologist C. G. Lange, i.e., that emotion is not the cause but the consequence of bodily changes. An outstanding investigator of the physiology of the emotions was Walter Cannon (1871–1945), who authored the concept of homeostasis by which the body reacts to maintain what Claude Bernard had earlier called the *milieu intérieur*.

The behaviorism theory, offered by American psychologist John B. Watson in 1912, combined the mechanistic concepts of Democritus, Epicurus, and the seventeenth century philosopher Thomas Hobbes with modern experimentation and knowledge of the nervous system; it held that behavior was a physiologic response to environmental stimuli, mental processes were physical movements, thinking was merely subvocal speech.

The most revolutionary development in psychology was the emergence of the various psychoanalytic schools. The father of this new approach was the Austrian Sigmund Freud (1856–1939) who postulated that the unconscious and not the conscious constitutes the major part of the human mind; he introduced the concept of the psyche as composed of three parts, the ego, id, and superego; he also stressed the importance of infantile impressions on the formation of character or as roots of adult neuroses.

Freud's notable contribution to psychiatry was to emphasize the concept that man is a total biologic and historical organism; he was more interested in why his patients suffered neuroses than in what they were suffering from. He in effect changed the pathology of mental diseases from visual to auditory, making it possible to "listen" to a neurosis instead of merely observing its symptoms, as was done in Charcot's time.

The impact of Freudian theories and therapeutic methods on Western civilization in the twentieth century is incalculable. Apart from reorientating medical thought, his concepts profoundly influenced art, music, design, religious teaching, educational methods, and exerted an enormous effect on Western literature by introducing the "stream of consciousness" technique and, by deepening writers' insight into human character.

One of Freud's disciples, Switzerland's Carl Gustav Jung (1875–1961) postulated two systems in the unconscious: the personal, made up of repressions or suppressed desires; and the archetypal, composed of inherited racial tendencies that constitute a "collective unconscious." For Alfred Adler (1870–1937), all psychic difficulties were rooted in a feeling of inferiority, derived from restrictions imposed by the environment on an individual's thirst for power and self-assertion; the term "inferiority complex" became a byword throughout the world.

A middle course between behaviorism and introspection was steered during these years by Adolf Meyer (1866–1950) who based his psychiatry on

what he called psychobiology; this made no sharp division between physiologic and psychologic factors, envisaged mental phenomena as integrations or sublimations by the frontal lobe of the brain of the primitive instinctive processes originating in the brain stem. He also emphasized that normal and sick persons must be studied against their environments.

Developed in the second half of the twentieth century was physiodynamic psychiatry, which attempted to integrate the newest biochemical and endocrinologic discoveries with mental processes, e.g., the different secretion and elimination of serotonin in mental health and disease. Widely used by this new school were hallucinogenic drugs such as mescaline to produce physical and mental changes similar to those found in mental illness.

Other techniques developed in psychiatry during this era were the use of insulin shock to treat some psychoses, introduced by Manfred Sakel (1900–1957), treatment by convulsive shock induced by pentylenetetrazol, discovered by Laszlo Joseph Meduna (b. 1896), the widely used electroshock therapy introduced by Italy's Ugo Cerletti (b. 1877) and L. Bini, and the debatable method of treating some psychoses by prefrontal lobotomy first demonstrated by Egas Moniz (1874–1956).

THE PHYSICIAN. The role of the physician during this century was both expanded and intensified: the

"Big Four" leaders plan a world made safe for democracy: from left, Vittorio Orlando, Lloyd George, Georges Clemenceau, Woodrow Wilson.

BROWN BROS.

Lenin, founder of Bolshevik communism, ruler after the 1917 revolution, addressing a Russian street crowd. He was a spellbinding orator.

public consciousness of the importance of health gave him a broadening responsibility in society; at the same time the rapid advances in medical science made it difficult for him to keep abreast of the times.

At the century's start the general practitioner functioned largely alone: he could still carry all of medicine's essential knowledge in his head and virtually its entire pharmaceutic armamentarium in his bag; the greater part of his practice was conducted in his office or in the patient's home; hospitals were then largely used for the indigent.

By midcentury this picture had radically changed: the physician functioned as a member of a team, at his disposal were colleagues trained in many specialties, an array of technicians, the facilities of laboratories, blood, tissue, and organ banks, the enormous resources of pharmaceutic manufacturers. Also behind him stood a towering structure of basic and applied research under the auspices of universities, foundations, voluntary organizations, government authorities, drug companies. Developments in his own and allied fields were reported in some 1200 clinical and preclinical journals; to help him keep abreast of the flood of literature a physician could use abstracting services, newsletters, tape recording devices, medical radio and television programs.

A modern development is group practice, in which a number of physicians join forces to create a medi-

BROWN BROS.

Dr. Sun Yat-sen, a physician, led the revolution ending Manchu rule.

EUROPEAN

Teheran Conference, 1943, at which Allied leaders Stalin, Roosevelt, and Churchill planned "Overlord," invasion of Europe.

cal center with technical personnel shared by the group; many such associations are organized under industrial, trade union, or health insurance plans.

Public responsibility for medical care ranged from complete government control, as in the communist countries, through combinations of state medicine and private practice, as in Great Britain and the Scandinavian countries; in the United States a variety of health plans, based on insurance, were developed to meet the growing demand for medical care.

In the new concept of his role the physician was expected not only to diagnose and treat illness but to prevent it by periodic examination and immunization, also to follow recovery with rehabilitation techniques.

The physician's social status has been one of respect; the shortage of physicians in the United States has caused his services to be much in demand, resulting in a fairly high economic level. On the other hand, his training costs multiplied: between the twelve years from college entrance to beginning of practice, the medical student requires $20,000 for tuition and living costs; to society (in the United States) the cost is an additional $4000 per student per year.

On the world scene the number of physicians increased by 39 per cent between 1950 and 1958; the expectation was that the need for physicians would remain far from satisfied for many decades as peoples in underdeveloped areas strove to improve their standards of living and medical care.

THE DISCOVERERS. The new vistas opened by nineteenth century pioneers led to these far-reaching discoveries: nutrition took its major step toward a scientific status when the English biochemist Frederick Gowland Hopkins (later knighted) demonstrated in the first decade that other factors besides proteins, carbohydrates, and fats were essential to normal growth and health; in 1912 Casimir Funk in Switzerland named these factors "vitamins" or vital amines.

George R. Minot's discovery in Boston in 1926 that liver was specific for pernicious anemia began the conquest of that disease, also the study of diet and hematology. Experiments with rats on a polished rice diet gave the clue to beriberi, confirmed the concept of deficiency diseases.

Claude Bernard's doctrine of internal secretions and Thomas Addison's earlier description of the disease named for him had laid the foundations of en-

General Charles DeGaulle, Free French war leader, parades through Paris shortly after city's liberation.

bacterial culture plate in London in 1928 in the small cluttered laboratory of Dr. Alexander Fleming (1881–1955) further extended man's frontier of struggle against pathogenic organisms. The penicillin, as Fleming named his discovery, lay dormant as a laboratory curiosity until World War II when it was improved and developed by England's Howard A. Florey (b. 1898), and Ernst B. Chain (b. 1906) and contributed enormously to reducing the casualties from wounds.

Penicillin was followed by the discovery of streptomycin in 1944 by Dr. Selman A. Waksman (b. 1888) and his assistants; from then on the discovery of new antibiotics, such as the tetracycline family, became the work of biochemist teams in pharmaceutic companies, virtually marking the end of the previous century's lone investigator.

THE SURGEONS. The rich armamentarium of antibiotics and improved techniques and drugs in anesthesia have given twentieth century surgeons a powerful incentive to break down the last barriers to the scalpel. The most spectacular advances were made in devising machines that could "by-pass" the heart and kidneys, permitting the surgeon to operate on open hearts, an unheard-of procedure only twenty years ago.

Equally unorthodox was the development of "replacement" surgery, in which diseased portions of vessels (or a trachea) are either by-passed or replaced by plastic tubing. Surgeons are now able not only to replace some organs or tissues (such as the cornea) but they can supplement a defective organ, such as the heart, by implanting a battery-operated pacemaker in the chest cavity.

As an adjunct to surgery, all the resources of the electronic age have been used to build prosthetic devices and apparatus for the handicapped, such as tiny almost invisible transistorized hearing aids. Electric and electronic machines are also used in a variety of devices to aid in rehabilitation of the maimed or diseased.

docrinology; the English physiologist George Redmayne Murray applied the new science in his successful treatment of a cretin with an extract of sheep thyroid. The new century opened with Jokichi Takamine's isolation of adrenalin in 1901, Ernest Henry Starling's theory of hormones as chemical messengers in 1905; there followed a stream of endocrine discoveries, plus the identification and later the synthesis of hormones. In 1921 the Toronto orthopedic surgeon Frederick G. Banting, working with his assistant Charles H. Best, extracted insulin from dog pancreas, thereby saving millions of people from what was a dread disease.

A new era in chemotherapy was launched in 1935 when Germany's Gerhard Domagk (b. 1895) discovered the antibacterial properties of sulfanilamide, the forerunner of the sulfonamides that became the twentieth century's first "miracle drugs." Overnight the treatment of infectious diseases was revolutionized, notably in pneumonia and peritonitis, and an age-old hazard in surgery was greatly reduced.

A stray spore of *Penicillium notatum* landing on a

Symbol of world's striving for peace and freedom in the United Nations General Assembly in New York.

Among the outstanding surgeons of this era were Alexis Carrel, who revolutionized surgery of the vascular system; Ernst Wertheim who developed the radical operation for cervical cancer; Rudolf Matas who introduced the technique of laryngeal intubation; Evarts Ambrose Graham who worked in gastroenterology; John Benjamin Murphy who did epoch-making work in the resection of damaged vessels; Friedrich Trendelenburg who introduced gastrostomy; Sir William Arbuthnot Lane who introduced innovations in the treatment of fractures, William Stewart Halstead who developed the famous supraclavicular operation for breast cancer; and Harvey Cushing, the prince of neurologic surgeons.

THE INVESTIGATORS. The Rockefeller Institute for Medical Research in 1901 departed from the European pattern of a laboratory built around an individual, such as the Pasteur Institute, offered instead facilities to groups of collaborating investigators. Other such institutes sprang up, some dedicated to specific fields (the John McCormick Institute for Infectious Diseases in 1902, the Phipps Institute for Tuberculosis in 1903, the Phipps Psychiatric Clinic in 1913); at first they were the expression of public responsibility of private individuals who had become millionaires in the rapid growth of the country; later they were supported by public contribution or by government; at midcentury the National Institutes of Health in Bethesda, Maryland, were the keystone in the United States of a vast structure of publicly and privately supported laboratories and projects at institutes, hospitals, universities, medical schools, and college science departments.

Genetics, virology, molecular structure of the cell, the brain and nervous system, endocrine glands, tissue biochemistry, enzymes, cell metabolism, these were some fields of outstanding research interest; under special scrutiny were the mental and degenerative diseases, and the age-old enemy, cancer. An outstanding contribution to twentieth century medicine was the discovery by Dr. Jonas Salk in 1954 of a killed-virus vaccine against poliomyelitis, followed later by Dr. Alfred Sabin's live-virus vaccine against the same disease.

In Europe outstanding medical research is being done in such centers as the Pasteur Institute in Paris, the Robert Koch Institute in Berlin, and the Lister Institute in London; a famous South American center is the Oswaldo Cruz Institute in Brazil; Japan has its great Kitasato Institute for Infectious Diseases in Tokyo.

NEW SPECIALTIES. Man's lengthening reach into time and space generated new medical specialties; most dramatic of these was space medicine in which man prepared to explore the universe beyond earth's atmosphere. Higher and faster flight raised problems of acceleration, pressure, thermal extremes, weight-

PIX

Theodore Dreiser

Marcel Proust

lessness, nutrition, excretion, physiologic cycles, sensory and psychologic distortions, genetic hazards from cosmic rays.

Outgrowth of the atomic age was atomic medicine, the use of radioactive substances in diagnosis by radioisotopes, and in therapy to control malignant processes. Of increasing importance was the preventive aspect of this branch in protecting workers from dangerous exposure and populations from radioactive wastes and foods contaminated by fallout from nuclear bomb tests.

The shrinking of the earth by jet plane travel and the increase in world travel for science, business, and recreation led to the first International Symposium on Health and Travel in 1955. Immunization, advice on food, clothing, psychologic stresses, and maintenance of health in exotic environments became the concern of the physician in his daily practice.

Medical geography, or the ecology of man, developed as a specialty when medicine launched worldwide attacks on such ancient scourges as malaria, trachoma, hookworm, leprosy, schistosomiasis, endemic, parasitic, and deficiency diseases. Local gov-

James Joyce

George Bernard Shaw

W. Somerset Maugham

Romain Rolland

Thomas Mann

WRITERS OF THE TWENTIETH CENTURY
The main currents of contemporary fiction stem from nineteenth century France. In the tradition of Zola's social-realist novels were writers like Dreiser, Maugham, who saw the individual dominated by the mores of society and wrote of the external forces that shaped their characters' destinies. Derived from Flaubert are the great introspective novels, psychologic documents like Proust's A la recherche du temps perdu and Joyce's Ulysses, which reveal their characters not so much as social animals but as sensitive personalities reacting within society.

ernments received aid in funds, clinical and research facilities, drugs, and especially in trained medical personnel; sources of aid were private foundations, individual governments, and international organizations such as the World Health Organization. It is probable that before the century's end medicine will have conquered malaria, tuberculosis, and trachoma, just as it has conquered such old disease entities as diphtheria and yellow fever.

In industrial medicine, physicians supervised working conditions, sanitation, ventilation; they also made periodic checks on the health of executives and personnel, gave advice on how to prevent fatigue, avoid unphysiologic working postures, reduce accidents and the occupational diseases that were the bane of the industrial revolution.

MILITARY MEDICINE. In its first sixty years the century recorded at least one major international or civil war in each decade; as always in history, war's urgency accelerated medicine's progress; many procedures improvised in an emergency earned a permanent place in medical practice.

The plague of World War I was typhus, which raged among the Austrian and Russian armies; German and Allied forces were protected by more thorough sanitation, especially by the control of lice infestation. The war was followed by a world-wide epidemic of influenza, which is estimated to have killed ten million people.

In World War II troops were subjected to numerous immunization routines, thereby greatly reducing the danger of epidemics in exotic climates; prophylaxis and education considerably reduced the incidence of venereal disease. The mortality rate from disease in the armed forces in World War II was one per 1000, compared with 19 per 1000 in World War I. Oustanding advances were made in plastic surgery and in the techniques of rehabilitation of the disabled.

GLOBAL MEDICINE. The same longing for peace and mutual aid that at first inspired the creation of the United Nations led to the founding in 1948 of the World Health Organization (WHO). This organization functions as a coordinating authority on international health projects and problems; it assists governments in programs of maternal and child health,

D. W. Griffith, creative pioneer of cinema photography.

sanitation, mental health, seeks to improve standards of health teaching and training. With a staff of 2000 persons working in Geneva on a budget contributed by 100 member states ($18 million in 1961), the organization is currently embarked on a world-wide effort to eradicate malaria; during 1961 more than 800 projects in 130 countries and territories received WHO assistance.

Highly effective were the global campaigns against syphilis, smallpox, tuberculosis, yaws; in Asia and Africa its field teams examined sixty million persons, treated one third with penicillin; in its first decade WHO succeeded in reducing by one half the number of malaria sufferers, with notable successes in the Near East and Asia.

Also working on a world scale is the international voice of organized medicine, the World Medical Association (WMA), a confederation of fifty national medical associations representing 750,000 physicians. This body was initiated in 1945; it is non-governmental and advances the professional interests of physicians, expresses their aspiration in international forums, promotes medical research and cooperation between physicians and public health officers, expedites the international flow of drugs, is the promulgator of an international code of medical ethics.

COMMUNICATIONS. The dissemination of medical knowledge at one time depended on word of mouth and a few great compilations; today it depends on a vast and varied network of communication in words, spoken and printed, pictures both still and moving; medical communication has become an industry in itself, employing special techniques and media.

Medical journals, which were an innovation of the seventeenth century, numbered about 1200 by 1910; by midcentury they had increased tenfold, with approximately 5000 being published in the United States alone.

An innovation of the century was medical and scientific journalism for laymen: physicians and professional scientific and medical journalists wrote books, articles, and columns in periodicals dealing not only with health and disease but also with basic biologic and physiologic data.

Most novel addition to medical journalism is the magazine *MD*, which presents the physician with all the important news in medicine and also publishes articles on music, art, literature, sport, travel, personalities, set in their historical background; the *MD* concept approaches the physician in his triple role as professional man, as a human being thirsting for knowledge, and as a member of his social environment.

After World War II films became a standard medium in medical communications; widely recognized was their value in demonstrating new techniques in surgery and rehabilitation, and in public health education. Medical films became standard fare at medical gatherings, were shown on both closed and open television programs; beginning in 1941 the American Medical Association maintained a special committee on motion pictures and television and an extensive library of scientifically validated films for rental at small fees to individuals and organizations; other suppliers were foundations, medical schools, and pharmaceutic firms.

Dr. Henry E. Sigerist whose ambition was to make physicians aware of the historic role of their profession, their social, cultural duties as individuals.

One of the first closed-circuit television programs for a medical audience was a telecast of a surgical procedure from Johns Hopkins in 1947; in the same year Cleveland physicians saw a symposium of carcinoma of the stomach, televised from Omaha. The 1949 AMA meeting saw the first medical telecasts in color; in 1951 the first coast-to-coast color telecasts were shown. Postgraduate "refresher" courses and equivalent symposia were annually attended by 70 per cent of American physicians; these also were brought to a wide audience by a series of closed circuit television programs.

THE MEDICAL HISTORIANS. While medicine forged ahead at an unprecedented pace, it also returned to its fountainheads of the past with new approaches to the research, study, and teaching of medical history. Great physicians of the past had included the history of medicine in their lectures; in eighteenth century America the leading teachers of the Philadelphia School, such as Benjamin Rush, also taught history.

Beginning in the nineteenth century, medical history began to be treated as a separate subject; in 1876 the newborn Johns Hopkins University appointed to a lectureship in medical history John Shaw Billings, first librarian of the Surgeon General's Library.

As early as the eighteenth century, great physicians had begun the preservation and study of medical works of historic interest, with such collections as that of William Hunter in Glasgow, Oliver Wendell Holmes in Boston, Sir William Osler at McGill University, Harvey Cushing, Arnold C. Klebs, and John F. Fulton at Yale; outstanding American historical

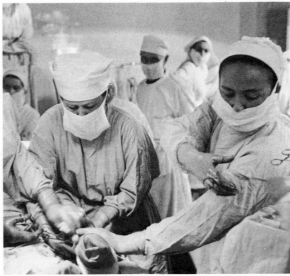

Women played an increasingly important role in medicine in the Twentieth century. Only 5 per cent of U.S. doctors are women; they outnumber men in U.S.S.R.

collections are in Tulane University, the University of Kansas School of Medicine, and the University of California medical school libraries.

By the twentieth century a generation of scholars in all countries had contributed a store of historiographic research material. Sound scholarship, eloquent writing, and a blend of science and humanism marked twentieth century medical history as exemplified by army surgeon-historian Fielding H. Garrison, whose *Introduction to the History of Medicine*, first issued in 1913 and revised four times by 1929 was the most widely known work of its kind; other notable contributions were the work of Victor Robinson, late professor of medical history at Temple University, and the standard classic work of Italy's Arturo Castiglioni. Illuminating the field was the humanist and sociologic influence of the late Henry E. Sigerist, professor of the subject at the Welch Medical Library, whose monumental work was prematurely cut short by death in 1957. Historians in special fields were England's Sir Ronald Ross in the history of public health and bacteriologist Ronald Hare in the history of infectious diseases.

At midcentury several medical schools offered courses in the history of medicine; national and international societies were in existence; so were a number of journals devoted to the discipline.

Some other outstanding names in the development of the history of medicine are Germany's Karl Sudhoff, founder of the Institut für Geschichte der Medizin at Leipzig in 1905, Max Neuburger, writer on a number of aspects of medicine, and Paul Diepgen; Gregorio Marañón and Pedro Laín Entralgo of Spain, Suhely Ünver of Turkey; Laignel-Lavastine and Ernest Wickersheimer of France; Douglas Guthrie of Scotland; Charles Singer of England; Logan Clen-

Shown with American pathologist William Henry Welch is Karl Sudhoff, left, medical historian who founded the Institut fur Geschichte der Medizin.

Among the century's most significant discoveries were those of Charles H. Best, left, and Dr. Frederick G. Banting, background portrait, who successfully extracted insulin in 1921, and Gerhard Domagk, right, discoverer of the antibacterial effect of sulfanilamides and launched a new period in drug treatment of infectious diseases.

dening, Ralph Major, among others, in the United States.

The increasing interest in the history of medicine is evidence that the twentieth century physician is still groping to understand his full role in society; the depth of perception afforded by a study of the past thus becomes a powerful philosophic and sociologic tool in shaping the physician's fate.

WOMEN IN MEDICINE. Johns Hopkins University in 1893 opened its medical school with a stipulation in its endowment that women were not to be barred because of their sex; at present all but two of more than eighty American medical schools are open to women.

The new century began with 7387 registered women physicians; twenty years later the proportion had risen to 5 per cent of the profession; at the start of the sixth decade approximately 8000 of the 220,000 physicians in the United States were women. Women physicians made outstanding contributions in this period: the first woman member of Harvard's medical faculty, Dr. Alice Hamilton, pioneered in the field of industrial toxicology; Dr. Sara Jordan was an internationally known gastroenterologist at Boston's Lahey Clinic; the late Dr. Gerty T. Cori was the first woman physician to win the Nobel Prize (1947), shared with her husband for the synthesis of glycogen; Dr. Leona Baumgartner is New York City's Commissioner of Health. In the Soviet Union the medical profession is 75 per cent women; a woman is Minister of Public Health. The American Medical Women's Association, founded in 1915, in 1958 had

Dr. Selman Waksman and colleagues discovered streptomycin. He was awarded the 1952 Nobel Prize.

39 branches in the United States, was affiliated with the international association linking 19 women's medical societies in other countries.

PUBLIC HEALTH. Drastic changes in man's environment advanced the frontiers of public health and preventive medicine to new positions. As gains along the bacteriologic front were consolidated, new enemies emerged: chemical air and water pollution from industrial and radioactive wastes; the rising incidence of mental diseases, probably caused by the stress of modern living; motor vehicle casualties.

Long-range dangers to health have been recognized: oil wash from ships that pollutes beaches and gums up the wings of seabirds, causing slow extinction and a possible imbalance of man's ecology; wide-scale use of detergents that clog sewage treatment plants; chemical sprays that upset insect balance.

The most serious potential public health problem is the threat to human health and possible genetic damage to fetuses by thermonuclear fallout; still unresolved is the extent of damage from concentrations of strontium-90 and other radioisotopes to food and human tissue.

Reaching their apogee in the twentieth century were huge professionally organized and efficiently operated voluntary health agencies dedicated to the control or eradication of dangerous diseases of childhood and unfathomed degenerative diseases.

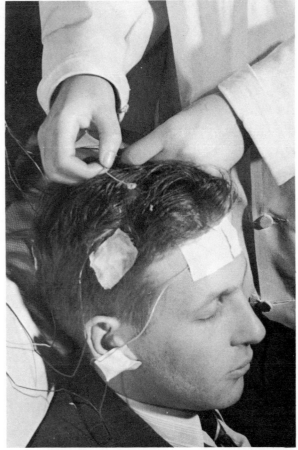

BLACK STAR

Terminals of an electroencephalograph applied to the scalp to record electric currents developed in the brain.

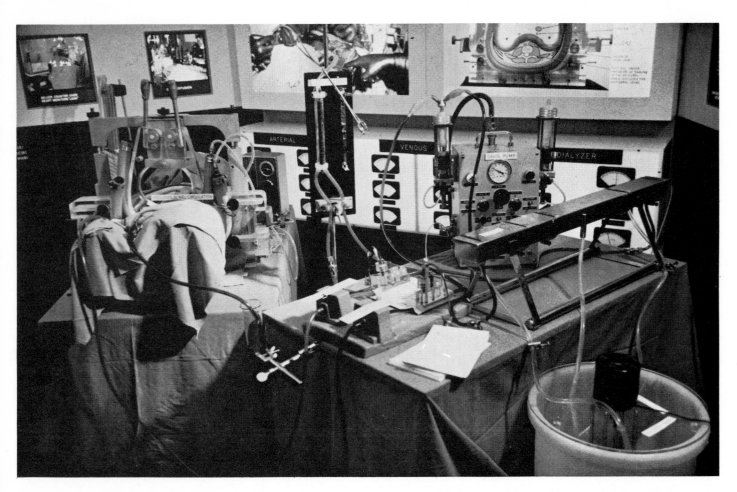

Artificial kidney exhibited at New York American Medical Association meeting. This circulates the patient's blood outside the body to remove nonprotein nitrogen, toxic substances, thus substituting for patient's renal function.

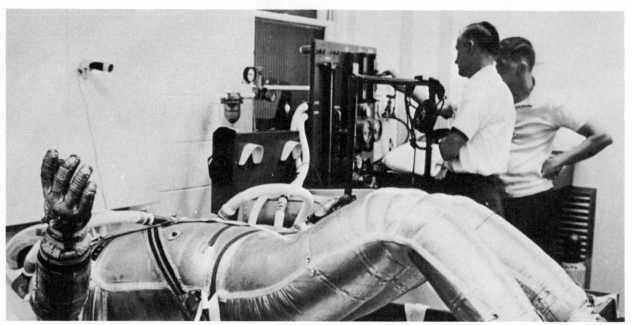

Medicine of the future will require increasingly close interdisciplinary collaboration for man's conquest of space. Shown is Astronaut Shepard's space suit worn in first manned-rocket flight, submitted to enormous gravity stress.

TRENDS AND PERSPECTIVES. The common infectious diseases that had plagued the civilized world throughout its history were one by one conquered in this century; within sight is the conquest of viral diseases; farther in the future is the prevention and successful treatment of cardiovascular diseases, metabolic diseases, degenerative diseases, cancer, schizophrenia and other mental ills.

The decline in both numbers and quality of medical school candidates, the resulting decline in the ratio of physicians to population poses grave problems; a prediction was that government aid would be increasingly enlisted for building medical schools, subsidizing the growing cost of medical education for students of highest qualifications.

As it marches toward the twenty-first century, the medical profession can look back on ten thousand years of history and prehistory, on innumerable follies but also uncounted glories, on an unbroken tradition of helping fellow human beings, on a sense of dedication that exists in no other profession. Supported on every hand by numerous sciences and technologies, medicine can face the future with confidence, secure in the age-old knowledge that man will always require the help and the compassion of another man.

Notes

II ARCHAIC MEDICINE

1. On occasion, walls were built before the cities.
2. Mesopotamians recognized over 6000 demons.
3. The seventh, fourteenth, nineteenth, twenty-first, twenty-eighth.
4. Based on the empiric observation that the liver contained more blood than any other organ.
5. Their ethnic origin is obscure.
6. Titles: Overseer of the Cosmetic Box, Overseer of the Cosmetic Pencil, Sandal-Bearer to the King.
7. Unlike the Mesopotamian society where social classes were rigidly stratified.
8. In a liaison or courtship the woman frequently took the initiative with passionate love letters.
9. Yet in many popular rituals Osiris was portrayed with enlarged genitals, sometimes with a triple phallus.
10. Also Akhenaton or Ikhnaton, meaning Spirit of Aten.
11. Including erotic literature and art.
12. In spite of the widespread practice of mummification, Egypt made no contribution to the understanding of anatomy.
13. A solid mass of over two million limestone blocks weighing 2½ tons and covering 13 acres.
14. Homer sang of "Egypt teeming with drugs, the land where each is a physician, skillful beyond all men." Herodotus described Egypt as the home of specialists.
15. Meaning "he who cometh in peace."
16. Principal ones: Ebers, Brugsch, Edwin Smith and Kahun. The Ebers Papyrus probably dates back to 1550 B.C.; the Edwin Smith deals with surgery, and the Kahun with gynecology.
17. Emulating the sacred ibis which uses its long bill as a rectal syringe.
18. Kahun (1900), Edwin Smith (1600), Ebers (1550), Hearst (1550), Erman (1550), London (1350), Berlin (1350), Chester Beatty (1200). They have been ably summarized by the late medical historian, Dr. Henry E. Sigerist.

III GREEK MEDICINE

1. Early Cretan language, recently deciphered, derived from Akkadian of ancient Sumer; hence possibly the "Achaeans" mentioned by Homer were Mesopotamians who came to Crete, then colonized Acheae in Greece.
2. About $6 million.

IV ROMAN MEDICINE

1. They introduced the chariot into Italy, an artifact that became the linchpin of Roman military and civil communications.
2. Legend claims that the Cloaca Maxima, Rome's great sewer, was started by Tarquinus Priscus, an Etruscan king.
3. Tanners maintained large vats outside their shops into which urine could be deposited, to be used in tanning.
4. Hurrying to his dying brother, Tiberius covered 600 miles in three days.
5. About $2,000.

V BYZANTINE MEDICINE

1. The end is usually accepted as 476 A.D.
2. Constantine was only baptized on his deathbed. It is not true as often claimed that he made Christianity the state religion.
3. Founded as Byzantium by Greeks in 658 B.C., it was captured by the Romans in 196 A.D.
4. Theodora gave asylum to an expelled Patriarch for twelve years.
5. Separated into Blues and Greens: this division also served to distinguish political and religious differences.
6. In the Tenth century it consisted of 180 vessels.
7. Animal and nature fables with a moral.
8. They are patrons of physicians and apothecaries, are remembered daily in the Mass.

VI ARABIAN MEDICINE

1. A queen of Saba (Sheba) is supposed to have visited Solomon (I Kings, 10) around 950 B.C., but her existence is historically doubtful.
2. The Moslem calendar begins from this date, called the Hegira.
3. Its site is the present Iranian town of Shushtar, 280 miles southeast of Baghdad.
4. Many of these notions were borrowed from Hebraic sources.
5. Menstruating women, as in Hebraic law, were considered unclean.
6. King Yunan in the *Thousand and One Nights* is cured of his maladies by playing polo.
7. The notion that so-called Arabic numerals in use today were invented by Arabs dies hard: they more probably were imported from India.
8. Benjamin of Tudela in 1160 founded 61 well-run hospitals in Baghdad.
9. Arabs wrested southern Spain from the quarreling bar-

279

barian Visigoths in 711, having landed from North Africa on the Rock of Gibraltar.

10. Including the famous occultist Michael Scot who introduced the study of Aristotle into Oxford university.
11. Over 3000 miles as the falcon flies.
12. Some of his medical ideas are found in the Koran.
13. Bukht-Yishu: delivered by Jesus.
14. Known to the Renaissance as Mesue the Elder.
15. Known to the West as Joannitius.
16. Gabriel Bakhtishu, physician to Harun al-Rashid, is estimated to have earned about a million dollars from his practice.
17. Translated into Latin in the Thirteenth century and called *Liber Continens*, and many times printed, its influence on European medicine was enormous.
18. Some titles have a contemporary ring: *On the fact that even skillful physicians cannot heal all disease; Why people prefer quacks and charlatans to skilled physicians; Why frightened patients easily forsake even the skilled physician.*
19. Among the first Arabic medical works to be translated into Latin by Constantinus Africanus in the Eleventh century, who conveniently ascribed them to himself.
20. A practical bit of advice: collect a fee when the illness is at its height; the cured patient is very forgetful.
21. Overindulgence and disregard for his own regimen did not prevent him from living to the then ripe age of 57.
22. He was persecuted by both Moslems and Christians for denying the immortality of the individual soul.
23. Possibly a compendium of Greek and Persian chemistry, produced under one name.
24. Some terms derived from Arabic: alcohol, alkali, syrup, sugar, julep.
25. Gifts from Caliph Harun al-Rashid to Frankish King Charlemagne were said to have included a majolica jar.

VII MEDIEVAL MEDICINE

1. Other servile dues: the *merchet*, a fine for marriage; the *heriot*, seizure of a family's best beast on the death of a tenant.
2. Usually a married woman, as unmarried girls were kept in seclusion.
3. Fully: Knights of the Order of the Hospital of St. John of Jerusalem.
4. This remarkable order survives to this day in the British St. John's Ambulance Brigade which did valorous medical service in both world wars.
5. Oddly, these included three books on diseases of women.
6. Notably his *De Minutione Sanguinis sive de Phlebotomia*.
7. Cistercian monks were discouraged from contact with physicians; if a monk underwent lithotomy he also had to undergo a penance.
8. With the exception of the Italian mercantile cities.
9. The market place was the only part of a town protected by public health regulations, such as the ban on refuse within 1000 paces of the place.
10. Virchow listed over 100 German towns in which hospitals of the Holy Spirit were founded.
11. The Dame Trot of later folklore. Some authorities think Trotula may have been a physician's wife.
12. Modern scholars believe it was written by the Catalan physician, Arnold of Villanova.
13. From the custom of addressing any body, such as a guild as *universitas vestra*, the whole of you.
14. He recommended wine, not knowing of its antiseptic qualities.
15. Of the twenty-nine inquests recorded in Oxford in the early Fourteenth century, thirteen were for murders committed by students. In this university, as at most others in Europe, students were outside town jurisdiction and could only be punished by their university authorities.
16. He was jailed for fourteen years for some of his astrologic contentions. Uncannily he predicted oarless ships, rapid vehicles not drawn by animals, flying machines, machines for raising enormous weights, bridges without supports.
17. Nevertheless he was in 1316 condemned to the stake and his remains were burned, though tradition holds that the body was hidden and the Inquisitors had to be satisfied with burning an effigy.
18. Physicians were usually called Doctor or Master.
19. Master Pancius de Controne, first physician, even lent some £4,000 to the king in 1337.
20. Now Feodosya in the U.S.S.R.; ironically it is a health spa.
21. This social change was accompanied by a series of bloody peasants' risings, including the Peasants' War in Germany and the Wat Tyler rebellion of 1381 in England.
22. Probably erysipelas.

VIII RENAISSANCE MEDICINE

1. Approximately Fourteenth to Sixteenth centuries.
2. Gunpowder reduced the usefulness of medieval castles.
3. Commonly attributed to Johann Gutenberg, but this is dubious.
4. Epitome of princely cruelty was Cesare Borgia (1476-1507), unequaled in treachery and unscrupulous opportunism. His vices have become legendary.
5. From the cultivation of *humanitas*.
6. One of the prototypes in Castiglione's *Book of the Courtier*.
7. Fuchsia was named for him.
8. Generally believed is that it was a virulent form of influenza.
9. Other names were spotted or petechial fever, *Morbus Hungaricus*.
10. Fracastoro doubted that syphilis was brought from America by Columbus' men because it appeared simultaneously in countries far apart, also because astrologers had predicted its coming years before.
11. He is variously reported to have died at 48 in a tavern brawl, from mercury fumes, from cancer of the liver, from sheer dissipation.
12. The battle of Crécy in 1346 is the usually accepted starting point of gunpowder wars.
13. The story that this was a penance for having unwittingly dissected a Spanish nobleman who was still alive is very doubtful.
14. Servetus quarreled with John Calvin, was burned as a heretic in Geneva in 1553.

IX BAROQUE MEDICINE

1. From Arabic *buraq*, an irregularly shaped pearl, also Spanish *barrueco*. The word became the name of an architectural and esthetic style.
2. Most famous is Rembrandt's *The Lesson in Anatomy of Dr. Tulp*.
3. I may be reduced to live without happiness, but none can convince me to live without honor.
4. Invited by Queen Christina to teach her philosophy, Descartes succumbed to the cold climate and died of pneumonia in Stockholm.

5. Derived from Paracelsus' *chaos.*
6. Curiously, it was illustrated by architect Sir Christopher Wren.
7. The notion of an intimate connection between heart and blood was also much in the air: there were numerous references to both in Shakespeare's plays: "As dear to me as are the ruddy drops/That visit my sad heart." *Julius Caesar.*
8. One eminent patient was Lord Chancellor Sir Francis Bacon.
9. The invention of the microscope is ascribed to Galileo by Italians, to Zacharias Janssen by the Dutch.
10. He was the first to transfuse blood from one animal to another.
11. Named after the Countess of Chinchon (*polvos de la condesa*) as it was used to treat her malaria. First printed mention in Europe is by Pedro Barba of Seville in 1642. Also called Peruvian bark.
12. He was also martyr to vesical calculi.
13. Plague physicians wore a long red or black leather gown, leather gauntlets and mask, with glass-covered openings for the eyes and a long beak filled with fumigants and antiseptics.
14. *Le Malade imaginaire; Le médecin malgré lui.*
15. It also listed human urine, much praised by Madame de Sévigné.

X MEDICINE IN THE ENLIGHTENMENT

1. About this time developed the practice of playing village cricket in which a duke might play with a drayman.
2. The most famous are those of the duc de Saint-Simon, written between 1739 and 1751.
3. Horace Walpole's copy of a Gothic castle built near London in 1747 set off the fashion for medieval architecture.
4. George Frederick Handel, the Bach family, Wolfgang Amadeus Mozart.
5. Benjamin Franklin performed the same fecund task in the American colonies through clubs, tracts, libraries, an academy, and the immensely popular *Poor Richard's Almanac.*
6. Fahrenheit, Réaumur, Celsius, using mercury and alcohol.
7. He was guillotined during the Reign of Terror.
8. Eponyms: Morgagni's cartilage, caruncle, cataract, column, crypt, disease, forearm, fossa, frenum, glands, and many more.
9. Inventor of the Voltaic pile, ancestor of the storage battery.
10. He was so famous that when a letter was sent from China to "Boerhaave of Europe" he received it.
11. Also remembered for the *liquor Swietenii*, corrosive sublimate used to treat syphilis.
12. Edinburgh's medical school was founded by surgeon John Monro, father of Alexander *primus.*
13. Hence the name Limey.
14. Brown himself died of excesses of both alcohol and laudanum.
15. Worth about $100,000 today.
16. London physician Richard Brocklehurst brought tears to Dr. Samuel Johnson's eyes with his offer of a £100 annuity.
17. A square and a street are named after him in London.
18. First named the "louisette" in honor of Dr. Louis.
19. He had been inspired by the humane treatment of the insane in an asylum in Saragossa, Spain.
20. Jenner was subsequently loaded with honors and gifts.

XI NINETEENTH CENTURY MEDICINE

1. Kingsley was an ardent advocate of Christian Socialism.
2. About 1000 newspapers in Europe at the start of the century grew to about 13,000 at the end.
3. Working with Löeffler.

XII TWENTIETH CENTURY MEDICINE

1. Said he: "I am myself and my circumstance."

Spectacles were in wide use in the Renaissance. Ready-made,
they were fitted to customer by trial and error.

Bibliography

GENERAL

Ackerknecht, Erwin H.: *A Short History of Medicine*, New York, Ronald Press, 1955.

Ashley-Montagu, M. F., Ed.: *Studies and Essays in the History of Science and Learning, offered in Homage to George Sarton*, New York, Henry Schuman, 1947.

The Cambridge Ancient History, New York, Cambridge University Press, 1923-51. 12 vols.

The Cambridge Modern History, New York, Cambridge University Press, 1902-12. 13 vols.

Castiglioni, Arturo: *A History of Medicine*, tr. E. B. Krumbhaar, New York, Knopf, 1947.

Dampier, Sir William Cecil: *A History of Science and its Relations with Philosophy and Religion*, New York, Cambridge University Press, 1961.

Fahraeus, Robin: *Historia de la medicina*, Barcelona, Editorial Gustavo Gili, S.A., 1956.

Frazer, James George: *The Golden Bough*, London, Macmillan, 1951.

Garrison, Fielding H.: *An Introduction to the History of Medicine*, Philadelphia, Saunders, 1929.

Guthrie, Douglas: *A History of Medicine*, Philadelphia, Lippincott, 1958.

Laignel-Lavastine, M., Ed.: *Histoire générale de la medecine*, Paris, Albin Michel Editeur, 1936, 1938, 1949. 3 vols.

Laín, Entralgo Pedro: *Clasicos de la medicina*, Madrid, Ediciones el Centauro, 1947. 50 vols. (Five published).

Laín, Entralgo Pedro: *Historia de la medicina*, Barcelona, Editorial Científico Médica, 1954.

Martí-Ibáñez, Félix: *The Fabric of Medicine*. To be published.

Martí-Ibáñez, Félix: *A Prelude to Medical History*, New York, MD Publications, 1961.

Martí-Ibáñez, Félix: *Ariel: Essays on the Arts and the History and Philosophy of Medicine*, New York, MD Publications, 1962.

Mettler, Cecilia: *History of Medicine*, Philadelphia, Blakiston, 1947.

Packard, Francis R.: *History of Medicine in the United States*, New York, Hoeber, 1931. 2 vols.

Robinson, Victor: *The Story of Medicine*, New York, The New Home Library, 1943.

Rosen, George: *A History of Public Health*, New York, MD Publications, 1958.

Shryock, Richard H.: *The Development of Modern Medicine*, New York, Knopf, 1947.

Singer, Charles, Holmyard, E. J., Hall, A. R., and Williams, T. I., Eds.: *A History of Technology*, New York, Oxford University Press, 1954-1958. 5 vols.

Singer, Charles: *A Short History of Scientific Ideas to 1900*, New York, Oxford University Press, 1959.

Sudhoff, Karl: *Essays in the History of Medicine*, New York, Medical Life Press, 1926.

Thorndike, Lynn: *A History of Magic and Experimental Science*, New York, Macmillan, 1923-1958. 8 vols.

Walker, Kenneth: *The Story of Medicine*, New York, Oxford University Press, 1955.

Wells, H. G.: *Outline of History*, Garden City, Garden City Books, 1949. 2 vols.

PREHISTORIC AND MAGIC MEDICINE

Ashley-Montagu, J. F.: *Introduction to Physical Anthropology*, Springfield, Ill., Thomas, 1951.

Harley, George Way: *Native African Medicine, with special reference to its practice in the Mano tribe of Liberia*, Cambridge, Mass., Harvard University Press, 1941.

Hoebel, E. A.: *Man in the Primitive World*, McGraw-Hill Series in Sociology and Anthropology, New York, McGraw-Hill, 1958.

Leroi-Gourhan, A.: *Prehistoric Man*, New York, Philosophical Library, 1957.

MacCurdy, G. G.: *Human Origins, a Manual of Prehistory*, New York, Appleton, 1926. 2 vols.

Moodie, Roy Lee: *The Antiquity of Disease*, Chicago, University of Chicago Press, 1923.

Moodie, Roy Lee: *Paleopathology, an Introduction to the Study of Ancient Evidences of Disease*, Urbana, University of Illinois Press, 1923.

Murray, Raymond W.: *Man's Unknown Ancestors*, Milwaukee, Bruce, 1943.

Osburn, Henry Fairfield: *Men of the Old Stone Age*, New York, Scribner, 1924.

Raphael, Max: *Prehistoric Cave Paintings*, New York, Pantheon, 1945.

Tyler, John M.: *The New Stone Age in Northern Europe*, New York, Scribner, 1921.

Sigerist, Henry E.: *A History of Medicine*, New York, Oxford University Press, 1955, v. 1.

Lissner, Ivar: *Man, God and Magic*, New York, Putnam, 1961.

ARCHAIC MEDICINE

Breasted, James Henry: *The Edwin Smith Surgical Papyrus*, Chicago, University of Chicago Press, 1930.

Breasted, James Henry: *History of Egypt, from the Earliest Times to the Persian Conquest*, London, Hodder and Stoughton, 1951.

Capart, Jean: *Egyptian Art, Introductory Studies,* tr. W. R. Dawson, London, Allen and Unwin, 1923.

Dawson, Warren Royal: *Magician and Leech,* London, Methuan, 1929.

Driver, Godfrey and Miles, John C.: *The Assyrian Laws,* New York, Oxford University Press, 1935.

Ebbell, B.: *The Papyrus Ebers, the Greatest Egyptian Medical Document,* London, Oxford University Press, 1937.

Hall, H. R. H.: *The Ancient History of the Near East,* London, Methuan, 1932.

Hurry, Jamieson B.: *Imhotep the Vizier and Physician of King Zozer and Afterwards the Egyptian God of Medicine,* London, Oxford University Press, 1928.

Jastrow, Morris: *The Civilization of Babylonia and Assyria,* Philadelphia, Lippincott, 1915.

Jastrow, Morris: *The Religion of Babylonia and Assyria,* Boston, Ginn, 1898.

Leake, Chauncey D.: *The Old Egyptian Medical Papyri,* Lawrence, Kansas, The University of Kansas Press, 1952.

Lefebvre, Gustave: *Essai sur la médecine Égyptienne de l'époque Pharaonique,* Paris, Presses Universitaires de France, 1956.

Lloyd, Seton: *The Art of the Ancient Near East,* London, Thames and Hudson, 1961.

Moret, Alexandre: *The Nile and Egyptian Civilization,* New York, Knopf, 1927.

Muthu, D. Chowry: *A Short Account of the Antiquity of Hindu Medicine and Civilization,* London, Baillière, Tindall & Co., 1930.

Olmstead, Albert TenEyck: *The History of Assyria,* New York, Scribner, 1923.

Peet, T. Eric: *A Comparative Study of the Literature of Egypt, Palestine, and Mesopotamia,* London, Oxford University Press, 1931.

Ruffer, Marc Armand: *Studies in the Paleopathology of Egypt,* Chicago, University of Chicago Press, 1921.

Scott, Nora E.: *The Home Life of the Ancient Egyptians,* New York, The Metropolitan Museum of Art, 1944.

Smith, Grafton Elliot and Dawson, Warren Royal: *Egyptian Mummies,* London, Allen and Unwin 1924.

Thompson, R. Campbell: *The Assyrian Herbal,* London, Luzac, 1924.

Thompson, R. Campbell: *Assyrian Medical Texts from the Originals in the British Museum,* London, 1923.

Wilhelm, Richard: *A Short History of Chinese Civilization,* tr. J. Joshua, New York, Viking Press, 1929.

GREEK MEDICINE

Breasted, James H.: *Ancient Times, a History of the Early World,* Boston, Ginn, 1944.

Dinsmoor, W. B.: *Architecture of Ancient Greece,* London, T. Batsford, 1950.

Durant, Will: *The Life of Greece,* New York, Simon and Schuster, 1939.

Edelstein, E. J. and L.: *Asclepius, a Collection and Interpretation of the Testimonies,* Baltimore, Johns Hopkins Press, 1946. 2 vols.

Freeman, Kenneth J.: *Schools of Hellas, an Essay on the Practice and Theory of Ancient Greek Education from 600 to 300 B.C.,* London, Macmillan, 1907.

Gardner, Ernest A.: *Ancient Athens,* New York, Macmillan, 1907.

Glotz, Gustav: *The Greek City and its Institutions,* London, Kegan Paul, Trench Trubner, 1929.

Guthrie, W. K. C.: *The Greek Philosophers from Thales to Aristotle,* New York, Philosophical Library, 1950.

Heidel, William A.: *Hippocratic Medicine, Its Spirit and Method,* New York, Columbia University Press, 1941.

Hurd-Mead, Kate C.: *A History of Women in Medicine from the Earliest Times to the Beginning of the Nineteenth Century,* Haddam, Conn., Haddam Press, 1938.

Jones, William H. S.: *Hippocrates,* London, Heinemann, 1923-31. 4 vols.

Jones, William H. S.: *Philosophy and Medicine in Ancient Greece,* Baltimore, Johns Hopkins Press, 1946.

Kerenyi, C.: *The Gods of the Greeks,* tr. Norman Cameron, New York, Thames & Hudson, 1951.

Lund, Fred B.: *Greek Medicine,* New York, Hoeber, 1936.

Sarton, George: *A History of Science. Ancient Science through the Golden Age of Greece,* Cambridge, Mass., Harvard University Press, 1952.

Sarton, George: *A History of Science. Hellenistic Science and Culture in the Last Three Centuries B.C.,* Cambridge, Mass., Harvard University Press, 1959.

Sigerist, Henry E.: *A History of Medicine,* New York, Oxford University Press, 1961, v. 2.

Singer, Charles Joseph: *Greek Biology and Greek Medicine,* New York, Oxford University Press, 1922.

Warrack, John: *Greek Sculpture,* London, Simpkin, Marshall, Hamilton Kent, 1912.

Whibley, Leonard: *A Companion to Greek Studies,* edited for the Syndics of the University Press, Cambridge University Press, 1916.

Wycherly, R. E.: *How the Greeks Built Cities,* London, Macmillan, 1949.

Zimmern, Alfred: *The Greek Commonwealth. Politics and Economics in Fifth-Century Athens,* New York, Modern Library, 1956.

ROMAN MEDICINE

Allbutt, Sir Thomas C.: *Greek Medicine in Rome,* London, Macmillan, 1921.

Carcopino, J.: *Daily Life in Ancient Rome,* New Haven, Yale University Press, 1940.

Dill, Samuel: *Roman Society from Nero to Marcus Aurelius,* New York, Meridian Library, 1956.

Gordon, Benjamin Lee: *Medicine Throughout Antiquity,* Philadelphia, Davis, 1949.

Gossen, H.: "Hygiene in Ancient Rome," *Ciba Symposium,* vol. 1, no. 2, May, 1939.

Gossen, H.: "The Legacy of Greece and Medical Thought in Ancient Rome," *Ciba Symposium,* vol. 1, no. 2, May, 1939.

Gossen, H.: "The Physician in Ancient Rome," *Ciba Symposium,* vol. 1, no. 2, May, 1939.

Gossen, H.: "Superstition in Roman Medicine," *Ciba Symposium,* vol. 1, no. 2, May, 1939.

Gossen, H.: "The Therapeutic Methods of the Roman Physician," *Ciba Symposium,* vol. 1, no. 2, May, 1939.

Hutton, Edward: *Rome,* New York, David McKay, 1950.

Lewis, Naphtali and Reinhold, Meyer, Eds.: *Roman Civilization, Selected Readings,* New York, Columbia University Press, 1955. 2 vols.

Neuburger, Max: *History of Medicine,* tr. Ernest Playfair, London, Frowde, 1910-1925, 2 vols.

Osler, Sir William: *The Evolution of Modern Medicine,* New Haven, Yale University Press, 1923.

Poland, F., Reisinger, E., and Wagner, R.: *The Culture of Ancient Greece and Rome; a General Sketch,* tr. J. H. Freese, Boston, Little, Brown, 1926.

Scott, William A.: "Practice of Medicine in Ancient Rome," *Canadian Anaesthetists' Society Journal,* 2:281-290, July, 1955.

ARABIAN MEDICINE

Arbuthnot, F. F.: *Arabic Authors,* London, Heinemann, 1890.

Arnold, Thomas and Guillaume, Alfred, Eds.: *The Legacy of Islam,* New York, Oxford University Press, 1931.

Browne, Edward G.: *Arabian Medicine,* London, Cambridge University Press, 1921.

Campbell, Donald: *Arabian Medicine and its Influence on the Middle Ages,* London, Kegan Paul, Trench, Trubner & Co., 1926, 2 v.

Elgood, Cyril: *A Medical History of Persia and the Eastern Caliphate,* London, Cambridge University Press, 1951.

Farrukh, Omar A.: *The Arab Genius in Science and Philosophy,* American Council of Learned Societies, Near Eastern Translations, Program No. 10, American Council of Learned Societies, Washington D.C., 1954.

Gruner, O. C.: *A Treatise on the Canon of Medicine of Avicenna,* London, Luzac, 1930.

Hitti, Philip K.: *History of the Arabs,* London, Macmillan, 1949.

Kertram, Thomas: *The Arabs,* New York, Doubleday Doran, 1937.

Osler, Sir William: *The Evolution of Modern Medicine,* New Haven, Yale University Press, 1923.

Whipple, Allen O.: "Role of the Nestorians as a Connecting Link between Greek and Arabic Medicine," *Bulletin of the New York Academy of Medicine,* 12:446, 1936.

Stenn, Frederick: "The Symbol of Medicine," *Quarterly Bulletin Northwestern University Medical School,* 32:74-87, Spring, 1958.

Whatmough, Joshua: *The Foundations of Roman Italy,* New York, Humanities Press, 1957.

BYZANTINE MEDICINE

Aetios of Amida: *Aetios of Amida: The Gynaecology and Obstetrics of the VIth Century, A.D.,* tr. James V. Ricci, Philadelphia, Blakiston, 1950.

Barker, Ernest: *Social and Political Thought in Byzantium: From Justinian I to the Last Palaeologus,* New York, Oxford University Press, 1957.

Baynes, Norman H., and Moss, H. St. L. B., Eds.: *Byzantium: An Introduction to East Roman Civilization,* New York, Oxford University Press, 1957.

Buckler, Georgina: *Anna Commena: A Study,* London, Oxford University Press, 1929.

Diehl, Charles: *Byzantium: Greatness and Decline,* New Brunswick, Rutgers University Press, 1957.

Guerdan, Rene: *Byzantium: Its Triumph and its Tragedy,* New York, Putnam, 1957.

Hamilton, J. Arnott: *Byzantine Architecture and Decoration,* London, Batsford, 1956.

Keenan, Sister Mary Emily: "St. Gregory of Nazianzus and Early Byzantine Medicine," *Bulletin of the History of Medicine,* 9:8-31, 1941.

Meyer, Peter: *Byzantine Mosaics,* New York, Oxford University Press, 1951.

Neuberger, Max: *History of Medicine,* tr. Ernest Playfair, London, Oxford University Press, 1910, v. 1.

Paulus Aegineta: *The Seven Books of Paulus Aegineta,* tr. F. Adams, London, Sydenham Society, 1844-1847. 3 vols.

Rice, D. Talbot: *Byzantine Art,* Harmondsworth, Middlesex, Penguin, 1954.

Runciman, Steven: *Byzantine Civilization,* New York, Meridian Books, 1956.

MEDIEVAL MEDICINE

Allbutt, T. C.: *Science and Medieval Thought,* London, Clay, 1901.

Crombie, A. C.: *Medieval and Early Modern Science,* Garden City, Doubleday, 1959. 2 vols.

Davis, R. H. C.: *A History of Medieval Europe, from Constantin to Saint Louis,* New York, Longmans, Green, 1958.

Harington, Sir John: *The School of Salernum,* Roma, Edizioni Saturnia, 1953.

Hecker, J. F. K.: *The Epidemics of the Middle Ages,* London, Sydenham Society, 1844.

MacKinney, Loren C.: *Early Medieval Medicine, with Special Reference to France and Chartres,* Baltimore, John Hopkins Press, 1937.

Painter, Sidney: *A History of the Middle Ages,* 284-1500, New York, Knopf, 1953.

Pirenne, H.: *Medieval Cities,* Princeton University Press, 1939.

Rashdall, H.: *The Universities of Europe in the Middle Ages,* New York, Oxford University Press, 1936.

Riesman, David: *The Story of Medicine in the Middle Ages,* New York, Hoeber, 1935.

Sarton, George: *Galen of Pergamon,* Lawrence, Kansas, University of Kansas Press, 1954.

Sarton, George: *Introduction to the History of Science,* Washington, Carnegie Institution, 1931. 3 vols.

Stephenson, Carl: *Medieval History; Europe from the Second to the Sixteenth Century,* New York, Harper, 1951.

Taylor, Henry Osborn: *The Medieval Mind; A History of the Development of Thought and Emotion in the Middle Ages,* Cambridge, Mass., Harvard University Press, 1951. 2 vols.

Walsh, James J.: *Medieval Medicine,* London, Black, 1920.

Walsh, James J.: *The Thirteenth, Greatest of Centuries,* New York, Fordham University Press, 1952.

RENAISSANCE MEDICINE

Burckhardt, Jacob: *The Civilization of the Renaissance in Italy,* New York, Harper, 1958.

Castiglione, A.: *The Renaissance of Medicine in Italy,* Baltimore, Johns Hopkins Press, 1934.

Cushing, Harvey: *A Bio-bibliography of Andreas Vesalius,* ed. J. F. Fulton, New York, Schuman, 1943.

Fulton, John F.: *Michael Servetus: Humanist and Martyr,* New York, Herbert Reichner, 1953.

Gordon, Benjamin Lee: *Medieval and Renaissance Medicine,* New York, Philosophical Library, 1959.

Hearnshaw, F. J. C., Ed.: *The Social and Political Ideas of some Great Thinkers of the Renaissance and Reformation,* London, Harrap, 1925.

Hudson, W. H.: *The Story of the Renaissance,* New York, Henry Holt, 1912.

Hale, John Rigby: *England and the Italian Renaissance: The Growth of Interest in Its History and Arts,* London, Faber and Faber, 1954.

McMurrich, J. P.: *Leonardo da Vinci, the Anatomist,* Baltimore, Williams and Wilkins, 1930.

Packard, Francis R.: *Life and Times of Ambroise Paré,* New York, Hoeber, 1925.

Pagel, Walter: *Paracelsus: An Introduction to Philosophical Medicine in the Era of the Renaissance,* New York, S. Karger, 1958.

Sarton, George: *Appreciation of Ancient and Medieval Science during the Renaissance,* New York, A. S. Barnes, 1961.

Sarton, George: *Six Wings: Men of Science in the Renaissance,* Bloomington, Indiana University Press, 1957.

285

Sellery, G. C.: *The Renaissance; Its Nature and Origins,* Madison, University of Wisconsin Press, 1950.

Singer, C.: *The Discovery of the Circulation of the Blood,* London, Bell, 1922.

Symonds, J. A.: *The Renaissance in Italy,* New York, Putnam, 1960, 2 vols.

Whitteridge, Gweneth, Ed.: *William Harvey's De Moto Locali Animalium 1627,* New York, Cambridge University Press, 1959.

BAROQUE MEDICINE

Bell, W. G.: *The Great Plague in London in 1665,* New York, Dodd, Mead, 1924.

Clark, G. N.: *The Seventeenth Century,* New York, Oxford University Press, 1929.

Clay, Reginald S. and Court, Thomas H.: *The History of the Microscope,* London, Griffin, 1932.

Dobell, Clifford: *Antony van Leeuwenhoek and his "Little Animals,"* New York, Harcourt, 1932.

Gotch, Sir Francis: *Two Oxford Physiologists,* New York, Oxford University Press, 1908.

Ogg, David: *Europe in the Seventeenth Century,* London, Black, 1948.

Ornstein, Martha: *The Role of Scientific Societies in the Seventeenth Century,* Chicago, University of Chicago Press, 1938.

Pevsner, Nikolaus: *Outline of European Architecture,* New York, Scribner, 1948.

Reddaway, W. F.: *A History of Europe from 1715-1814,* London, Methuan, 1936.

Riesman, D.: *Thomas Sydenham,* New York, Hoeber, 1926.

Willey, Basil: *The Seventeenth Century Background,* London, Chatto & Windus, 1946.

Wolf, Abraham: *History of Science, Technology, and Philosophy in the Sixteenth and Seventeenth Centuries,* London, Allen & Unwin, 1935.

MEDICINE IN THE AGE OF ENLIGHTENMENT

Allen, A. B.: *18th Century England; Costume, Life, etc.,* London, Rockcliff, 1955.

Andrews, A.: *The 18th Century; Manners and Customs,* London, Chapman, 1856.

Comrie, John D.: *History of Scottish Medicine,* London, Ballière, Tindall & Cox, 1927.

Dobson, A.: *Eighteenth Century Vignettes,* New York, Dodd, Mead, 1896.

Hale, S.: *Men and Manners of the 18th Century,* Philadelphia, Jacobs, 1898.

Hayes, C. J. H.: *Modern Europe to 1870,* New York, Macmillan, 1953.

Kesten, H.: *Casanova,* New York, Harper, 1955.

Lacroix, P.: *The 18th Century; Institutions, Customs, and Manners,* New York, Scribner, 1876.

King, L. S.: *The Medical World of the 18th Century,* Chicago, Chicago University Press, 1958.

Kobler, J.: *The Reluctant Surgeon (John Hunter),* New York, Doubleday, 1960.

Major, R. H.: *A History of Medicine,* Springfield, Ill., Thomas, 1954, v. 2.

Nicholls, G. B. T.: *Europe in the 18th Century,* London, Harrap, 1929.

Pi Suñer, A.: *Classics of Biology,* London, Pitman, 1955.

Willey, Basil: *The Eighteenth Century Background,* London, Chatto & Windus, 1940.

NINETEENTH CENTURY MEDICINE

Arago, F.: *Biographies of Distinguished Scientific Men,* Boston, Ticknor, 1859.

Brown, G.: *Nineteenth Century European Civilization,* New York, Galaxy, 1936.

Friedel, Egon: *A Cultural History of the Modern Age,* New York, Knopf, 1954, v. 3.

Guedalla, P.: *The Hundred Years,* London, Hodder & Stoughton, 1936.

Haagensen, C. D. and Lloyd, W. E.: *A Hundred Years of Medicine,* New York, Sheridan, 1943.

de Kruif, Paul: *Microbe Hunters,* New York, Pocket Books, 1950.

Olmsted, J. M. D.: *Charles-Édouard Brown-Séquard; A 19th Century Neurologist and Endocrinologist,* Baltimore, Johns Hopkins Press, 1946.

Olmsted, J. M. D., and Olmsted, E. Harris: *Claude Bernard; The Experimental Method in Medicine,* New York, Henry Schuman, 1952.

Pusey, W. A.: *A Doctor in the 1870's and 1880's,* Springfield, Ill., Thomas, 1932.

Quennell, Marjorie and C. H. B.: *A History of Everyday Things in England 1851-1914,* New York, Putnam, 1958.

Saunders, J. J.: *The Age of Revolution,* New York, Roy Publishers, 1949.

Seaman, L. C. B.: *From Vienna to Versailles,* New York, Coward McCann, 1956.

Singer, C.: *A Short History of Science in the Nineteenth Century;* New York, Oxford University Press, 1941.

Thomson, J. A.: *The Science of Life, an Outline of the History of Biology and its Recent Advances,* Chicago, Stone, 1899.

Thorwald, Jürgen: *The Century of the Surgeon,* New York, Pantheon, 1958.

TWENTIETH CENTURY MEDICINE

Crouzet, M.: *L'Époque Contemporaine,* Paris, P. U. F., 1957.

Commings, S.: *Man and the Universe,* New York, Random House, 1947.

Einstein, A.: *Out of my Later Years,* New York, Philosophical Library, 1950.

Galdston, Iago: *Progress in Medicine,* New York, Knopf, 1940.

Kirchner, W.: *Western Civilization since 1500,* New York, Barnes & Noble, 1960.

Marshall, A.: *Economics of Industry,* London, Macmillan, 1928.

Martí-Ibáñez, Félix: *Centaur: Essays on the History of Medical Ideas,* New York, MD Publications, 1958.

Martí-Ibáñez, Félix, Ed.: *Henry E. Siegerist on the History of Medicine,* New York, MD Publications, 1960.

Oakley, C. A.: *Men at Work,* London, Hodder & Stoughton, 1945.

Roemer, Milton I., Ed.: *Henry E. Sigerist on the Sociology of Medicine,* New York, MD Publications, 1960.

Stewart, R. W.: *A Textbook of Light,* London, University Tutorial Press, 1920.

Taylor, F. S.: *The Century of Science,* London, Heinemann, 1941.

Thompson, S. P.: *Electricity and Magnetism,* London, Macmillan, 1921.

Thomson, G.: *The Foreseeable Future,* New York, Viking Press, 1960.

Sullivan, J. W. N., and Grierson, W.: *Outline of Modern Belief,* London, Newnes, 1936.

Whitehead, A. N.: *Symbolism, Its Meaning and Effect,* New York, Capricorn, 1959.

Index

PICTURE CREDIT LIST

A NOTE ON THE TYPE AND DESIGN

The text of this book has been set in Caledonia, created by William Addison Dwiggins, distinguished type and book designer, and cut by the Mergenthaler Linotype Company in 1938. Caledonia, the ancient name for what is now called Scotland, was first intended to resemble Scotch Roman, but Dwiggins later used as a basis for his design the types cut for William Bulmer by William Martin in the 1790's.

The chapter title and initial letter of each chapter are set in Perpetua, a type face designed in 1927 by Eric Gill, pupil of the famous calligrapher Edward Johnston. Other faces designed by Gill include Bunyan, Joanna, and Felicity Italic.

This book was printed by Livermore and Knight Co. of Providence, R. I., and bound by The Book Press of Brattleboro, Vt. The paper used is Warren's Bookman offset.

The typography, and binding, are by Christopher Simon, with the production assistance of Herbert Mordana Associates.